THE AGE OF BIG BUSINESS

TEXTBOOK EDITION

∴

THE YALE CHRONICLES
OF AMERICA SERIES
ALLEN JOHNSON
EDITOR

GERHARD R. LOMER
CHARLES W. JEFFERYS
ASSISTANT EDITORS

THE AGE
OF BIG BUSINESS

A CHRONICLE OF THE
CAPTAINS OF INDUSTRY
BY BURTON J. HENDRICK

TORONTO: GLASGOW, BROOK & CO.
NEW YORK: UNITED STATES PUBLISHERS
ASSOCIATION, INC.

Copyright, 1919, by Yale University Press

Printed in the United States of America

CONTENTS

CONTENTS

THE AGE OF BIG BUSINESS

∴

CHAPTER I

INDUSTRIAL AMERICA AT THE END OF THE CIVIL WAR

A COMPREHENSIVE survey of the United States, at
the end of the Civil War, would reveal a state of
society which bears little resemblance to that of
today. Almost all those commonplace fundamen-
tals of existence, the things that contribute to
our bodily comfort while they vex us with economic
and political problems, had not yet made their
appearance. The America of Civil War days
was a country without transcontinental railroads,
without telephones, without European cables, or
wireless stations, or automobiles, or electric lights,
or sky-scrapers, or million-dollar hotels, or trolley
cars, or a thousand other contrivances that today
supply the conveniences and comforts of what we
call our American civilization. The cities of that

period, with their unsewered and unpaved streets, their dingy, flickering gaslights, their ambling horse-cars, and their hideous slums, seemed appropriate settings for the unformed social life and the rough-and-ready political methods of American democracy. The railroads, with their fragile iron rails, their little wheezy locomotives, their wooden bridges, their unheated coaches, and their kerosene lamps, fairly typified the prevailing frontier business and economic organization. But only by talking with the business leaders of that time could we have understood the changes that have taken place in fifty years. For the most part we speak a business language which our fathers and grandfathers would not have comprehended. The word "trust" had not become a part of their vocabulary; "restraint of trade" was a phrase which only the antiquarian lawyer could have interpreted; "interlocking directorates," "holding companies," "subsidiaries," "underwriting syndicates," and "community of interest" — all this jargon of modern business would have signified nothing to our immediate ancestors. Our nation of 1865 was a nation of farmers, city artisans, and industrious, independent business men, and small-scale manufacturers. Millionaires, though they were not unknown, did not swarm all over the land. Luxury, though it had made great progress in the latter years of the war, had not become the American standard of well-being. The industrial story of the United States in the last fifty years is the story of the most amazing economic transformation that the world has ever known; a change which is fitly typified in the evolution of the independent oil-driller of western Pennsylvania into the Standard Oil Company, and of the ancient open air forge on the banks of the Allegheny into the United States Steel Corporation.

The slow, unceasing ages had been accumulating a priceless inheritance for the American people. Nearly all of their natural resources, in 1865, were still lying fallow, and even undiscovered in many instances. Americans had begun, it is true, to exploit their more obvious, external wealth, their forests and their land; the first had made them one of the world's two greatest shipbuilding nations, while the second had furnished a large part of the resources that had enabled the Federal Government to fight what was, up to that time, the greatest war in history. But the extensive prairie plains whose settlement was to follow the railroad extensions of the sixties and the seventies — Kansas,

Nebraska, Iowa, Oklahoma, Minnesota, the Dako-
tas — had been only slightly penetrated. This
region, with a rainfall not too abundant and not
too scanty, with a cultivable soil extending from
eight inches to twenty feet under the ground, with
hardly a rock in its whole extent, with scarcely a
tree, except where it bordered on the streams, has
been pronounced by competent scientists the finest
farming country to which man has ever set the
plow. Our mineral wealth was likewise lying everywhere ready to the uses of the new generation.
The United States now supplies the world with half
its copper, but in 1865 it was importing a considerable part of its own supply. It was not till 1859
that the first "oil gusher" of western Pennsylvania
opened up an entirely new source of wealth.
Though we had the largest coal deposits known to
geologists, we were bringing large supplies of this
indispensable necessity from Nova Scotia. It has
been said that coal and iron are the two mineral
products that have chiefly affected modern civilization. Certainly the nations that have made the
greatest progress industrially and commercially
— England, Germany, America — are the three
that possess these minerals in largest amount.
From sixty to seventy per cent of all the known

coal deposits in the world were located in our national domain. Nature had given no other nation anything even remotely comparable to the four hundred and eighty square miles of anthracite in western Pennsylvania and West Virginia. Enormous fields of bituminous lay in those Appalachian ranges extending from Pennsylvania to Alabama, in Michigan, in the Rocky Mountains, and in the Pacific regions. In speaking of our iron it is necessary to use terms that are even more extravagant. From colonial times Americans had worked the iron ore plentifully scattered along the Atlantic coast, but the greatest field of all, that in Minnesota, had not been scratched. From the settlement of the country up to 1869 it had mined only 50,000,000 tons of iron ore; while up to 1910 we had produced 685,000,000 tons. The streams and waterfalls that, in the next sixty years, were to furnish the power that would light our cities, propel our street-cars, drive our transcontinental trains across the mountains, and perform numerous domestic services, were running their useless courses to the sea.

Industrial America is a product of the decades succeeding the Civil War; yet even in 1865 we were a large manufacturing nation. The leading characteristic of our industries, as compared with present conditions, was that they were individualized. Nearly all had outgrown the household stage, the factory system had gained a foothold in nearly every line, even the corporation had made its appearance, yet small-scale production prevailed in practically every field. In the decade preceding the War, vans were still making regular trips through New England and the Middle States, leaving at farmhouses bundles of straw plait, which the members of the household fashioned into hats. The farmers' wives and daughters still supplemented the family income by working on goods for city dealers in ready-made clothing. We can still see in Massachusetts rural towns the little shoe shops in which the predecessors of the existing factory workers soled and heeled the shoes which shod our armies in the early days of the Civil War. Every city and town had its own slaughter house; New York had more than two hundred; what is now Fifth Avenue was frequently encumbered by large droves of cattle, and great stockyards occupied territory which is now used for beautiful clubs, railroad stations, hotels, and the highest class of retail establishments.

In this period before the Civil War comparatively small single owners, or frequently copartnerships, controlled practically every industrial field. Individual proprietors, not uncommonly powerful families which were almost feudal in character, owned the great cotton and woolen mills of New England. Separate proprietors, likewise, controlled the iron and steel factories of New York State and Pennsylvania. Indeed it was not until the War that corporations entered the iron industry, now regarded as the field above all others adapted to this kind of organization. The manufacture of sewing machines, firearms, and agricultural implements started on a great scale in the Civil War; still, the prevailing unit was the private owner or the partnership. In many manufacturing lines the joint stock company had become the prevailing organization, but even in these fields the element that so characterizes our own age, that of combination, was exerting practically no influence.

Competition was the order of the day: the industrial warfare of the sixties was a free-for-all. A mere reference to the status of manufactures in which the trust is now the all-prevailing fact will make the contrast clear. In 1865 thousands of independent companies were drilling oil in Pennsylvania and there were more than two hundred which

were refining the product.   Nearly four hundred
and fifty operators were mining coal, not even
dimly foreseeing the day when their business would
become a great railroad monopoly.   The two hundred companies that were making mowers and
reapers, seventy-five of them located in New York
State, had formed no mental picture of the future
International Harvester Company.   One of our
first large industrial combinations was that which
in the early seventies absorbed the manufacturers
of salt; yet the close of the Civil War found fifty
competing companies making salt in the Saginaw
Valley of Michigan.   In the same State, about fifty
distinct ownerships controlled the copper mines,
while in Nevada the Comstock Lode had more
than one hundred proprietors.   The modern trust
movement has now absorbed even our lumber and
mineral lands, but in 1865 these rich resources
were parceled out among a multiplicity of owners.
No business has offered greater opportunities to the
modern promoter of combinations than our street
railways.   In 1865 most of our large cities had
their leisurely horse-car systems, yet practically
every avenue had its independent line.   New York
had thirty separate companies engaged in the business of local transportation.   Indeed the Civil War

period developed only one corporation that could be described as a "trust" in the modern sense. This was the Western Union Telegraph Company. Incredible as it may seem, more than fifty companies, ten years before the Civil War, were engaged in the business of transmitting telegraphic messages. These companies had built their telegraph lines precisely as the railroads had laid their tracks; that is, independent lines were constructed connecting two given points. It was inevitable, of course, that all these scattered lines should come under a single control, for the public convenience could not be served otherwise. This combination was effected a few years before the War, when the Western Union Telegraph Company, after a long and fierce contest, succeeded in absorbing all its competitors. Similar forces were bringing together certain continuous lines of railways, but the creation of huge trunk systems had not yet taken place. How far our industrial era is removed from that of fifty years ago is apparent when we recall that the proposed capitalization of $15,000,000, caused by the merging of the Boston and Worcester and the Western railroads, was widely denounced as "monstrous" and as a corrupting force that would destroy our Republican institutions.

Naturally this small-scale ownership was reflected in the distribution of wealth. The "swollen fortunes" of that period rested upon the same foundation that had given stability for centuries to the aristocracies of Europe. Social preëminence in large cities rested almost entirely upon the ownership of land. The Astors, the Goelets, the Rhinelanders, the Beekmans, the Brevoorts, and practically all the mighty families that ruled the old Knickerbocker aristocracy in New York were huge landed proprietors. Their fortunes thus had precisely the same foundation as that of the Prussian Junkers today. But their accumulations compared only faintly with the fortunes that are commonplace now. How many "millionaires" there were fifty years ago we do not precisely know. The only definite information we have is a pamphlet published in 1855 by Moses Yale Beach, proprietor of the *New York Sun*, on the "Wealthy Men of New York." This records the names of nineteen citizens who, in the estimation of well-qualified judges, possessed more than a million dollars each. The richest man in the list was William B. Astor, whose estate is estimated at $6,000-000. The next richest man was Stephen Whitney, also a large landowner, whose fortune is listed at

$5,000,000. Then comes James Lenox, again a landed proprietor, with $3,000,000. The man who was to accumulate the first monstrous American fortune, Cornelius Vanderbilt, is accredited with a paltry $1,500,000. Mr. Beach's little pamphlet sheds the utmost light upon the economic era preceding the Civil War. It really pictures an industrial organization that belongs as much to ancient history as the empire of the Cæsars. His study lists about one thousand of New York's "wealthy citizens." Yet the fact that a man qualified for entrance into this Valhalla who had $100,000 to his credit and that nine-tenths of those so chosen possessed only that amount shows the progress concentrated riches have made in sixty years. How many New Yorkers of today would look upon a man with $100,000 as "wealthy"?

The sources of these fortunes also show the economic changes our country has undergone. Today, when we think of our much exploited millionaires, the phrase "captains of industry" is the accepted description; in Mr. Beach's time the popular designation was "merchant prince." His catalogue contains no "oil magnates" or "steel kings" or "railroad manipulators"; nearly all the industrial giants of ante-bellum times — as distinguished from the socially prominent whose wealth was inherited — had heaped together their accumulations in humdrum trade. Perhaps Peter Cooper, who had made a million dollars in the manufacture of isinglass and glue, and George Law, whose gains, equally large, represented fortunate speculations in street railroads, faintly suggest the approaching era; yet the fortunes which are really typical are those of William Aspinwall, who made $4,000,000 in the shipping business, of A. T. Stewart, whose $2,000,000 represented his earnings as a retail and wholesale dry goods merchant, and of Peter Harmony, whose $1,000,000 had been derived from happy trade ventures in Cuba and Spain. Many of the reservoirs of this ante-bellum wealth sound strangely in our modern ears. John Haggerty had made $1,000,000 as an auctioneer; William L. Coggeswell had made half as much as a wine importer; Japhet Bishop had rounded out an honest $600,000 from the profits of a hardware store; while Phineas T. Barnum ranks high in the list by virtue of $800,000 accumulated in a business which it is hardly necessary to specify. Indeed his name and that of the great landlords are almost the only ones in this list that have descended to posterity. Yet they were the

Rockefellers, the Carnegies, the Harrimans, the Fricks, and the Henry Fords of their day.

Before the Civil War had ended, however, the transformation of the United States from a nation of farmers and small-scale manufacturers to a highly organized industrial state had begun. Probably the most important single influence was the War itself. Those four years of bitter conflict illustrate, perhaps more graphically than any similar event in history, the power which military operations may exercise in stimulating all the productive forces of a people. In thickly settled nations, with few dormant resources and with practically no areas of unoccupied land, a long war usually produces industrial disorganization and financial exhaustion. The Napoleonic wars had this effect in Europe; in particular they caused a period of social and industrial distress in England. The few years immediately following Waterloo marked a period when starving mobs rioted in the streets of London, setting fire to the houses of the aristocracy and stoning the Prince Regent whenever he dared to show his head in public, when cotton spindles ceased to turn, when collieries closed down, when jails and workhouses were overflowing with a wretched proletariat, and when gaunt and homeless women and children crowded the country highways. No such disorders followed the Civil War in this country, at least in the North and West. Spiritually the struggle accomplished much in awakening the nation to a consciousness of its great opportunities. The fact that we could spend more than a million dollars a day — expenditures that hardly seem startling in amount now, but which were almost unprecedented then — and that soon after hostilities ceased we rapidly paid off our large debt, directed the attention of foreign capitalists to our resources, and gave them the utmost confidence in this new investment field. Immigration, too, started after the war at a rate hitherto without parallel in our annals. The Germans who had come in the years preceding the Civil War had been largely political refugees and democratic idealists, but now, in much larger numbers, began the influx of north and south Germans whose dominating motive was economic. These Germans began to find their way to the farms of the Mississippi Valley; the Irish began once more to crowd our cities; the Slavs gravitated towards the mines of Pennsylvania; the Scandinavians settled whole counties of certain northwestern States; while the Jews began that conquest of the tailoring

industries that was ultimately to make them
the clothiers of a hundred million people. For
this industrial development, America supplied
the land, the resources, and the business leaders,
while Europe furnished the liquid capital and the
laborers.

Even more directly did the War stimulate our
industrial development. Perhaps the greatest
effect was the way in which it changed our transportation system. The mere necessity of constantly transporting hundreds of thousands of
troops and war supplies demanded reconstruction
and reëquipment on an extensive scale. The
American Civil War was the first great conflict in
which railroads played a conspicuous military part,
and their development during those four years
naturally left them in a strong position to meet the
new necessities of peace. One of the first effects
of the War was to close the Mississippi River;
consequently the products of the Western farms
had to go east by railroad, and this fact led to
that preëminence of the great trunk lines which
they retain to this day. Almost overnight Chicago became the great Western shipping center,
and though the river boats lingered for a time on
the Ohio and the Mississippi they grew fewer year

by year. Prosperity, greater than the country had ever known, prevailed everywhere in the North throughout the last two years of the War.

So, too, feeding and supplying an army of millions of men laid the foundation of many of our greatest industries. The Northern soldiers in the early days of the war were clothed in garments so variegated that they sometimes had trouble in telling friend from foe, and not infrequently they shot at one another; so inadequately were our woolen mills prepared to supply their uniforms! But larger government contracts enabled the proprietors to reconstruct their mills, install modern machines, and build up an organization and a prosperous business that still endures. Making boots and shoes for Northern soldiers laid the foundation of America's great shoe industry. Machinery had already been applied to shoe manufacture, but only to a limited extent; under the pressure of war conditions, however, American inventive skill found ways of performing mechanically almost all the operations that had formerly been done by hand. The McKay sewing machine, one of the greatest of our inventions, which was perfected in the second year of the war, did as much perhaps as any single device to keep our soldiers well shod and comfortable. The necessity of feeding these same armies created our great packing plants. Though McCormick had invented his reaper several years before the war, the new agricultural machinery had made no great headway. Without this machinery, however, our Western farmers could never have harvested the gigantic crops which not only fed our soldiers but laid the basis of our economic prosperity. Thus the War directly established one of the greatest, and certainly one of the most romantic, of our industries — that of agricultural machinery.

Above all, however, the victory at Appomattox threw upon the country more than a million unemployed men. Our European critics predicted that their return to civil life would produce dire social and political consequences. But these critics were thinking in terms of their own countries; they failed to consider that the United States had an immense unoccupied domain which was waiting for development. The men who fought the Civil War had demonstrated precisely the adventurous, hardy instincts which were most needed in this great enterprise. Even before the War ended, a great immigration started towards the mines and farms of the trans-Mississippi

country. There was probably no important town
or district west of the Alleghanies that did not
absorb a considerable number. In most instances,
too, our ex-soldiers became leaders in these new
communities. Perhaps this movement has its
most typical and picturesque illustration in the
extent to which the Northern soldiers opened up
the oil-producing regions of western Pennsylvania.
Venango County, where this great development
started, boasted that it had more ex-soldiers than
any similar section of the United States.

The Civil War period also forced into prominence
a few men whose methods and whose achievements
indicated, even though roughly and indistinctly,
a new type of industrial leadership. Every period has its outstanding figure and, when the Civil
War was approaching its end, one personality had
emerged from the humdrum characters of the time
— one man who, in energy, imagination, and genius, displayed the forces that were to create a new
American world. Although this man employed his
great talents in a field, that of railroad transportation, which lies outside the scope of the present
volume, yet in this comprehensive view I may take
Cornelius Vanderbilt as the symbol that links the
old industrial era with the new. He is worthy of

more detailed study than he has ever received, for in personality and accomplishments Vanderbilt is the most romantic figure in the history of American finance. We must remember that Vanderbilt was born in 1794 and that at the time we are considering he was seventy-one years old. In the matter of years, therefore, his career apparently belongs to the ante-bellum days, yet the most remarkable fact about this remarkable man is that his real life work did not begin until he had passed his seventieth year. In 1865 Vanderbilt's fortune, consisting chiefly of a fleet of steamboats, amounted to about $10,000,000; he died twelve years later, in 1877, leaving $104,000,000, the first of those colossal American fortunes that were destined to astound the world. The mere fact that this fortune was the accumulated profit of only ten years shows perhaps more eloquently than any other circumstance that the United States had entered a new economic age. That new factor in the life of America and the world, the railroad, explains his achievement. Vanderbilt was one of the most astonishing characters in our history. His physical exterior made him perhaps the most imposing figure in New York. In his old age, at seventy-three, Vanderbilt married his second wife, a beautiful

Southern widow who had just turned her thirtieth year, and the appearance of the two, sitting side by side in one of the Commodore's smartest turnouts, driving recklessly behind a pair of the fastest trotters of the day, was a common sight in Central Park. Nor did Vanderbilt look incongruous in this brilliant setting. His tall and powerful frame was still erect, and his large, defiant head, ruddy cheeks, sparkling, deep-set black eyes, and snowy white hair and whiskers, made him look every inch the Commodore. These public appearances lent a pleasanter and more sentimental aspect to Vanderbilt's life than his intimates always perceived. For his manners were harsh and uncouth; he was totally without education and could write hardly half a dozen lines without outraging the spelling-book. Though he loved his race-horses, had a fondness for music, and could sit through long winter evenings while his young wife sang old Southern ballads, Vanderbilt's ungovernable temper had placed him on bad terms with nearly all his children — he had had thirteen, of whom eleven survived him — who contested his will and exposed all his eccentricities to public view on the ground that the man who created the New York Central system was actually insane. Vanderbilt's methods and his temperament presented such a contrast to the commonplace minds which had previously dominated American business that this explanation of his career is perhaps not surprising. He saw things in their largest aspects and in his big transactions he seemed to act almost on impulse and intuition. He could never explain the mental processes by which he arrived at important decisions, though these decisions themselves were invariably sound. He seems to have had, as he himself frequently said, almost a seer-like faculty. He saw visions, and he believed in dreams and in signs. The greatest practical genius of his time was a frequent attendant at spiritualistic seances; he cultivated personally the society of mediums, and in sickness he usually resorted to mental healers, mesmerists, and clairvoyants. Before making investments or embarking in his great railroad ventures, Vanderbilt visited spiritualists; we have one circumstantial account of his summoning the wraith of Jim Fiske to advise him in stock operations. His excessive vanity led him to print his picture on all the Lake Shore bonds; he proposed to New York City the construction in Central Park of a large monument that would commemorate, side by side, the names of Vanderbilt and Washington; and he actually erected a large statue to himself in his new Hudson River station in St. John's Park. His attitude towards the public was shown in his remark when one of his associates told him that "each and every one" of certain transactions which he had just forced through "is absolutely forbidden by the statutes of the State of New York." "My God, John!" said the Commodore, "you don't suppose you can run a railroad in accordance with the statutes of the State of New York, do you?" "Law!" he once roared on a similar occasion, "What do I care about law? Hain't I got the power?"

These things of course were the excrescences of an extremely vital, overflowing, imaginative, energetic human being; they are traits that not infrequently accompany genius. And the work which Vanderbilt did remains an essential part of our economic organization today. Before his time a trip to Chicago meant that the passenger changed trains seventeen times, and that all freight had to be unloaded at a similar number of places, carted across towns, and reloaded into other trains. The magnificent railroad highway that extends up the banks of the Hudson, through the Mohawk Valley, and alongside the borders of Lake Erie — a water line route nearly the entire distance — was all but

useless. It is true that not all the consolidation
of these lines was Vanderbilt's work. In 1853
certain millionaires and politicians had linked together the several separate lines extending from
Albany to Buffalo, but they had managed the new
road so wretchedly that the largest stockholders in
1867 begged Vanderbilt to take over the control.
By 1873 the Commodore had acquired the Hudson
River. extending from New York to Albany, the
New York Central extending from Albany to Buffalo, and the Lake Shore which ran from Buffalo to
Chicago. In a few years these roads had been consolidated into a smoothly operating system. If, in
transforming these discordant railroads into one,
Vanderbilt bribed legislatures and corrupted courts,
if he engaged in the largest stock-watering operations on record up to that time, and took advantage
of inside information to make huge winnings on the
stock exchange, he also ripped up the old iron rails
and relaid them with steel, put down four tracks
where formerly there had been two, replaced wood-
en bridges with steel, discarded the old locomotives
for new and more powerful ones, built splendid new
terminals, introduced economies in a hundred directions, cut down the hours required in a New
York–Chicago trip from fifty to twenty-four, made

his highway an expeditious line for transporting freight, and transformed railroads that had formerly been the playthings of Wall Street and that frequently could not meet their pay-rolls into exceedingly profitable, high dividend paying properties. In this operation Vanderbilt typified the era that was dawning — an era of ruthlessness, of personal selfishness, of corruption, of disregard of private rights, of contempt for law and legislatures, and yet of vast and beneficial achievement. The men of this time may have traveled roughshod to their goal, but after all, they opened up, in an amazingly short time, a mighty continent to the uses of mankind. The triumph of the New York Central and Hudson River Railroad under Vanderbilt, a triumph which dazzled European investors as well as our own, and which represented an entirely different business organization from anything the nation had hitherto seen, appropriately ushered in the new business era whose outlines will be sketched in the succeeding pages.

had for generations been known as Oil Creek. The neighboring farmers used to collect the oil and use it to grease their wagon axles; others, more enterprising, made a business of gathering the floating substance, packing it in bottles, and selling it broadcast as a medicine. The most famous of these concoctions, "Seneca Oil," was widely advertised as a sure cure for rheumatism, and had an extensive sale in this country. "Kier's Rock Oil" afterwards had an even more extended use. Samuel M. Kier, who exploited this comprehensive cure-all, made no lasting contributions to medical science, but his method of obtaining his medicament led indirectly to the establishment of a great industry. In this western Pennsylvania region salt manufacture had been a thriving business for many years; the salt was obtained from salt water by means of artesian wells. This salt water usually came to the surface contaminated with that same evil-smelling oil which floated so constantly on top of the rivers and brooks. The salt makers spent much time and money "purifying" their water from this substance, never apparently suspecting that the really valuable product of their wells was not the salt water they so carefully preserved, but the petroleum which they threw away. Samuel M. Kier was originally a salt manufacturer; more canny than his competitors, he sold the oil which came up with his water as a patent medicine. In order to give a mysterious virtue to this remedy, Kier printed on his labels the information that it had been "pumped up with salt water about four hundred feet below the earth's surface." His labels also contained the convincing picture of an artesian well — a rough woodcut which really laid the foundation of the Standard Oil Company.

In the late fifties Mr. George H. Bissell had become interested in rock oil, not as an embrocation and as a cure for most human ills, but as a light-giving material. A professor at Dartmouth had performed certain experiments with this substance which had sunk deeply into Bissell's imagination. So convinced was this young man that he could introduce petroleum commercially that he leased certain fields in western Pennsylvania and sent a specimen of the oil to Benjamin Silliman, Jr., Professor of Chemistry at Yale. Professor Silliman gave the product a more complete analysis than it had ever previously received and submitted a report which is still the great classic in the scientific literature of petroleum. This report informed Bissell that the substance could be refined cheaply and easily, and that, when refined, it made a splendid illuminant, besides yielding certain by-products, such as paraffin and naphtha, which had a great commercial value. So far, Bissell's enterprise seemed to promise success, yet the great problem still remained: how could he obtain this rock oil in amounts large enough to make his enterprise a practical one? A chance glimpse of Kier's label, with its picture of an artesian well, supplied Bissell with his answer. He at once sent E. L. Drake into the oil-fields with a complete drilling equipment, to look, not for salt water, but for oil. Nothing seems quite so obvious today as drilling a well into the rock to discover oil, yet so strange was the idea in Drake's time that the people of Titusville, where he started work, regarded him as a lunatic and manifested a hostility to his enterprise that delayed operations for several months. Yet one day in August, 1859, the coveted liquid began flowing from "Drake's folly" at the rate of twenty-five barrels a day.

Because of this performance Drake has gone down to fame as the man who "discovered oil." In the sense that his operation made petroleum available to the uses of mankind, Drake was its discoverer, and his achievement seems really a

greater one than that of the men who first made
apparent our beds of coal, iron, copper, or even
gold.   For Drake really uncovered an entirely new
substance.   And the country responded spontane-
ously to Drake's success.   For anything approaching the sudden rush to the oil-fields we shall have to
go to the discovery of gold in California ten years
before.   Men flocked into western Pennsylvania by
the thousands; fortunes were made and lost almost
instantaneously.   Oil flowed so plentifully in this
region that it frequently ran upon the ground, and
the "gusher," which threw a stream of the precious liquid sometimes a hundred feet and more into the air, became an almost every-day occurrence.
The discovery took the whole section by surprise; there were no towns, no railways, and no
wagon roads except a few almost impassable lumber trails.   Yet, almost in a twinkling, the whole
situation changed; towns sprang up overnight,
roads were built, over which teamsters could carry
the oil to the nearest shipping points, and the great
trunk lines began to extend branches into the regions.   The one thing, next to Drake's well, that
made the oil available, was the discovery, which
was made by Samuel Van Syckel, that a two-inch
pipe, starting at the well, could convey the oil for

several miles to the nearest railway station. In a few years the whole oil region of Venango County was an inextricable tangle of these primitive pipe lines.

Thus, before the Civil War had ended, the western Pennsylvania wilderness had been transformed into the busy headquarters of a new industry. Companies had been formed, many of them the wildest stock-jobbing operations, refineries had been started, in a few years the whalers of New England had almost lost their occupation, but millions of American homes, that had hitherto had to spend the long winter evenings almost in darkness, suddenly found themselves flooded with light. In Cleveland, in Pittsburgh, in Philadelphia, in New York, and in the oil regions, the business of refining and selling petroleum had reached extensive proportions. Europe, although it had great undeveloped oil-fields of its own, drew upon this new American enterprise to such an extent that, eleven years after Drake's "discovery," petroleum had taken fourth place among our exported articles.

The very year that Bissell had organized his petroleum company a boy of sixteen had obtained his first job in a produce commission office on a dock in Cleveland. As the curtain rises on the career of

John D. Rockefeller, we see him perched upon a high stool, adding up figures and casting accounts, faithfully doing every odd office job that came his way, earning his employer's respect for his industry, his sobriety, and his unmistakable talents for business. Nor does this picture inadequately visualize Rockefeller's whole after-life, and explain the business qualities that made possible his unexampled success. It is, indeed, the scene to which Mr. Rockefeller himself most frequently reverts when, in his famous autobiographical discourses to his Cleveland Sunday School, he calls our attention to the rules that inevitably lead to industrial prosperity. "Thrift, thrift, Horatio," is the one idea upon which the great captain of the oil business has always insisted. Many have detected in these habits of mind only the cheese-paring activities of a naturally narrow spirit. Rockefeller's old Cleveland associates remember him as the greatest bargainer they had ever known, as a man who had an eye for infinite details and an unquenchable patience and resource in making economies. Yet Rockefeller was clearly more than a pertinacious haggler over trifles. Certainly such a diagnosis does not explain a man who has built up one of the world's greatest organizations and accumulated the largest fortune which has ever been placed at the disposal of one man. Indeed, Rockefeller displayed unusual business ability even before he entered the oil business. A young man who, at the age of nineteen, could start a commission house and do a business of nearly five hundred thousand the first year must have had commercial capacity to an extraordinary degree.

Fate had placed Rockefeller in Cleveland in the days when the oil business had got well under way. In the early sixties a score or so of refineries had started in this town, many of which were making large profits. It is not surprising that Rockefeller, gazing at these black and evil-smelling buildings from the vantage point of his commission office, should have felt an impulse to join in the gamble. He plunged into this new activity at the age of twenty-three. He possessed two great advantages over most of his adventurous competitors; one was a heavy bank account, representing his earnings in the commission business, and the other a partner, Samuel Andrews, who was generally regarded as a mechanical genius in the production of illuminating oil. At the beginning, therefore, Rockefeller had the two essentials which largely explain his subsequent career; an adequate liquid capital and high technical resources. In the first few years the Rockefeller houses — he rapidly organized three, one after another — competed with a large number of other units in the oil business on somewhat more than even terms. At this time Rockefeller was merely one of a large number of successful oil refiners, yet during these early days a grandiose scheme was taking shape in that quiet, insinuating, far-reaching brain. He said nothing about it, even to his closest associates, yet it filled his every waking hour. For this young man was taking a comprehensive sweep of the world and he saw millions of people, in the Americas, in Europe, and in Asia, whose need for the article in which he dealt would grow more insistent every day. He saw that he was handling a product which was becoming as much a necessity of life as the air itself. The young man reached out to grasp this business. "All of it," we can picture Rockefeller saying to himself, "all of it shall be mine." Any study of Rockefeller's career must lead to the conclusion that, before he had reached his thirtieth year, he had determined to monopolize this growing necessity. The mere fact that this young man could form such a stupendous plan indicates that in him we are meeting for the first time a new type

of industrial leader. At that time monopolies
were unknown in the United States. That certain
old English Kings had frequently granted exclusive trading privileges to favored merchants most
educated Americans knew; and their knowledge of
monopolies extended little further than this. Yet
about 1868 John D. Rockefeller started consciously
to revive this ancient practice, and to bring under
one ownership the magnificent industry to which
Drake's sensational discovery had given rise.

Daring as was this conception, the resourceful-
ness and the skill with which Rockefeller executed
it were more startling still. Merely to catalogue,
one by one, the achievements of the ten succeeding fruitful years, almost takes one's breath away.
Indeed the whole operation proceeded with such
a Napoleonic rapidity of action that the outside
world had hardly grasped Rockefeller's intention
before the monopoly had been made complete. We
catch one glimpse of Rockefeller, in 1868, as head of
the prosperous house of Rockefeller, Andrews, and
Flagler, and eight years afterwards we see him once
more, this time the man who controlled practically
the entire petroleum business of the world. His
career of conquest began in 1870, when the firm
of Rockefeller, Andrews, and Flagler, joining hands

with several large capitalists in Cleveland and New York, was incorporated under the name of the Standard Oil Company of Ohio. In 1870 about twenty-five independent refineries, many of them prosperous and powerful, were manufacturing oil in the city of Cleveland; two years afterward this new Standard Oil Company had absorbed all of them except five. In these two critical years the oil business of the largest refining center in the United States had thus passed into Rockefeller's hands. By 1874 the greatest refineries in New York and Philadelphia had likewise merged their identity with his own. When Rockefeller began his acquisition, there were thirty independent refineries operating in Pittsburgh, all of which, in four or five years, passed one by one under his control. The largest refineries of Baltimore surrendered in 1875.

These capitulations left only one important refining headquarters in the United States which the Standard had not absorbed. This was that section of western Pennsylvania where the oil business had had its origin. The mere fact that this area was the headquarters of the oil supply gave it great advantages as a place for manufacturing the finished product. The oil regions regarded these advantages as giving them the right to dominate the growing industry, and they had frequently proclaimed the doctrine that the business belonged to them. They hated Rockefeller as much as they feared him, yet at the very moment when the Titusville operators were hanging him in effigy and posting the hoardings with cabalistic signs against his corporation, this mysterious, almost uncanny power was encircling them. Men who one night were addressing public meetings denouncing the Standard influence would suddenly sell out their holdings the next day. In 1875 John D. Archbold, a brilliant young refiner who had grown up in the oil regions and who had gained much local fame as opponent of the Standard, appeared in Titusville as the President of the Acme Oil Company. At that time there were twenty-seven independent refineries in this section. Archbold began buying and leasing these establishments for his Acme Company, and in about four years practically every one had passed under his control. The Acme Company was merely a subsidiary of the Standard Oil.

These rapid purchasing campaigns gave the Standard ninety per cent of all the refineries in the United States, but Rockefeller's scheme comprehended more than the acquisition of refineries. In the main the Rockefeller group left the production

of crude oil in the hands of the private drillers, but
practically every other branch of the business
passed ultimately into their hands.   Both the New
York Central and the Erie railroads surrendered
to the Standard the large oil terminal stations
which they had maintained for years in New York.
As a consequence, the Standard obtained complete
supervision of all oil sent by railroad into New
York, and it also secured the machinery of a complete espionage system over the business of competitors.   The Standard acquired companies which
had built up a large business in marketing oil.
Even more dramatic was its success in gathering
up, one after another, these pipe lines which represented the circulatory system of the oil industry.
In the early days these pipe lines were small and
comparatively simple affairs.   They merely carried
the crude oil from the wells to railroad centers;
from these stations the railroads transported it to
the refineries at Cleveland, New York, and other
places. At an early day the construction and management of these pipe lines became a separate industry. And now, in 1873, the Standard Oil Company secured possession of a one-third interest in
the largest of these privately owned companies, the
American Transfer Company.   Soon afterward the

United Pipe Line Company went under their control. In 1877 the Empire Transportation Company, a large pipe line and refining corporation which the Pennsylvania Railroad had controlled for many years, became a Standard subsidiary.

Meanwhile certain hardy spirits in the oil regions had conceived a much more ambitious plan. Why not build great underground mains directly from the oil regions to the seaboard, pump the crude oil directly to the city refineries, and thus free themselves from dependence on the railroads? At first the idea of pumping oil through pipes over the Alleghany Mountains seemed grotesque, but competent engineers gave their indorsement to the plan. A certain "Dr." Hostetter built for the Columbia Conduit Company a trunk pipe line that extended thirty miles from the oil regions to Pittsburgh. Hardly had Hostetter completed his splendid project when the Standard Oil capitalists quietly appeared and purchased it! For four years another group struggled with an even more ambitious scheme, the construction of a conduit, five hundred miles long, from the oil regions to Baltimore. The American people looked on admiringly at the splendid enterprise whose projectors, led by General Haupt, the builder of the Hoosac Tunnel, struggled against bankruptcy, strikes, railroad opposition, and hostile legislatures, in their attempts to push their pipe line to the sea. In 1879 the Tidewater Company first began to pump their oil, and the American press hailed their achievement as something that ranked with the laying of the Atlantic Cable and the construction of the Brooklyn Bridge. But in less than two years the Rockefeller interest had entered into agreements with the Tidewater Company that practically placed this great seaboard pipe line in its hands.

Thus in less than ten years Rockefeller had realized his ambitious dream; he now controlled practically everything concerned in the manufacture and sale of petroleum. The change had come about so stealthily, so secretly, and even so remorselessly that it impressed the public almost as the work of some uncanny genius. What were the forces, personal and economic, that had produced this new phenomenon in our business life? In certain particulars the Standard Oil monopoly was the product of well-understood principles. From his earliest days John D. Rockefeller had struggled to eliminate the middleman. He established factories to build his own barrels, to make his own acids; he created his own selling firms, and, instead of paying large storage charges, he constructed his own warehouses in New York. From his earliest days as a refiner, he had adopted the principle of paying no man a profit, and of performing all the intermediate acts that had formerly resulted in large tribute to middlemen. Moreover, the Standard Oil Company was apparently the first great American industrial enterprise that realized the necessity of operating with an abundant capital. Not the least of Mr. Rockefeller's achievements was his success in associating with the new company men having great financial standing — Amasa Stone, Benjamin Brewster, Oliver Jennings, and the like, capitalists whose banking resources, placed at the disposition of the Standard, gave it an immense advantage over its rivals. While his competitors were "kiting" checks and waiting, hat in hand, on the good nature of the money lenders, Rockefeller always had a large bank balance, upon which he could instantly draw for his operations.

Nor must we overlook the fact that the Standard group contained a large number of exceedingly able men. "They are mighty smart men," said the despairing W. H. Vanderbilt, in 1879, when pressed to give his reasons for granting rebates to the Rockefeller group. "I guess if you ever had to deal

with them you would find that out." In Rockefeller the corporation possessed a man of tireless
industry and unshakable determination. Nothing
could turn him aside from the work to which he had
put his hand. Public criticism and even denuncia-
tion, while he resented it as unjust and regarded it
as the product of a general misunderstanding, never
caused the leader of Standard Oil even momenta-
rily to flinch. He was a man of one idea, and he
worked at it day and night, taking no rest or recrea-
tion, skillfully turning to his purpose every little
advantage that came his way. His associates —
men like Flagler, Archbold, and Rogers — also had
unusual talents, and together they built up the
splendid organization that still exists. They ex-
acted from their subordinates the last ounce of attention and energy and they rewarded generously
everybody who served them well. They showed
great judgment in establishing refineries at the
most strategic points and in giving up localities,
such as Boston and Portland, which were too far
removed from their supplies. They established a
marketing system which enabled them to bring
their oil directly from their own refineries to the re-
tailer, all in their own tank cars and tank wagons.
They extended their markets in foreign countries,

so that now the Standard sells the larger part of its products outside the United States. They established chemical research laboratories which devised new and inexpensive methods for refining the product and developed invaluable by-products, such as paraffin, naphtha, vaseline, and lubricating oils. It is impossible to study the career of the Standard Oil Company without concluding that we have here an example of a supreme business intelligence working in a field which gave the widest possible scope of action.

A high quality of organization, however, does not completely explain the growth of this monopoly. The Standard Oil Company was the beneficiary of methods that have deservedly received great public opprobrium. Of these the one that stands forth most conspicuously is the railroad rebate. Those who have attempted to trace the very origin of the Rockefeller preëminence to railroad discrimination have not entirely succeeded. Only the most hazy evidence exists that the firm of Rockefeller, Andrews, and Flagler greatly profited from rebates. In fact, refined oil was not transported from Cleveland to the seaboard by railroad until 1870, the year that this firm dissolved; practically all of the product then went by way of the Great Lakes and the Erie Canal. Possibly the Rockefeller firm did get occasional rebates on crude oil from the oil regions to the refineries, but so did their competitors. It is therefore not likely that such favors had great influence in making this single firm the most successful in the largest refining center. With the organization of the Standard Oil Company, however, rebates became a more important consideration.

The turning-point in the history of the oil industry came when the Rockefeller interests acquired the Cleveland refineries. The details concerning this act of generalship are fairly well known. The South Improvement Company is a corporation that necessarily bulks large in the history of the Standard Oil. Mr. Rockefeller and his associates have always disclaimed the parentage of this organization. They assert — and their assertion is doubtless true — that the only responsible begetters were Thomas A. Scott, President of the Pennsylvania Railroad, and certain refineries in Pittsburgh and Philadelphia which, though they were afterwards absorbed by the Standard, were at that time their competitors. These refiners and the Pennsylvania, over which the Standard Oil then was making no shipments, thus represented a group,

composed of railroads and refiners, which was antagonistic to the Rockefeller interests. The South
Improvement Company was an association of refiners with which the railroads, chiefly the Pennsylvania, the New York Central, and the Erie, made
exclusive contracts for shipping oil. Under these
contracts rates to the seaboard were to be generally raised, though the members of the South Improvement Company were to receive liberal rebates. The refiners of Cleveland and Pittsburgh
were to get lower rates than the refiners located
in the oil regions. But the clause in these contracts that caused the greatest amazement and
indignation was one which gave the inside group
rebates on every barrel of oil shipped by its
competitors.

It would be difficult to imagine any transaction
more wicked than these contracts. Carried into
execution they inevitably meant the extinction of
every refiner who had not been admitted into the
inside ring. Of the two thousand shares of the
South Improvement Company, the gentlemen who
were at that time most conspicuously identified
with the Standard Oil Company subscribed to five
hundred and forty. Mr. Rockefeller has always
protested that he did not favor the scheme and that

he became a party to it simply because he could not afford to antagonize the powerful Pennsylvania Railroad, which had originated it. When the details became public property, a wave of indignation swept from the Atlantic to the Pacific; the oil regions, which would have been the heaviest sufferers, shut down their wells and so cut off the supply of crude oil; the New York newspapers started a "crusade" against the South Improvement group and Congress ordered an investigation. So fiercely was the public wrath aroused that the railroads ran to cover, abrogated the contracts, signed an agreement promising never more to grant rebates to any one, while the Pennsylvania Legislature repealed the charter of the South Improvement Company. This particular scheme, therefore, never came to maturity.

Before the South Improvement Company ended its corporate existence, however, a great change had taken place in the oil situation. Practically all the refineries in Cleveland had passed into the control of the Standard Oil Company. The Standard has always denied that there was any connection between the purchase of these great refineries and the organization of the South Improvement Company. But there is much evidence sustaining a

contrary view, for many of these refiners afterward
went on the witness stand and told circumstantial
stories, all of which made precisely the same point.
This was that the Standard men had come to them,
shown the contracts which had been made by the
South Improvement Company, and argued that,
under these new conditions, the refineries left outside the combination could not long survive. The
Standard's rivals were therefore urged to "come
in," to take Standard stock in return for their
refineries, or, if they preferred, to sell outright.
Practically all saw the force in this argument and
sold — in most cases taking cash.

The acquisition of these Cleveland refineries
made inevitable the Rockefeller conquest of the oil
industry. Up to that time the Standard had refined about fifteen hundred barrels a day, and now
suddenly its capacity jumped to more than twelve
thousand barrels. This one strategic move had
made Rockefeller master of about one-third of all
the oil business in the United States, and this fact
explains the rapidity with which the other citadels
fell. There is no evidence that the Standard exercised any pressure upon the great refineries in New
York, Pittsburgh, and Philadelphia. Indeed these
concerns manifested an eagerness to join. The

fact that, unlike the Cleveland refiners, many of
the firms in these other cities took Standard stock,
and so became parts of the new organization, is
in itself significant. They evidently realized that
they were casting their fortunes with the winning
side. The huge shipments which the Standard now
controlled explain this change in front. Every day
Mr. Rockefeller could send from Cleveland to the
seaboard a train, sixty cars long, loaded with
the blue barrels containing his celebrated liquid.
That was a consideration for which any railroad
would at that time sell its soul. And the New
York Central road promptly made this sacrifice.
Hardly had the ink dried on its written promise
not to grant any rebates when it began granting
them to the Standard Oil Company.

In those days the railroad rate was not the sacred, immutable thing which it subsequently became, although the argument for equal treatment
of shippers existed theoretically just as strongly
forty years ago as it does today. The rebate
was just as illegal then as it is at present; there
was no precise statute, it is true, which made it
unlawful until the Interstate Commerce Act was
passed in 1887; but the common law had always
prohibited such discriminations. In the seventies

and eighties, however, railroad men like Cornelius Vanderbilt and Thomas A. Scott were less interested in legal formalities than in getting freight. They regarded transportation as a commodity to be bought and sold, like so much sugar or wheat or coal, and they believed that the ordinary principles which regulated private bargaining should also regulate the sale of the article in which they dealt. According to this reasoning, which was utterly false and iniquitous, but generally prevalent at the time, the man who shipped the largest quantities of oil should get the lowest rate.

The purchase of the Cleveland refineries made the Standard Oil group the largest shippers and therefore they obtained the most advantageous terms for transporting their product. Under these conditions they naturally obtained the monopoly, the extent of which has been already described. Their competitors could rage, hold public meetings, start riots, threaten to lynch Mr. Rockefeller and all his associates, but they could not long survive in face of these advantages. The only way in which the smaller shippers could overcome this handicap was by acquiring new methods of transportation. It was this necessity that inspired the construction of pipe lines; but the Standard, as already described, succeeded in absorbing these just about as rapidly as they were constructed.

Not only did the Standard obtain railroad rebates but it developed the most death-dealing methods in its system of marketing its oil. In these campaigns it certainly overstepped the boundaries of legitimate business, even according to the prevailing morals of its own or of any other time. While it probably did not set fire to rival refineries, as it has sometimes been accused of doing, it undoubtedly did resort to somewhat Prussian methods of destroying the foe. This great corporation divided the United States into several sections, over each of which it appointed an agent, who in turn subdivided his territory into smaller divisions, each one of which likewise had its captain. The order imperatively issued to each agent was, "Sell all the oil that is sold in your district." To these instructions he was rigidly held; success in accomplishing his task meant advancement and an increased salary, with a liberal pension in his old age, whereas failure meant a pitiless dismissal. He was expected to supervise not only his own business, but that of his rivals as well, to obtain access to their accounts, their shipments, and their customers. It has been asserted, and the assertion has been supported by considerable evidence, that these agents did not hesitate to bribe railroad employees and in this way get access to their competitors' bills of lading and records of their shipments, and that they would even bribe dealers to cancel such orders and take the oil from them at a lower price. This information laid the foundation for those price-cutting campaigns that have brought the name of the Standard Oil into such disfavor. And when the Standard cut, it cut to kill; the only purpose was to drive the competitor from the field, and, when this had been accomplished, the price of oil would promptly go up again. The organization of "bogus companies," started purely for the purpose of eliminating competitors, seems to have been a not infrequent practice. This latter method emphasizes another quality that accompanied the Standard's operations and so largely explains its unpopularity — the secrecy with which it so commonly worked. Though the independent oil refiners were combating the most powerful financial power of the time, they were frequently fighting in the dark, never knowing where to deliver their blows.

This same characteristic was manifested in the form of corporate existence which the Standard adopted. The first great "trust" was a trust not only in name but in fact. The Standard introduced not only a new economic development into our national organization; it introduced a new word into our language and an issue into American politics that provided sustenance for the presidential campaigns of twenty-five years. From the beginning the Standard Oil had always been a close corporation. Originally it had had only ten stockholders, and this number had gradually grown until, in 1881, there were forty-one. These men had adopted a new and secretive method of combining their increasing possessions into a single ownership. In 1873 the Standard Company had increased its capital stock (originally $1,000,000) to $3,500,000, the new certificates being exchanged for interests in the great New York and Philadelphia refineries. The Standard Oil Company of Ohio never had a larger capital stock than that. As additional properties were acquired, the interests were placed in the hands of trustees, who held them for the joint benefit of the stockholders in the original company. In 1882 this idea was carried further, for then the Standard Oil Trust was organized. The fact that the properties lay in so many different States, many of which had laws intended to curb corporations, was evidently what led to this form of consolidation. A trust was formed, consisting of nine trustees, who held, for the benefit of the Standard Oil stockholders, all the stock in the Standard and in the subsidiary companies. Instead of certificates of stock the trustees issued certificates of trust amounting to $70,000,000. Each Standard stockholder received twenty of these certificates for each share which he held of Standard stock. These certificates could be bought and sold and passed on by inheritance precisely the same as stocks.

Ingenious as was this legal device, it did not stand the test of the courts. In 1892 the Ohio Supreme Court declared the Standard Oil Trust a violation of the law and demanded its dissolution. The persistent attempts of the Standard to disregard this order increased its reputation for lawlessness. Finally, in 1899, after Ohio had brought another action, the trust was dissolved. The Standard interests now reorganized all their holdings under the name of the Standard Oil Company of New Jersey. Again, in 1911, the United States Supreme Court declared this combination a violation of the Sherman Anti-Trust Act, and ordered its dissolution. By this time the Standard capitalists had learned the value of public opinion as a corporate asset, and made no attempt to evade the order of the court. The Standard Oil Company of New Jersey proceeded to apportion among its stockholders the stock which it held in thirty-seven other companies — refineries, pipe lines, producing companies, marketing companies, and the like. Chief Justice White, in rendering his decision, specifically ordered that, in dissolving their combination, the Standard should make no agreement, contractual or implied, which was intended still to retain their properties in one ownership. As less than a dozen men owned a majority interest in the Standard Oil Company of New Jersey, these same men naturally continued to own a majority interest in the subsidiary companies. Though the immediate effect of this famous decision therefore was not to cause a separation in fact, this does not signify that, as time goes on, such a real dissolution will not take place. It is not unlikely that, in a few years, the transfers of the stock by inheritance or sale will weaken the consolidated interest to a point where the companies that made up the Standard Company will be distinct and competitive.

This is more likely to be the case since, long before the decision of 1911, the Standard Oil Company had ceased to be a monopoly. In the early nine-

ties there came to the front in the oil regions
a man whose organizing ability and indomitable
will suggested the Standard Oil leaders themselves.
This man's soul burned with an intense hatred of
the Rockefeller group, and this sentiment, as much
as his love of success, inspired all his efforts. There
is nothing finer in American business history than
the fifteen years' battle which Lewis Emery, Jr.,
fought against the greatest financial power of the
day. In 1901 this long struggle met with complete success. Its monuments were the two great
trunk pipe lines which Emery had built from
the Pennsylvania regions to Marcus Hook, near
Philadelphia, one for pumping refined and one for
pumping crude. The Pure Oil Company, Emery's
creation, has survived all its trials and has done
an excellent business. And meanwhile other independents sprang up with the discovery of oil in
other parts of the country. This discovery first
astonished the Standard Oil men themselves; when
someone suggested to Archbold, thirty-five years
ago, that the mid-continent field probably contained large oil supplies, he laughed, and said that
he would drink all the oil ever discovered outside
of Pennsylvania. In these days a haunting fear
pursued the oil men that the Pennsylvania field

would be exhausted and that their business would be ended. This fear, as developments showed, had a substantial basis; the Pennsylvania yield began to fail in the eighties and nineties, until now it is an inconsiderable element in this gigantic industry. Ohio, Indiana, Illinois, Kansas, Oklahoma, Texas, California, and other States in turn became the scene of the same exciting and adventurous events that had followed the discovery of oil in Pennsylvania. The Standard promptly extended its pipe lines into these new areas, but other great companies also took part in the development. These companies, such as the Gulf Refining Company and the Texas Refining Company, have their gathering pipe lines, their great trunk lines, their marketing stations, and their export trade, like the Standard; the Pure Oil Company has its tank cars, its tank ships, and its barges on the great rivers of Europe. The ending of the rebate system has stimulated the growth of independents, and the production of crude oil and the market demand in a thousand directions has increased the business to an extent which is now far beyond the ability of any one corporation to monopolize. The Standard interests refine perhaps something more than fifty per cent of the crude oil produced in this country.

But in recent years, Standard Oil has meant more than a corporation dealing in this natural product. It has become the synonym of a vast financial power reaching in all directions. The enormous profits made by the Rockefeller group have found investments in other fields. The Rockefellers became the owners of the great Mesaba iron ore range in Minnesota and of the Colorado Fuel and Iron Company, the chief competitor of United States Steel. It is the largest factor in several of the greatest American banks. Above all, it is the single largest railroad power in America today.

CHAPTER III

THE EPIC OF STEEL

It was the boast of a Roman Emperor that he had found the Eternal City brick and left it marble. Similarly the present generation of Americans inherited a country which was wood and have transformed it into steel. That which chiefly distinguishes the physical America of today from that of forty years ago is the extensive use of this metal. Our fathers used steel very little in railway transportation; rails and locomotives were usually made of iron, and wood was the prevailing material for railroad bridges. Steel cars, both for passengers and for freight, are now everywhere taking the place of the more flimsy substance. We travel today in steel subways, transact our business in steel buildings, and live in apartments and private houses which are made largely of steel. The steel automobile has long since supplanted the wooden carriage; the steel ship has displaced the iron and wooden vessel. The American farmer now encloses his lands with steel wire, the Southern planter binds his cotton with steel ties, and modern America could never gather her abundant harvests without her mighty agricultural implements, all of which are made of steel. Thus it is steel that shelters us, that transports us, that feeds us, and that even clothes us.

This substance is such a commonplace element in our lives that we take it for granted, like air and water and the soil itself; yet the generation that fought the Civil War knew practically nothing of steel. They were familiar with this metal only as a curiosity or as a material used for the finer kinds of cutlery. How many Americans realize that steel was used even less in 1865 than aluminum is used today? Nearly all the men who have made the American Steel Age — such as Carnegie, Phipps, Frick, and Schwab — are still living and some of them are even now extremely active. Thirty-five years ago steel manufacture was regarded, even in this country, as an almost exclusively British industry. In 1870 the American steel maker was the parvenu of the trade. American railroads purchased their first steel rails in England, and the early American steel makers went to Sheffield for their expert workmen. Yet, in little more than ten years, American mills were selling agricultural machinery in that same English town, American rails were displacing the English product in all parts of the world, American locomotives were drawing English trains on English railways, and American steel bridges were spanning the Ganges and the Nile. Indeed, the United States soon surpassed England. In the year before the World War the United Kingdom produced 7,500,000 tons of steel a year, while the United States produced 32,000,000 tons. Since the outbreak of the Great War, the United States has probably made more steel than all the rest of the world put together. "The nation that makes the cheapest steel," says Mr. Carnegie, "has the other nations at its feet." When some future Buckle analyzes the fundamental facts in the World War, he may possibly find that steel precipitated it and that steel determined its outcome.

Three circumstances contributed to the rise of this greatest of American industries: a new process for cheaply converting molten pig iron into steel, the discovery of enormous deposits of ore in several sections of the United States, and the entrance into the business of a hardy and adventurous group of manufacturers and business men. Our steel industry is thus another triumph of American inventive skill, made possible by the richness of our mineral resources and the racial energy of our people. An elementary scientific discovery introduced the great steel age. Steel, of course, is merely iron which has been refined — freed from certain impurities, such as carbon, sulphur, and phosphorus. We refine our iron and turn it into steel precisely as we refine our sugar and petroleum. From the days of Tubal Cain the iron worker had known that heat would accomplish this purification; but heat, up to almost 1865, was an exceedingly expensive commodity. For ages iron workers had obtained the finer metal by applying this heat in the form of charcoal, never once realizing that unlimited quantities of another fuel existed on every hand. The man who first suggested that so commonplace a substance as air, blown upon molten pig iron, would produce the intensest heat and destroy its impurities, made possible our steel railroads, our steel ships, and our steel cities. When William Kelly, an owner of iron works near Eddyville, Kentucky, first proposed this method in 1847, he met with the ridicule which usually greets the pioneer inventor. When Henry Bessemer, several years afterward, read a paper before the British Association for the Advancement of Science, in which he advocated the same principle, he was roared down as "a crazy Frenchman," and the savants were so humiliated by the suggestion that they voted to make no record of his "silly paper" in their official minutes.   Yet these two men, the American Kelly and the Englishman Bessemer, were the creators of modern steel.   The records of the American Patent Office clearly show that Kelly made "Bessemer" steel many years before Bessemer.   In 1870 the American Government refused to extend Bessemer's patent in this country on the ground that William Kelly had a prior claim; in spite of this, Bessemer was undoubtedly the man who developed the mechanical details and gave the process a universal standing.

Though the Bessemer process made possible the production of steel by tons instead of by pounds, it would never in itself have given the nation its present prëeminence in the steel industry.   Iron had been mined in the United States for two centuries on a small scale, the main deposits being located in the Lake Champlain region of New York and in western Pennsylvania.   But these, and a hundred other places located along the Atlantic coast, could not have produced ore in quantities sufficient to satisfy the yawning jaws of the Bessemer converters. As this new method poured out the liquid in thousands of tons, and as the commercial demand extended in a dozen different directions, the cry went up from the furnaces for more ore. And again Nature, which has favored America in so many directions, came to her assistance. Manufacturers in the steel regions began to recall strange stories which had been floating down for many years from the wilderness surrounding Lake Superior. The recollection of a famous voyage made in this region by Philo M. Everett, as far back as 1845, now laid siege to the imagination of the new generation of ironmasters. For years the Indians had told Everett of the "mountains of iron" that lay on the Minnesota shore of Lake Superior and had described their wonders in words that finally impelled this hardy adventurer to make a voyage of exploration. For six weeks, in company with two Indian guides, Everett had navigated a small boat along the shores of the Lake, covering a distance that now takes only a few hours. The Indians had long regarded this silent, red iron region with a superstitious reverence, and now, as the little party approached, they refused to complete the journey.

"Iron Mountain!" they said, pointing northward along the trail — "Indian not go near; white man go!" The sight which presently met Everett's eyes repaid him well for his solitary tramp in the forest. He found himself face to face with a "mountain a hundred and fifty feet high, of solid ore, which looked as bright as a bar of iron just broken." Other explorations subsequently laid open the whole of the Minnesota fields, including the Mesaba, which developed into the world's greatest iron range. America has other regions rich in ore, particularly in Alabama, located alongside the coal and limestone so necessary in steel production; yet it has drawn two-thirds of its whole supply from these Lake Superior fields. Not only the quantity, which is apparently limitless, but the quality explains America's leadership in steel making.

Mining in Minnesota has a character which is not duplicated elsewhere. When we think of an iron mine, we naturally picture subterranean caverns and galleries, and strange, gnome-like creatures prowling about with pick and shovel and drill. But mining in this section is a much simpler proceeding. The precious mineral does not lie concealed deep within the earth; it lies practically upon the surface. Removing it is not a question of blasting with dynamite; it is merely a matter of lifting it from the surface of the earth with a huge steam shovel. "Miners" in Minnesota have none of the conventional aspects of their trade. They operate precisely as did those who dug the Panama Canal. The railroad cars run closely to the gigantic red pit. A huge steam shovel opens its jaws, descends into an open amphitheater, licks up five tons at each mouthful, and, swinging sideways over the open cars, neatly deposits its booty. It is not surprising that ore can be produced at lower cost in the United States than even in those countries where the most wretched wages are paid. Evidently this one iron field, to say nothing of others already worked, gives a permanence to our steel industry.

Not only did America have the material resources; what is even more important, she had also the men. American industrial history presents few groups more brilliant, more resourceful, and more picturesque than that which, in the early seventies, started to turn these Minnesota ore fields into steel — and into gold. These men had all the dash, all the venturesomeness, all the speculative and even the gambling instinct, needed for one of the greatest industrial adventures in our annals. All had sprung from the simplest and humblest

origins. They had served their business appren-
ticeships as grocery clerks, errand boys, telegraph
messengers, and newspaper gamins. For the most
part they had spent their boyhood together, had
played with each other as children, had attended
the same Sunday schools, had sung in the same
church choirs, and, as young men, had quarreled
with each other over their sweethearts. The Pittsburgh group comprised about forty men, most of
whom retired as millionaires, though their names
for the most part signify little to the present-day
American. Kloman, Coleman, McCandless, Shinn,
Stewart, Jones, Vandervoort — are all important
men in the history of American steel.   Thomas
A. Scott and J. Edgar Thomson, men associated
chiefly with the creation of the Pennsylvania Railroad, also made their contributions. But three or
four men towered so preëminently above their associates that today when we think of the human
agencies that constructed this mighty edifice, the
names that insistently come to mind are those of
Carnegie, Phipps, Frick, and Schwab.

Books have been written to discredit Carnegie's
work and to picture him as the man who has stolen
success from the labor of greater men. Yet Carnegie
is the one member of a brilliant company who had

the indispensable quality of genius. He had none of the plodding, painstaking qualities of a Rockefeller; he had the fire, the restlessness, the keen relish for adventure, and the imagination that leaped far in advance of his competitors which we find so conspicuous in the older Vanderbilt. Carnegie showed these qualities from his earliest days. Driven as a child from his Scottish home by hunger, never having gone to school after twelve, he found himself, at the age of thirteen, living in a miserable hut in Allegheny, earning a dollar and twenty cents a week as bobbin-boy in a cotton mill, while his mother augmented the family income by taking in washing. Half a dozen years later Thomas Scott, President of the Pennsylvania Railroad, made Carnegie his private secretary. How well the young man used his opportunities in this occupation appeared afterward when he turned his wide acquaintanceship among railroad men to practical use in the steel business. It was this personal adaptability, indeed, that explains Carnegie's success. In the narrow, methodical sense he was not a business man at all; he knew and cared nothing for its dull routine and its labyrinthine details. As a practical steel man his position is a negligible one. Though he was profoundly impressed by his first sight of a Bessemer converter, he had little interest in the every-day process of making steel. He had also many personal weaknesses: his egotism was marked, he loved applause, he was always seeking opportunities for self-exploitation, and he even aspired to fame as an author and philosopher. The staid business men of Pittsburgh early regarded Carnegie with disfavor; his daring impressed them as rashness and his bold adventures as the plunging of the speculator. Yet in all its aspects Carnegie's triumph was a personal one. He was perhaps the greatest commercial traveler this country has ever known. While his more methodical associates plodded along making steel, Carnegie went out upon the highway, bringing in orders by the millions. He showed this same personal quality in the organization of his force. As a young man, entirely new to the steel industry, he selected as the first manager of his works Captain Bill Jones; his amazing judgment was justified when Jones developed into America's greatest practical genius in making steel. "Here lies the man" — Carnegie once suggested this line for his epitaph — "who knew how to get around him men who were cleverer than himself." Carnegie inspired these men with his own energy and restlessness; the spirit of the whole establishment automatically became that of the pushing spirit of its head. This little giant became the most remorseless pace-maker in the steel regions. However astounding might be the results obtained by the Carnegie works the captain at the head was never satisfied. As each month's output surpassed that which had gone before, Carnegie always came back with the same cry of "More." "We broke all records for making steel last week!" a delighted superintendent once wired him and immediately he received his answer, "Congratulations. Why not do it every week?" This spirit explains the success of the Carnegie Company in outdistancing all its competitors and gaining a worldwide preëminence for the Pittsburgh district. But Carnegie did not make the mistake of capitalizing all this prosperity for himself; his real greatness as an American business man consists in the fact that he liberally shared the profits with his associates. Ruthless he might be in appropriating their last ounce of energy, yet he rewarded the successful men with golden partnerships. Nothing delighted Carnegie more than to see the man whom he had lifted from a puddler's furnace develop into a millionaire.

Henry Phipps, still living at the age of seventy-

eight, was the only one of Carnegie's early associates who remained with him to the end. Like
many of the others, Phipps had been Carnegie's
playmate as a boy, so far as any of them, in those
early days, had opportunity to play; like all his
contemporaries also, Phipps had been wretchedly
poor, his earliest business opening having been as
messenger boy for a jeweler. Phipps had none of
the dash and sparkle of Carnegie. He was the
plodder, the bookkeeper, the economizer, the man
who had an eye for microscopic details. "What
we most admired in young Phipps," a Pittsburgh
banker once remarked, "is the way in which he
could keep a check in the air for three or four
days." His abilities consisted mainly in keeping
the bankers complaisant, in smoothing the ruf-
fled feelings of creditors, in cutting out unnecessary expenditures, and in shaving prices.

Carnegie's other two more celebrated associates,
Henry C. Frick and Charles M. Schwab, were
younger men. Frick was cold and masterful, as
hard, unyielding, and effective as the steel that
formed the staple of his existence. Schwab was
enthusiastic, warm-hearted, and happy-go-lucky;
a man who ruled his employees and obtained his
results by appealing to their sympathies. The men

of the steel yards feared Frick as much as they loved "Charlie" Schwab. The earliest glimpses which we get of these remarkable men suggest certain permanent characteristics: Frick is pictured as the sober, industrious bookkeeper in his grandfather's distillery; Schwab as the rollicking, whistling driver of a stage between Loretto and Cresson. Frick came into the steel business as a matter of deliberate choice, whereas Schwab became associated with the Pittsburgh group more or less by accident.

The region of Connellsville contains almost 150 square miles underlaid with coal that has a particular heat value when submitted to the process known as coking. As early as the late eighties certain operators had discovered this fact and were coking this coal on a small scale. It is the highest tribute to Frick's intelligence that he alone foresaw the part which this Connellsville coal was to play in building up the Pittsburgh steel district. The panic of 1873, which laid low most of the Connellsville operators, proved Frick's opportunity. Though he was only twenty-four years old he succeeded, by his intelligence and earnestness, in borrowing money to purchase certain Connellsville mines, then much depreciated in price. From that

moment, coke became Frick's obsession, as steel
had been Carnegie's. With his early profits he purchased more coal lands until, by 1889, he owned ten
thousand coke ovens and was the undisputed "coke
king" of Connellsville. Several years before this,
Carnegie had made Frick one of his marshals, coke
having become indispensable to the manufacture of
steel, and in 1889 the former distiller's accountant
became Carnegie's commander-in-chief. Probably
the popular mind associates Frick chiefly with the
importation of Slavs as workmen, with the terrible
strikes that followed in consequence at Homestead,
with the murderous attack made upon him by
Berkman, the anarchist, and with his bitter, long-
drawn-out quarrel with Andrew Carnegie. Frick's
stormy career was naturally the product of his
character.

On the other hand, temperamental pliability
and lovableness were the directing traits of the
man who, in his way, made contributions quite as
solid to the extension of the Pittsburgh steel industry. Schwab worked with the human material
quite as successfully as other men worked with
iron ore, Bessemer furnaces, and coal. He handled
successfully what was perhaps the greatest task
in management ever presented to a manufacturer

when to him fell the job of reorganizing the Homestead Works after the strike of 1892 and of transforming thousands of riotous workmen into orderly and interested producers of steel. In three or four years practically every man on the premises had become "Charlie" Schwab's personal friend, and the Homestead property which, until the day he took charge, had been a colossal failure, had developed into one of the most profitable holdings of the Carnegie Company. As his reward Schwab, at the age of thirty-four, was made President of the Carnegie corporation. Only sixteen years before he had entered the steel works as a stake driver at a dollar a day.

When the Carnegie group began operations in the early seventies, American steel, as a British writer remarked, was a "hot-house product"; yet in 1900 the Carnegie partners divided $40,000,000 as the profits of a single year. They had demonstrated that the United States, despite the high prices that prevailed everywhere, could make steel more cheaply than any other country. Foreign observers have offered several explanations for this achievement. American makers had an endless supply of cheap and high-grade ore, cheaper coke, cheaper transportation, and workmen of a superior skill.   We must give due consideration to the fact that their organization was more flexible than those of older countries, and that it regulated promotion exclusively by merit and gave exceptional opportunities to young men.   American steel makers also had scrap heaps whose size astounded the foreign observers; they never hesitated to discard the most expensive plants if by so doing they could reduce the cost of steel rails by a dollar a ton.   Machinery for steel making had a more extensive development in this country than in England or Germany.   Mr. Carnegie also enjoyed the advantages of a high protective tariff, though about 1900 he discovered that his extremely healthy infant no longer demanded this form of coddling.   But probably the Carnegie Company's greatest achievement was the abolition of the middleman.   In a few years it assembled all the essential elements of steel making in its own hands.   Frick's entrance into the combination gave the concern an unlimited supply of the highest grade of coking coal.   In a few years, the Carnegie interests had acquired great holdings in the Minnesota ore regions.

At first glance, the Pittsburgh region seems hardly the ideal place for the making of steel.   Fortune first placed the industry there because all the raw materials, especially iron ore and coal, seemed to exist in abundance. But the discovery of the Minnesota ore field, which alone could supply this essential product in the amounts which the furnaces demanded, immediately deprived the Pittsburgh region of its chief advantage. As a result of this sudden development, the manufacturers of Pittsburgh awoke one morning and discovered that their ore was located a thousand miles away. To bring it to their converters necessitated a long voyage by water and rail, with several reloadings. They overcame these obstacles by developing machinery for handling ore and by acquiring the raw materials and the connecting links of transportation. Ore which had been lying in the wilds of Minnesota on Monday morning was thus brought to Pittsburgh and made into steel rails or bridges or structural shapes by Saturday night. The Carnegie Company first acquired sufficient mineral lands to furnish ore for several generations and organized an ore fleet which transported the products of the mines through the lakes to ports on Lake Erie, particularly Ashtabula and Conneaut. The purchase of the Bessemer and Lake Erie Railroad, which extended from Conneaut to Pittsburgh, made this great transportation route complete. Besides freeing their business from uncertainty, this elimination of middlemen naturally produced great economies.

Probably Andrew Carnegie's shrewdness in naming his first plant the J. Edgar Thompson Steel Works, after the powerful President of the Pennsylvania Railroad, and in making Thompson and his associate Scott partners, had much to do with his early success. These two gentlemen conferred two priceless favors upon the struggling enterprise. They became large purchasers of steel rails and their influence in this direction extended far beyond the Pennsylvania Railroad. What was perhaps even more important, they gave the Carnegie concerns railroad rebates. The use of rebates, as a method of stifling competition and building up a great industrial prosperity, is an offense which the popular mind associates almost exclusively with the Standard Oil Company, yet the Carnegie fortune, as well as that of John D. Rockefeller, received an artificial stimulation of this kind.

Though incomparably the greatest of the American steel companies, the Carnegie Steel Company by no means monopolized the field. In forty years, indeed, an enormous steel area had grown up, including western Pennsylvania, Ohio, Indiana, and

Illinois, practically all of it drawing its raw materials from those same teeming ore lands in the Lake Superior region.   Johnstown, Youngstown, Cleveland, Lorain, Chicago, and Joliet, became headquarters of steel production almost as important as Pittsburgh itself.   Two entirely new steel kingdoms, each with its own natural reservoirs of ore, grew up in Colorado and Alabama.   The Colorado Fuel and Iron Company, which possessed apparently inexhaustible mineral lands in Colorado, Wyoming, Utah, New Mexico, and California, itself produces not far from three million tons a year, almost half the present production of Great Britain.   The Alabama steel country has developed in even more spectacular fashion.   Birmingham, a hive of southern industry placed almost as if by magic in the leisurely cotton lands of the South, had no existence in 1870, when the Pittsburgh prosperity began. In the Civil War, the present site of a city with a population of 140,000 was merely a blacksmith shop in the fork of the roads.   Yet this district has advantages for the manufacture of steel that have no parallel elsewhere.   The steel companies which are located here do not have to bring their materials laboriously from a distance but possess, immediately at hand, apparently endless store of the three things needful for making steel — iron ore, coal, and limestone. All these territories have their personal romances and their heroes, many of them quite as picturesque as those of the Pittsburgh group.

It is doubtful indeed if American industry presents any figure quite as astonishing and variegated as that of John W. Gates, the man who educated farmers all over the world to the use of wire fencing. Half charlatan, half enthusiast, speculator, gambler, a man who created great enterprises and who also destroyed them, at times an up-building force and at other times a sinister influence, Gates completely typified a period in American history that, along with much that was heroic and splendid, had much also that was grotesque and sordid. The opera-bouffe performance that laid the foundations of Gates's great industry was in every way characteristic of this period. In 1871 Gates, then a clerk in a hardware store at twenty-five dollars a week, made his first attempt to sell barbed wire in the great cattle countries of the southwestern States. When the cattle men in Texas first saw this barbed wire, they ridiculed the idea that it could ever hold their steers. Gates selected a plaza in San Antonio, fenced it in with his new product, and invited the

enemies to bring along their wildest specimens.
About thirty of Texas' most ferocious cattle, placed
within the enclosure, spent a whole afternoon
plunging at the barbs in a useless and tormenting
attempt to escape. This spectacular demonstration of efficiency launched Gates fairly upon his
career. He immediately began to sell his new fencing on an enormous scale; in a few years the whole
world was demanding it, and it has become, as recent events have disclosed, a particularly formid-
able munition of war. The American Steel and
Wire Company, one of the greatest of American
corporations, was the ultimate outgrowth of that
lively afternoon in San Antonio.

In 1900 the Carnegie Steel Company was making
one-quarter of all the Bessemer steel produced in
the United States. It owned in abundance all the
properties which were essential to its completed
output — coal, limestone, steel ships, railroads, and
steel mills. In twenty-five years, from 1875 to
1900, this manufacturing enterprise had paid the
Carnegie group profits aggregating $133,000,000,
profits which, in the closing years of the century,
had increased at a stupendous rate. In 1898 Carnegie and his associates had divided $11,500,000,
in 1899 their earnings had grown to $25,000,000, and

in 1900 the aggregate had suddenly jumped to $40,-000,000. Of this latter sum Carnegie received $25,-000,000, Phipps $5,500,000, Frick $2,600,000, and Schwab $1,300,000. And Carnegie's little group could see no limit to the growth of their business and the expansion of their personal fortunes. Yet at that very moment Carnegie was planning to play the part of a Charles V. with the large empire which he had pieced together — to abdicate his throne, retire from business life, and spend his remaining days in quiet.

Many influences were impelling him to this decision. His triumph, stupendous as it had been, also had had its alloy of sorrow. Indeed this little Scotsman, now at the crowning of his glory, was one of the loneliest figures in the world. Practically all the forty men with whom he had been closely associated had vanished from the scene. He had quarreled with his playmate and lifelong partner, Henry Phipps, and was in the worst possible business and personal relations with Frick. He had no son to carry on his work. He had become greatly interested in his philanthropies, and he had declared that the man who died rich died disgraced. Moreover, new influences were rising in the steel trade with which Carnegie had little sympathy. Its national capital seemed to be shifting from Pittsburgh to Wall Street. New men who knew nothing about steel but who possessed an intimate acquaintance with stocks and bonds — J. Pierpont Morgan, George W. Perkins, and their associates — were branching out as controllers of large steel interests. Carnegie had no interest in Wall Street; he has declared that he never speculated in his life and that he would immediately dissociate himself from any partner who would do so. This Wall Street coterie, in the years from 1898 to 1900, had made several large combinations in the steel trade. That was the era when the trust mania had gained possession of the American mind and when its worst features displayed themselves. The Federal Steel Company, the American Bridge Company, the American Steel and Wire, the National Tube Company, all representing the assembling of large works which had been engaged as rivals in similar enterprises, were launched, with the usual accompaniments of "underwriting syndicates," watered stock, and Wall Street speculation. This sort of thing made no appeal to Andrew Carnegie. His huge enterprise had always remained essentially a copartnership, and he had frequently expressed his abhorrence of trusts.

Yet, in spite of his wish to retire from business and in spite of his avowed intention to die poor, Carnegie now adopted the policy of the Sibylline leaves to all prospective purchasers. Moore and Reid would have purchased his interest for $157,-000,000; when Rockefeller came along the price had risen to $250,000,000; when the oil man shook his head and retired, Carnegie immediately raised his price to $500,000,000. It is doubtful whether he would have sold at all had not his Wall Street competitors begun to encroach on a field which the little Scotsman understood quite as well as they — the production and merchandising of steel. The newly organized combinations were completing elaborate plans to go after Carnegie's business. Then Carnegie, who had practically retired from active life, again arrayed himself in his shirt-sleeves, abandoned his career of authorship, and resumed his early trade. His first attacks produced an immense reverberation in the House of Morgan. He purchased a huge tract at Conneaut and began building a gigantic plant for the manufacture of steel tubes, a business in which he had not hitherto engaged. This was a blow aimed at one of Morgan's pet new creations, the National Tube Company. Should Carnegie finish his works, there was no doubt the Morgan enterprise would be ruined, for the new plant would be far more modern and so could manufacture the product at a much lower price; and, with Charles M. Schwab as active manager, what possible chance would the older corporation have? But Carnegie struck his enemy at an even more vulnerable point. The Pennsylvania Railroad had a practical monopoly of traffic in and out of Pittsburgh, and Pittsburgh "created" more freight business than any other city in the world. Carnegie lent his powerful support to George J. Gould, who was then extending his railroad system into the preëmpted field and was also making surveys and had financed a company to build an entirely new railroad from Pittsburgh to the Atlantic Coast. As Carnegie himself controlled the larger part of the freight that made Pittsburgh such an essential feeder to railroads, his new enterprise caused the greatest alarm. At the same time Carnegie equipped a new and splendid fleet of ore ships, his purpose being to enter a field of transportation which John D. Rockefeller had found extremely profitable.

Such were the circumstances and such were the motives that gave birth to the world's largest corporation. All one night, so the story goes, Charles

M. Schwab and John W. Gates discussed the steel situation with J. Pierpont Morgan. There was only one possible solution, they said — Andrew Carnegie must be bought out. By the time the morning sun came through the windows Morgan had been convinced. "Go and ask him what he will sell for," he said to Schwab. In a brief period Schwab came back to Morgan with a letter which contained the following figures — five per cent gold bonds $303,450,000; preferred stock $98,277,100; common stock $90,279,000 — a total of over $492,-000,000. Carnegie demanded no cash; he preferred to hold a huge first mortgage on a business whose golden opportunities he knew so well. Morgan, who had been accustomed all his life to dictate to other men, had now met a man who was able to dictate to him. And he capitulated. The man who fifty-three years before had started life in a new country as a bobbin-boy at a dollar and twenty cents a week, now at the age of sixty-six retired from business the second richest man in the world. With him retired a miscellaneous assortment of millionaires whose fortunes he had made and whose subsequent careers in the United States and in Europe have given a peculiar significance to the name "Pittsburgh Millionaires." The United

States Steel Corporation, the combination that included not only the Carnegie Company but seventy per cent of all the steel concerns in the country, was really a trust made up of trusts. It had a capitalization of a billion and a half, of which about $700,000,000 was composed of the commodity usually known as "water"; but so greatly has its business grown and so capably has it been managed that all this liquid material has since been converted into more solid substance. The disappearance of Andrew Carnegie and his coworkers and the emergence of this gigantic enterprise completed the great business cycle in the steel trade. The age of individual enterprise and competition had passed — that of corporate control had arrived.

CHAPTER IV

THE TELEPHONE: "AMERICA'S MOST POETICAL
ACHIEVEMENT"

A DISTINGUISHED English journalist, who was visiting the United States, in 1917, on an important
governmental mission, had an almost sublime illustration of the extent to which the telephone had
developed on the North American Continent. Sitting at a desk in a large office building in New York,
Lord Northcliffe took up two telephone receivers
and placed one at each ear. In the first he heard
the surf beating at Coney Island, New York, and
in the other he heard, with equal distinctness,
the breakers pounding the beach at the Golden
Gate, San Francisco. Certainly this demonstration
justified the statement made a few years before
by another English traveler. "What startles and
frightens the backward European in the United
States," said Mr. Arnold Bennett, "is the efficiency and fearful universality of the telephone.

To me it was the proudest achievement and the most poetical achievement of the American people."

Lord Northcliffe's experience had a certain dramatic justice which probably even he did not appreciate. He is the proprietor of the London *Times*, a newspaper which, when the telephone was first introduced, denounced it as the "latest American humbug" and declared that it "was far inferior to the well-established system of speaking tubes." The London *Times* delivered this solemn judgment in 1877. A year before, at the Philadelphia Centennial Exposition, Don Pedro, Emperor of Brazil, picked up, almost accidentally, a queer cone-shaped instrument and put it to his ear. "My God! It talks!" was his exclamation; an incident which, when widely published in the press, first informed the American people that another of the greatest inventions of all times had had its birth on their own soil. Yet the initial judgment of the American people did not differ essentially from the opinion which had been more coarsely expressed by the leading English newspaper. Our fathers did not denounce the telephone as an "American humbug," but they did describe it as a curious electric "toy" and ridiculed the notion that it could ever have any practical value. Even after Alexander Graham Bell and his associates had completely demonstrated its usefulness, the Western Union Telegraph Company refused to purchase all their patent rights for $100,000! Only forty years have passed since the telephone made such an inauspicious beginning. It remains now, as it was then, essentially an American achievement. Other nations have their telephone systems, but it is only in the United States that its possibilities have been even faintly realized. It is not until Americans visit foreign countries that they understand that, imperfect as in certain directions their industrial and social organization may be, in this respect at least their nation is preëminent.

The United States contains nearly all the telephones in existence, to be exact, about seventy-five per cent. We have about ten million telephones, while Canada, Central America, South America, Great Britain, Europe, Asia, and Africa all combined have only about four million. In order to make an impressive showing, however, we need not include the backward peoples, for a comparison with the most enlightened nations emphasizes the same point. Thus New York City has more telephones than six European countries taken together

— Austria-Hungary, Belgium, Norway, Denmark, Italy, and the Netherlands. Chicago, with a population of 2,000,000, has more telephones than the whole of France, with a population of 40,000,-000. Philadelphia, with 1,500,000, has more than the Russian Empire, with 166,000,000. Boston has more telephones than Austria-Hungary, Los Angeles more than the Netherlands, and Kansas City more than Belgium. Several office buildings and hotels in New York City have more instruments than the kingdoms of Greece or Bulgaria. The whole of Great Britain and Ireland has about 650,000 telephones, which is only about 200,000 more than the city of New York.

Mere numbers, however, tell only half the story. It is when we compare service that American superiority stands most manifest. The London newspapers are constantly filled with letters abusing the English telephone system. If these communications describe things accurately, there is apparently no telephone vexation that the Englishman does not have to endure. Delays in getting connections are apparently chronic. At times it seems impossible to get connections at all, especially from four to five in the afternoon — when the operators are taking tea. Suburban

connections, which in New York take about ninety
seconds, average half an hour in London, and many
of the smaller cities have no night service. An
American thinks nothing of putting in a telephone:
he notifies his company and in a few days the instrument is installed. We take a thing like this
for granted. But there are places where a mere
telephone subscription, the privilege of having an
instrument installed, is a property right of considerable value and where the telephone service
has a "waiting list," like an exclusive club. In
Japan one can sell a telephone privilege at a good
price, its value being daily quoted on the Stock
Exchange. Americans, by constantly using the
telephone, have developed what may be called a
sixth sense, which enables them to project their
personalities over an almost unlimited area. In
the United States the telephone has become the one
all-prevailing method of communication. The
European writes or telegraphs while the American
more frequently telephones. In this country the
telephone penetrates to places which even the mails
never reach. The rural free delivery and other
forms of the mail service extend to 58,000 communities, while our 10,000,000 telephones encom-
pass 70,000. We use this instrument for all the

varied experiences of life, domestic, social, and commercial. There are residences in New York City that have private branch exchanges, like a bank or a newspaper office. Hostesses are more and more falling into the habit of telephoning invitations for dinner and other diversions. Many people find telephone conversations more convenient than personal interviews, and it is every day displacing the stenographer and the traveling salesman.

Perhaps the most noteworthy achievement of the telephone is its transformation of country life. In Europe, rural telephones are almost unknown, while in the United States one-third of all our telephone stations are in country districts. The farmer no longer depends upon the mails; like the city man, he telephones. This instrument is thus the greatest civilizing force we have, for civilization is very largely a matter of intercommunication. Indeed, the telephone and other similar agencies, such as the parcel post, the rural free delivery, better roads, and the automobile, are rapidly transforming rural life in this country. In several regions, especially in the Mississippi Valley, a farmer who has no telephone is in a class by himself, like one who has no mowing-machine. Thus the latest returns from Iowa, taken by the census as far back as 1907, showed that seventy-three per cent of all the farms — 160,000 out of 220,000 — had telephones and the proportion is unquestionably greater now. Every other farmhouse from the Atlantic to the Pacific contains at least one instrument. These statistics clearly show that the telephone has removed half the terrors and isolation of rural life. Many a lonely farmer's wife or daughter, on the approach of a suspicious-looking character, has rushed to the telephone and called up the neighbors, so that now tramps notoriously avoid houses that shelter the protecting wires. In remote sections, insanity, especially among women, is frequently the result of loneliness, a calamity which the telephone is doing much to mitigate.

In the United States today there is one telephone to every nine persons. This achievement represents American invention, genius, industrial organization, and business enterprise at their best. The story of American business contains many chapters and episodes which Americans would willingly forget. But the American Telephone and Telegraph Company represents an industry which has made not a single "swollen fortune," whose largest stockholder is the wife of Alexander Graham Bell, the inventor (a woman who, being totally deaf, has never talked over the telephone); which has not corrupted legislatures or courts; which has steadily decreased the prices of its products as business and profits have increased; which has never issued watered stock or declared fictitious dividends; and which has always manifested a high sense of responsibility in its dealings with the public.

Two forces, American science and American business capacity, have accomplished this result. As a mechanism, this American telephone system is the product not of one but of many minds. What most strikes the imagination is the story of Alexander Graham Bell, yet other names — Carty, Scribner, Pupin — play a large part in the story.

The man who discovered that an electric current had the power of transmitting sound over a copper wire knew very little about electricity. Had he known more about this agency and less about acoustics, Bell once said himself, he would never have invented the telephone. His father and grandfather had been teachers of the deaf and dumb and had made important researches in acoustics. Alexander Graham Bell, born in Edinburgh in March, 1847, and educated there and in London, followed the ancestral example. This experience

gave Bell an expert knowledge of phonetics that
laid the foundation for his life work. His invention, indeed, is clearly associated with his attempts
to make the deaf and dumb talk. He was driven
to America by ill-health, coming first to Canada,
and in 1871 he settled in Boston, where he accepted
a position in Boston University to introduce his
system of teaching deaf-mutes. He opened a
school of "Vocal Physiology," and his success in
his chosen field brought him into association with
the people who afterward played an important part
in the development of the telephone. Not a single
element of romance was lacking in Bell's experience; his great invention even involved the love
story of his life. Two influential citizens of Boston,
Thomas Sanders and Gardiner G. Hubbard, had
daughters who were deaf and dumb, and both
engaged Bell's services as teacher. Bell lived in
Sanders's home for a considerable period, dividing
his time between teaching his little pupil how to
talk and puttering away at a proposed invention
which he called a "harmonic telegraph." Both
Sanders and Hubbard had become greatly interested in this contrivance and backed Bell finan-
cially while he worked. It was Bell's idea that, by
a system of tuning different telegraphic receivers

to different pitches, several telegraphic messages could be sent simultaneously over the same wire. The idea was not original with Bell, although he supposed that it was and was entirely unaware that, at the particular moment when he started work, about twenty other inventors were struggling with the same problem. It was one of these other twenty experimenters, Elisha Gray, who ultimately perfected this instrument. Bell's researches have an interest only in that they taught him much about sound transmission and other kindred subjects and so paved the way for his great conception.

One day Hubbard and Sanders learned that Bell had abandoned his "harmonic telegraph" and was experimenting with an entirely new idea. This was the possibility of transmitting the human voice over an electric wire. While working in Sanders's basement, Bell had obtained from a doctor a dead man's ear, and it is said that while he was minutely studying and analyzing this gruesome object, the idea of the telephone first burst upon his mind. For years Bell had been engaged in a task that seemed hopeless to most men — that of making deaf-mutes talk. "If I can make a deaf-mute talk, I can make iron talk," he declared. "If I could make a current of electricity vary in intensity as the air varies in density," he said at another time, "I could transmit sound telegraphically." Many others, of course, had dreamed of inventing such an instrument. The story of the telephone concerns many men who preceded Bell, one of whom. Philip Reis, produced, in 1861, a mechanism that could send a few discordant sounds, though not the human voice, over an electric wire. Reis seemed to have based his work upon an article published in *The American Journal of Science* by Dr. C. G. Page, of Salem, Mass., in 1837, in which he called attention to the sound given out by an electric magnet when the circuit is opened or closed. The work of these experimenters involves too many technicalities for discussion in this place. The important facts are that they all involved different principles from those worked out by Bell and that none of them ever attained any practical importance. Reis, in particular, never grasped the essential principles that ultimately made the telephone a reality. His work occupies a place in telephone history only because certain financial interests, many years after his death, brought it to light in an attempt to discredit Bell's claim to priority as the inventor. An investigator who seems to have grasped more clearly the basic idea was the distinguished

American inventor Elisha Gray, already mentioned as the man who had succeeded in perfecting the "harmonic telegraph." On February 14, 1876, Gray filed a caveat in the United States Patent Office, setting forth pretty accurately the conception of the electric telephone. The tragedy in Gray's work consists in the fact that, two hours before his caveat had been put in, Bell had filed his application for a patent on the completed instrument.

The champions of Bell and Gray may dispute the question of priority to their heart's content; the historic fact is that the telephone dates from a dramatic moment in the year 1876. Sanders and Hubbard, much annoyed that Bell had abandoned his harmonic telegraph for so visionary an idea as a long distance talking machine, refused to finance him further unless he returned to his original quest. Disappointed and disconsolate, Bell and his assistant, Thomas A. Watson, had started work on the top floor of the Williams Manufacturing Company's shop in Boston. And now another chance happening turned Bell back once more to the telephone. His magnetized telegraph wire stretched from one room to another located in a remote part of the building. One day Watson accidentally plucked a piece of clock wire that lay near this telegraph wire, and Bell, working in another room, heard the twang. A few seconds later Watson was startled when an excited and somewhat disheveled figure burst into his room. "What was that?" shouted Bell. What had happened was clearly manifest; a sound had been sent distinctly over an electric wire. Bell's harmonic telegraph immediately went into the discard, and the young inventor — Bell was then only twenty-nine — became a man of one passionate idea. Yet final success did not come easily; the inventor worked day and night for forty weeks before he had obtained satisfactory results. It was on March 10, 1876, that Watson, in a distant room, picked up the first telephone receiver and heard these words, the first that had ever passed over a magnetized wire, "Come here, Watson; I want you." The speaking instrument had become a reality, and the foundation of the telephone, in all its present development, had been laid. When the New York and San Francisco line was opened in January, 1915, Alexander Graham Bell spoke these same words to his old associate, Thomas Watson, located in San Francisco, both men using the same instruments that had served so well on that historic occasion forty years before.

Though Bell's first invention comprehended the great basic idea that made it a success, the instrument itself bore few external resemblances to that which has become so commonplace today. If one could transport himself back to this early period and undergo the torture of using this primitive telephone, he would appreciate somewhat the labor, the patience, the inventive skill, and the business organization that have produced the modern telephone. In the first place you would have no separate transmitter and receiver. You would talk into a funnel-shaped contrivance and then place it against your ear to get the returning message. In order to make yourself heard, you would have to shout like a Gloucester sea-captain at the height of a storm. More than the speakers' voices would come over the wire. It seemed to have become the playground of a million devils; moanings, shriekings, mutterings, and noises of all kinds would constantly interrupt the flow of speech. To call up your "party" you would not merely lift the receiver as today; you would tap with a lead pencil, or some other appliance, upon the diaphragm of your transmitter. There were no separate telephone wires. The talking at first was done over the telegraph lines. The earliest "centrals" reminded most persons of madhouses, for the day of the polite, soft-spoken telephone girl had not arrived. Instead, boys were rushing around with the ends of wires which they were frantically attempting to peg into the holes of the primitive switchboard and so establish "connections." When not knocking down and fighting each other, these boys were swearing into transmitters at the customers; and it is said that the incurable profanity of these early "telephone boys" had much to do with their supersession by girls. In the early days of the telephone, each instrument had to carry its own battery, usually installed in a little box under the transmitter. The early telephone wires, even in the largest cities, were strung on poles, as they are in country and suburban districts today. In places like New York and Chicago, these thousands of overhanging wires not only destroyed the attractiveness of the thoroughfare, but constantly interfered with the fire department and proved to be public nuisances in other ways. A telephone wire, however, loses much of its transmitting power when placed under ground, and it took many years of experimenting before the engineers perfected these subways. In these early days, of course, the telephone was purely a local matter. Certain visionary enthusiasts had foreseen the possibility of a national, long distance system, but a large amount of labor, both in the laboratory and out, was to be expended before these aspirations could become realities.

The transformation of this rudimentary means of communication into the beautiful mechanism which we have today forms a splendid chapter in the history of American invention. Of all the details in Bell's apparatus the receiver is almost the only one that remains now what it was forty years ago. The story of the transmitter in itself would fill a volume. Edison's success in devising a transmitter which permitted talk in ordinary conversational tones — an invention that became the property of the Western Union Telegraph Company, which early embarked in the telephone business — at one time seemed likely to force the Bell Company out of business. But Emile Berliner and Francis Blake finally came to the rescue with an excellent instrument, and the suggestion of an English clergyman, the Reverend Henry Hummings, that carbon granules be used on the diaphragm, made possible the present perfect instrument. The magneto call bell — still used in certain backward districts — for many years gave fair results for calling purposes, but the automatic switch, which enables us to get central by merely picking up the receiver, has made possible our great urban service. It was several years before the telephone makers developed so essential a thing as a satisfactory wire. Silver, which gave excellent results, was obviously too costly, and copper, the other metal which had many desirable qualities, was too soft. Thomas B. Doolittle solved this problem by inventing a hard-drawn copper wire. A young man of twenty-two, John J. Carty, suggested a simple device for exorcising the hundreds of "mysterious noises" that had made the use of the telephone so agonizing. It was caused. Carty pointed out, by the circumstance that the telephone, like the telegraph, used a ground circuit for the return wire; the resultant scrapings and moanings and howlings were merely the multitudinous voices of mother earth herself. Mr. Carty began installing the metallic circuit in his lines — that is, he used wire, instead of the ground, to complete the circuit. As a result of this improvement the telephone was immediately cleared of these annoying interruptions. Mr. Carty, who is now Chief Engineer of the American Telephone and Telegraph Company, and the man who has superintended all its extensions in recent years, is one of the three or four men who have done most to create the present system. Another is Charles E. Scribner, who, by his invention of that intricate device, the multiple switchboard, has converted the telephone exchange into a smoothly working, orderly place. Scribner's multiple switchboard dates from about 1890. It was Mr. Scribner also who replaced the individual system of dry cells with one common battery located at the central exchange, an improvement which saved the Company 4,000,-000 dry cells a year. Then Barrett discovered a method of twisting fifty pairs of wires — since grown to 2400 pairs — into a cable, wrapping them in paper and molding them in lead, and the wires were now taken from poles and placed in conduits underground.

But perhaps the most romantic figure in telephone history, next to Bell, is that of a humble Servian immigrant who came to this country as a boy and obtained his first employment as a rubber in a Turkish bath. Michael I. Pupin was graduated from Columbia, studied afterward in Germany, and became absorbed in the new subject of electromechanics. In particular he became interested in a telephone problem that had bothered the greatest experts for years.   One thing that had prevented the great extension of the telephone, especially for long distance work, was the size of the wire.   Long distance lines up to 1900 demanded wire about one-eighth of an inch thick — as thick as a fair-sized lead pencil; and, for this reason, the New York–Chicago line, built in 1893, consumed 870,000 pounds of copper wire of this size.   Naturally the enormous expense stood in the way of any extended development.   The same thickness also interfered with cable extension.   Only about a hundred wires could be squeezed into one cable, against the eighteen hundred now compressed in the same area. Because of these shortcomings, telephone progress, about 1900, was marking time, awaiting the arrival of a thin wire that would do the work of a thick one. The importance of the problem is shown by the fact that one-fourth of all the capital invested in the telephone has been spent in copper.   Professor Pupin, who had been a member of the faculty of Columbia University since 1888, solved this problem in his quiet laboratory and, by doing so, won the greatest prize in modern telephone art.   His researches resulted in the famous "Pupin coil" by the expedient now known as "loading."   When the scientists attempt to explain this invention, they have to use all kinds of mathematical formulas and curves and, in fact, they usually get to quarreling among themselves over the points involved. What Professor Pupin has apparently done is to free the wire from those miscellaneous disturbances known as "induction." This Pupin invention involved another improvement unsuspected by the inventor, which shows us the telephone in all its mystery and beauty and even its sublimity. Soon after the Pupin coil was introduced, it was discovered that, by crossing the wires of two circuits at regular intervals, another unexplainable circuit was induced. Because this third circuit travels apparently without wires, in some manner which the scientists have not yet discovered, it is appropriately known as the phantom circuit. The practical result is that it is now possible to send three telephone messages and eight telegraph messages over two pairs of wires — all at the same time. Professor Pupin's invention has resulted in economies that amount to millions of dollars, and has made possible long distance lines to practically every part of the United States.

Thus many great inventive minds have produced the physical telephone. We can point to several men — Bell, Blake, Carty, Scribner, Barrett, Pupin

— and say of each one, "Without his work the present telephone system could not exist." But business genius, as well as mechanical genius, explains this achievement.   For the first four or five years of its existence, the new invention had hard sailing. Bell and Thomas Watson, in order to fortify their finances, were forced to travel around the country, giving a kind of vaudeville entertainment.   Bell made a speech explaining the new invention, while a cornet player, located in another part of the town, played solos, the music reaching the audience through several telephone instruments placed against the walls. Watson, also located at a distance, varied the program by singing songs via telephone.   These lecture tours not only gave Bell the money which he sorely needed but advertised the innovation.   There followed a few scattering attempts to introduce the telephone into every-day use and telephone exchanges were established in New York, Boston, Bridgeport, and New Haven.   But these pioneers had the hostility of the most powerful corporation of the day — the Western Union Telegraph Company — and they lacked aggressive leaders.

In 1878, Mr. Gardiner Hubbard, Bell's earliest backer, and now his father-in-law, became acquainted with a young man who was then serving in Washington as General Superintendent of the Railway Mail Service. This young man was Theodore N. Vail. His energy and enterprise so impressed Hubbard that he immediately asked Vail to become General Manager of the company which he was then forming to exploit the telephone. Viewed from the retrospection of forty years this offer certainly looks like one of the greatest prizes in American business. What it signified at that time, however, is apparent from the fact that the office paid a salary of $3500 a year and that for the first ten years Vail did not succeed in collecting a dollar of this princely remuneration. Yet it was a happy fortune, not only for the Bell Company but for the nation, that placed Vail at the head of this struggling enterprise. There was a certain appropriateness in his selection, even then. His granduncle, Stephen Vail, had built the engines for the first steamship to cross the Atlantic. A cousin had worked with Morse while he was inventing the telegraph. Vail, who was born in Carroll County, Ohio, in 1845, after spending two years as a medical student, suddenly shifted his plans and became a telegraph operator. Then he entered the Railway Mail service; in this service he completely revolutionized the system and introduced reforms that exist at the present time. A natural bent had apparently directed Vail's mind towards methods of communication, a fact that may perhaps explain the youthful enthusiasm with which he took up the new venture and the vision with which he foresaw and planned its future. For the chief fact about Vail is that he was a business man with an imagination. The crazy little machine which he now undertook to exploit did not interest him as a means of collecting tolls, floating stock, and paying dividends. He saw in it a new method of spreading American civilization and of contributing to the happiness and comfort of millions of people. Indeed Vail had hardly seen the telephone when a picture portraying the development which we are familiar with today unfolded before his eyes. That the telephone has had a greater development in America than elsewhere and that the United States has avoided all those mistakes of organization that have so greatly hampered its growth in other lands, is owing to the fact that Vail, when he first took charge, mapped out the comprehensive policies which have guided his corporation since.

Vail early adopted the "slogan" which has directed the Bell activities for forty years — "One

System! One Policy! Universal Service." In his mind a telephone company was not a city affair, or even a state affair; it was a national affair. His aim has been from the first a universal, national service, all under one head, and reaching every hamlet, every business house, factory, and home in the nation. The idea that any man, anywhere, should be able to take down a receiver and talk to any one, anywhere else in the United States, was the conception which guided Vail's labors from the first. He did not believe that a mass of unrelated companies could give a satisfactory service; if circumstances had ever made a national monopoly, that monopoly was certainly the telephone. Having in view this national, universal, articulating monopoly, Vail insisted on his second great principle, the standardization of equipment. Every man's telephone must be precisely like every other man's, and that must be the best which mechanical skill and inventive genius could produce. To make this a reality and to secure perfect supervision and upkeep, it was necessary that telephones should not be sold but leased. By enforcing these ideas Vail saved the United States from the chaos which exists in certain other countries, such as France, where each subscriber purchases his own instrument, making his selection from about forty different varieties. That certain dangers were inherent in this universal system Vail understood. Monopoly all too likely brings in excessive charges, poor service, and inside speculation; but it was Vail's plan to justify his system by its works. To this end he established a great engineering department which should study all imaginable mechanical improvements, with the results which have been described. He gave the greatest attention to every detail of the service and particularly insisted on the fairest and most courteous treatment of the public. The "please" which invariably accompanies the telephone girl's request for a number — the familiar "number, please" — is a trifle, but it epitomizes the whole spirit which Vail inspired throughout his entire organization. Though there are plenty of people who think that the existing telephone charges are too high, the fact remains that the rate has steadily declined with the extension of the business. Vail has also kept his company clear from the financial scandals that have disgraced so many other great corporations. He has never received any reward himself except his salary, such fortune as he possesses being the result of personal business ventures in South America during the twenty years from 1887 to 1907 that he was not associated with the Bell interests.

Vail's first achievement was to rescue this invention from the greatest calamity which would have befallen it. The Western Union Telegraph Company, which in the early days had looked upon the telephone as negligible, suddenly awoke one morning to a realization of its importance. This corporation had recently introduced its "printing telegraph," a device that made it possible to communicate without the intermediary operator. When news reached headquarters that subscribers were dropping this new contrivance and subscribing to telephones, the Western Union first understood that a competitor had entered their field. Promptly organizing the American Speaking Telephone Company, the Western Union, with all its wealth and prestige, proceeded to destroy this insolent pigmy. Its methods of attack were unscrupulous and underhanded, the least discreditable one being the use of its political influence to prevent communities from giving franchises to the Bell Company. But this corporation mainly relied for success upon the wholesale manner in which it infringed the Bell patents. It raked together all possible claimants to priority, from Philip Reis

to Elisha Gray, in its attempts to discredit Bell
as the inventor. The Western Union had only
one legitimate advantage — the Edison transmitter — which was unquestionably much superior to
anything which the Bell Company then possessed.
Many Bell stockholders were discouraged in face of
this fierce opposition and wished to abandon the
fight. Not so Vail. The mere circumstance that
the great capitalists of the Western Union had
taken up the telephone gave the public a confidence
in its value which otherwise it would not have had,
a fact which Vail skillfully used in attracting influential financial support. He boldly sued the
Western Union in 1878 for infringement of the Bell
patents. The case was a famous one; the whole
history of the telephone was reviewed from the
earliest days, and the evidence as to rival claimants
was placed on record for all time. After about a
year, Mr. George Gifford, perhaps the best patent
attorney of the day, who was conducting the case
for the Western Union, quietly informed his clients
that they could never win, for the records showed
that Bell was the inventor. He advised the Western Union to settle the case out of court and his
advice was taken. This great corporation war was
concluded by a treaty (November 10, 1879) in

which the Western Union acknowledged that Bell was the inventor, that his patents were valid, and agreed to retire from the telephone business. The Bell Company, on its part, agreed to buy the Western Union Telephone System, to pay the Western Union a royalty of twenty per cent on all telephone rentals, and not to engage in the telegraph business. Had this case been decided against the Bell Company it is almost certain that the telephone would have been smothered in the interest of the telegraph and its development delayed for many years.

Soon after the settlement of the Western Union suit, the original group which had created the telephone withdrew from the scene. Bell went back to teaching deaf-mutes. He has since busied himself with the study of airplanes and wireless, and has invented an instrument for transmitting sound by light. The new telephone company offered him $10,000 a year as chief inventor, but he replied that he could not invent to order. Thomas Sanders received somewhat less than $1,000,000 and lost most of it exploiting a Colorado gold mine. Gardiner Hubbard withdrew from business and devoted the last years of his life to the National Geographic Society. Thomas Watson, after retiring from the

8

telephone business, bought a ship-building yard near Boston, which has been successful.

In making this settlement with the Western Union, the Bell interests not only eliminated a competitor but gained great material advantages. They took over about 56,000 telephone stations located in 55 cities and towns. They also soon acquired the Western Electric Manufacturing Company, which under the control of the Western Union had developed into an important concern for the manufacture of telephone supplies. Under the management of the Bell Company this corporation, which now has extensive factories in Hawthorne, Ill., produces two-thirds of the world's telephone apparatus. With the Western Electric Vail has realized the fundamental conception underlying his ideal telephone system — the standardization of equipment. For the accomplishment of his idea of a national telephone system, instead of a parochial one, Mr. Vail organized, in 1881, the American Bell Telephone Company, a corporation that really represented the federalization of all the telephone activities of the subsidiary companies. The United States was divided into several sections, in each of which a separate company was organized to develop the telephone possibilities of that particular area. In 1899 the American Telephone and Telegraph Company took over the business and properties of the American Bell Company. The larger corporation built toll lines, connected these smaller systems with one another, and thus made it possible for Washington to talk to New York, New York to Chicago, and ultimately — Boston to San Francisco. An enlightened policy led the Bell Company frequently to establish exchanges in places where there was little chance of immediate profit. Under this stimulation the use of this instrument extended rapidly, yet it is in the last twenty years that the telephone has grown with accelerated momentum. In 1887 there were 170,000 subscribers in the United States, and in 1900 there were 610,000; but in 1906 the American Telephone and Telegraph Company was furnishing its service to 2,550,000 stations, and in 1916 to 10,000,000. Clearly it is only since 1900 that the telephone has become a commonplace of American existence. Up to 1900 it had grown at the rate of about 13,000 a year; whereas since 1900 it has grown at the rate of 700,000 a year. The explanation is that charges have been so reduced that the telephone has been brought within the reach of practically every business house and every family.

Until the year 1900 every telephone subscriber had to pay $240 a year, and manifestly only families in affluent circumstances could afford such a luxury. About that time a new system of charges known as the "message rate" plan was introduced, according to which the subscriber paid a moderate price for a stipulated number of calls, and a pro rata charge for all calls in excess of that number. Probably no single change in any business has had such an instantaneous effect. The telephone, which had hitherto been an external symbol of prosperity, suddenly became the possession of almost every citizen.

Other companies than the Bell interests have participated in this development. The only time the Bell Company has had no competitor, Mr. Vail has said, was at the Philadelphia Centennial in 1876. Some of this competition has benefited the public but much of it has accomplished little except to enrich many not over-scrupulous promoters. Groups of farmers who frequently started companies to furnish service at cost did much to extend the use of the telephone. Many of the companies which, when the Bell patents expired in 1895, sprang up in the Middle West, also manifested great enterprise and gave excellent service. These companies have made valuable contributions, of which perhaps the automatic telephone, an instrument which enables a subscriber to call up his "party" directly, without the mediation of "central," is the most ingenious. Although due acknowledgment must be made of the honesty and enterprise with which hundreds of the independents are managed, the fact remains that they are a great economic waste. Most of them give only a local service, no company having yet arisen which aims to duplicate the comprehensive national plans of the greater corporation. As soon as an independent obtains a foothold, the natural consequence is that every business house and private household must either be contented with half service, or double the cost of the telephone by subscribing to two companies. It is not unlikely that the "independents" have exercised a wholesome influence upon the Bell Corporation, but, as the principle of government regulation rather than individual competition has now become the established method of controlling monopoly, this influence will possess less virtue in the future. In addition to these independent enterprises, the telephone has unfortunately furnished an opportunity for stock-jobbing schemes on a considerable scale. The years from

1895 to 1905 witnessed the growth of many bubbles of this kind; one group of men organized not far from two hundred telephone companies. They would go into selected communities, promise a superior service at half the current rates, enlist the coöperation of "leading" business men, sell the stock largely in the city or town to be benefited, make large profits in the construction of the lines and the sale of equipment — and then decamp for pastures new. The multitudinous bankruptcies that followed in the wake of such exploiters at length brought their activities to an end.

CHAPTER V

THE DEVELOPMENT OF PUBLIC UTILITIES

THE streets of practically all American cities, as they appeared in 1870 and as they appear today, present one of the greatest contrasts in our industrial development. Fifty years ago only a few flickering gas lamps lighted the most traveled thoroughfares. Only the most prosperous business houses and homes had even this expensive illumination; most obtained their artificial light from the new illuminant known as kerosene. But it was the mechanism of city transportation that would have looked the strangest in our eyes. New York City had built the world's first horse-car line in 1832, and since that year this peculiarly American contrivance has had the most extended development. In 1870, indeed, practically every city of any importance had one or more railways of this type. New York possessed thirty different companies, each operating an independent system. In Philadelphia,

Chicago, St. Louis, and San Francisco the growth of urban transportation had been equally haphazard. The idea of combining the several street railways into one comprehensive corporation had apparently occurred to no one. The passengers, in their peregrinations through the city, had frequently to pay three or four fares; competition was thus the universal rule. The mechanical equipment similarly represented a primitive state of organization. Horses and mules, in many cases hideous physical specimens of their breeds, furnished the motive power. The cars were little "bobtailed" receptacles, usually badly painted and more often than not in a desperate state of disrepair. In many cities the driver presided as a solitary autocrat; the passengers on entrance deposited their coins in a little fare box. At night tiny oil lamps made the darkness visible; in winter time shivering passengers warmed themselves by pulling their coat collars and furs closely about their necks and thrusting their lower members into a heap of straw, piled almost a foot deep on the floor.

Who would have thought, forty years ago, that the lighting of these dark and dirty streets and the modernization of these local railway systems would have given rise to one of the most astounding chapters in our financial history and created hundreds, perhaps thousands, of millionaires? When Thomas A. Edison invented the incandescent light, and when Frank J. Sprague in 1887 constructed the first practicable urban trolley line, in Richmond, Virginia, they liberated forces that powerfully affected not only our social and economic life but our political institutions. These two inventions introduced a new phrase — "Public Utilities." Combined with the great growth and prosperity of the cities they furnished a fruitful opportunity to several particularly famous groups of financial adventurers. They led to the organization of "syndicates" which devoted all their energies, for a quarter of a century, to exploiting city lighting and transportation systems. These syndicates made a business of entering city after city, purchasing the scattered street railway lines and lighting companies, equipping them with electricity, combining them into unified systems, organizing large corporations, and floating huge issues of securities. A single group of six men — Yerkes, Widener, Elkins, Dolan, Whitney, and Ryan — combined the street railways, and in many cases the lighting companies, of New York, Philadelphia, Chicago, Pittsburgh, and at least a hundred towns and cities in Pennsylvania.

Connecticut, Rhode Island, Massachusetts, Ohio, Indiana, New Hampshire, and Maine. Either jointly or separately they controlled the gas and electric lighting companies of Philadelphia, Reading, Harrisburg, Atlanta, Vicksburg, St. Augustine, Minneapolis, Omaha, Des Moines, Kansas City, Sioux City, Syracuse, and about seventy other communities. A single corporation developed nearly all the trolley lines and lighting companies of New Jersey; another controlled similar utilities in San Francisco and other cities on the Pacific Coast. In practically all instances these syndicates adopted precisely the same plan of operation. In so far as their activities resulted in cheap, comfortable, rapid, and comprehensive transit systems and low-priced illumination, their activities greatly benefited the public. The future historian of American society will probably attribute enormous influence to the trolley car in linking urban community with urban community, in extending the radius of the modern city, in freeing urban workers from the demoralizing influences of the tenement, in offering the poorer classes comfortable homes in the surrounding country, and in extending general enlightenment by bringing about a closer human intercourse. Indeed, there is probably no single ínfluence that has contributed so much to the pleasure and comfort of the masses as the trolley car.

Yet the story that I shall have to tell is not a pleasant one. It is impossible to write even a brief outline of this development without plunging deeply into the two phases of American life of which we have most cause to be ashamed; these are American municipal politics and the speculative aspects of Wall Street. The predominating influences in American city life have been the great franchise corporations. Practically all the men that have had most to do with developing our public utilities have also had the greatest influence in city politics. In New York, Thomas F. Ryan and William C. Whitney were the powerful, though invisible, powers in Tammany Hall. In Chicago, Charles T. Yerkes controlled mayors and city councils; he even extended his influence into the state government, controlling governors and legislatures. In Philadelphia, Widener and Elkins dominated the City Hall and also became part of the Quay machine of Pennsylvania. Mark Hanna, the most active force in Cleveland railways, was also the political boss of the State. Roswell P. Flower, chief agent in developing Brooklyn Rapid Transit, had been Governor of New York; Patrick

Calhoun, who monopolized the utilities of San Francisco and other cities, presided likewise over the city's inner politics. The Public Service Corporation of New Jersey also comprised a large political power in city and state politics. It is hardly an exaggeration to say that in the most active period, that from 1880 to 1905, the powers that developed city railway and lighting companies in American cities were identically the same owners that had the most to do with city government. In the minds of these men politics was necessarily as much a part of their business as trolley poles and steel rails. This type of capitalist existed only on public franchises — the right to occupy the public streets with their trolley cars, gas mains, and electric light conduits; they could obtain these privileges only from complaisant city governments, and the simplest way to obtain them was to control these governments themselves. Herein we have the simple formula which made possible one of the most profitable and one of the most adventurous undertakings of our time.

An attempt to relate the history of all these syndicates would involve endless repetition. If we have the history of one we have the history of practically all. I have therefore selected, as typical, the operations of the group that developed the street railways and, to a certain extent, the public lighting companies, in our three greatest American cities — New York, Chicago, and Philadelphia.

One of the men who started these enterprises actually had a criminal record. William H. Kemble, an early member of the Philadelphia group, had been indicted for attempting to bribe the Pennsylvania Legislature; he had been convicted and sentenced to one year in the county jail and had escaped imprisonment only by virtue of a pardon obtained through political influence. Charles T. Yerkes, one of his partners in politics and street railway enterprises, had been less fortunate, for he had served seven months for assisting in the embezzlement of Philadelphia funds in 1873. It was this circumstance in Yerkes's career which impelled him to leave Philadelphia and settle in Chicago where, starting as a small broker, he ultimately acquired sufficient resources and influence to embark in that street railway business at which he had already served an extensive apprenticeship. Under his domination, the Chicago aldermen attained a depravity that made them notorious all over the world. They openly sold Yerkes the use of the streets for cash and constantly blocked the efforts which an infuriated populace made for reform. Yerkes purchased the old street railway lines, lined his pockets by making contracts for their reconstruction, issued large flotations of watered stock, heaped securities upon securities and reorganization upon reorganization and diverted their assets to business in a hundred ingenious ways.

In spite of the crimes which Yerkes perpetrated in American cities, there was something refreshing and ingratiating about the man. Possibly this is because he did not associate any hypocrisy with his depredations. "The secret of success in my business," he once frankly said, "is to buy old junk, fix it up a little, and unload it upon other fellows." Certain of his epigrams — such as, "It is the strap-hanger who pays the dividends" — have likewise given him a genial immortality. The fact that, after having reduced the railway system of Chicago to financial pulp and physical dissolution, he finally unloaded the whole useless mass, at a handsome personal profit, upon his old New York friends, Whitney and Ryan, and decamped to London, where he carried through huge transit enterprises, clearly demonstrated that Yerkes was a buccaneer of no ordinary caliber.

Yerkes's difficulties in Philadelphia indirectly made possible the career of Peter A. B. Widener. For Yerkes had become involved in the defalcation of the City Treasurer, Joseph P. Mercer, whose translation to the Eastern Penitentiary left vacant a municipal office into which Mr. Widener now promptly stepped.   Thus Mr. Widener, as is practically the case with all these street railway magnates, was a municipal politician before he became a financier.   The fact that he attained the city treasurership shows that he had already gone far, for it was the most powerful office in Philadelphia. He had all those qualities of suavity, joviality, firmness, and personal domination that made possible success in American local politics a generation ago.   His occupation contributed to his advancement.   In recent years Mr. Widener, as the owner of great art galleries and the patron of philanthropic and industrial institutions, has been a national figure of the utmost dignity.   Had you dropped into the Spring Garden Market in Philadelphia forty years ago, you would have found a portly gentleman, clad in a white apron, and armed with a cleaver, presiding over a shop decorated with the design — "Peter A. B. Widener, Butcher."   He was constantly joking with his customers and visitors, and in the evening he was accustomed to foregather with a group of well-chosen spirits who had been long famous in Philadelphia as the "all-night poker players." A successful butcher shop in Philadelphia in those days played about the same part in local politics as did the saloon in New York City. Such a station became the headquarters of political gossip and the meeting ground of a political clique; and so Widener, the son of a poor German bricklayer, rapidly became a political leader in the Twentieth Ward, and soon found his power extending even to Harrisburg. A few years ago Widener presided over a turbulent meeting of Metropolitan shareholders in Newark, New Jersey. The proposal under consideration was the transference of all the Metropolitan's visible assets to a company of which the stockholders knew nothing. When several of these stockholders arose and demanded that they be given an opportunity to discuss the projected lease, Widener turned to them and said, in his politest and blandest manner: "You can vote first and discuss afterward." Widener displayed precisely these same qualities of ingratiating arrogance and good-natured contempt as a Philadelphia politician. He was a man of big frame, alert and decisive in his movements.

and a ready talker; in business he was given much to living in the clouds — a born speculator — emphatically a "boomer." His sympathies were generous, at times emotional; it is said that he has even been known to weep when discussing his fine collection of Madonnas. He showed this personal side in his lifelong friendship and business association with William L. Elkins, a man much inferior to him in ability. Indeed, Elkins's great fortune was little more than a free gift from Widener, who carried him as a partner in all his deals. Elkins became Widener's bondsman when the latter entered the City Treasurer's office; the two men lived near each other on the same street, and this association was cemented when Widener's oldest son married Elkins's daughter. Elkins had started life as an entry clerk in a grocery store, had made money in the butter and egg business, had "struck oil" at Titusville in 1862, and had succeeded in exchanging his holdings for a block of Standard Oil stock. He too became a Philadelphia politician, but he had certain hard qualities — he was closefisted, slow, plodding — that prevented him from achieving much success.

For the other members of this group we must now change the scene to New York City. In the early eighties certain powerful interests had formed plans for controlling the New York transit fields. Prominent among them was William Collins Whitney, a very different type of man from the Philadelphians. Born in Conway, Massachusetts, in 1841, he came from a long line of distinguished and intellectual New Englanders. At Yale his wonderful mental gifts raised him far above his fellows; he divided all scholastic honors there with his classmate, William Graham Sumner, afterwards Yale's great political economist. Soon after graduation Whitney came to New York and rapidly forged ahead as a lawyer. Brilliant, polished, suave, he early displayed those qualities which afterward made him the master mind of presidential Cabinets and the maker of American Presidents. Physically handsome, loved by most men and all women, he soon acquired a social standing that amounted almost to a dictatorship. His early political activities had greatly benefited New York. He became a member of that group which, under the leadership of Joseph H. Choate and Samuel J. Tilden, accomplished the downfall of William M. Tweed. Whitney remained Tilden's political protégé for several years. Though highbred and luxury-loving, as a young man he was not averse to hard political work, and many old-timers still remember the days when "Bill" Whitney delivered cart-tail harangues on the lower east side.   By 1884 he had become the most prominent Democrat in New York — always a foe to Tammany — and as such he contributed largely to Cleveland's first election, became Secretary of the Navy in Cleveland's cabinet and that great President's close friend and adviser.   As Secretary of the Navy, Whitney, who found the fleet composed of a few useless hulks left over from the days of Farragut, created the fighting force that did such efficient service in the Spanish War.   The fact that the United States is now the third naval power is largely owing to these early activities of Whitney.

Certainly all this national service forms a strange prelude to Whitney's activities in the public utilities of New York and other cities.   Had he died, indeed, in his fiftieth year, his name would be renowned today as a worker for the highest ideals of American citizenship.   What suddenly made him turn his back upon his past, join his former enemies in Tammany Hall, and engage in these great speculative enterprises?   The simplest explanation is that, with his ability and ambition, Whitney had the luxurious tastes of a

Medici.   At the height of his career his financial
success found expression in a magnificent house
which he established on Fifth Avenue.   Its furnish-
ings were one of the wonders of New York.   Whitney ransacked the art treasures of Europe, stripped
medieval castles of their carvings and tapestries,
ripped whole staircases and ceilings from the repose
of centuries, and relaid them in this abode of splen-
dor, and here he entertained with a lavishness that
astounded New York.   This single exploit pictures
the man.   Everything that Whitney did and was
— his house, his financial transactions, his Wall
Street speculations, the rewards which he gave his
friends — assumed heroic proportions.   But these
things all demanded money.   The dilapidated
horse railways of New York offered him his most
convenient opportunity for amassing it.

But Whitney had not proceeded far when he
came face to face with a quiet and energetic young
man who had already made considerable progress
in the New York transit field.   This was a Vir-
ginian of South Irish descent who had started life
as a humble broker's clerk twelve or fourteen years
before.   His name was Thomas Fortune Ryan.
Few men have wielded greater power in American finance, but in 1884 Ryan was merely a

ruddy-faced, clean-cut, and clean-living Irishman
of thirty-three, who could be depended on to exe-
cute quickly and faithfully orders on the New York
Stock Exchange — even though they were small
ones — and who, in unostentatious fashion, had
already acquired much influence in Tammany Hall.
With his six feet of stature, his extremely slender
figure, his long legs, his long arms, his raiment —
which always represented the height of fashion and
tended slightly toward the flashy — Ryan made
a conspicuous figure wherever he went. He was
born in 1851, on a small farm in Nelson County,
Virginia. The Civil War, which broke out when
Ryan was a boy of ten, destroyed the family fortune and in 1868, when seventeen, he began life
as a dry-goods clerk in Baltimore, fulfilling the
tradition of the successful country boy in the large
city by marrying his employer's daughter. When
his father-in-law failed, in 1870, Ryan came to
New York, went to work in a broker's office, and
succeeded so well that, in a few years, he was able
to purchase a seat on the Stock Exchange. He
was sufficiently skillful as a broker to number Jay
Gould among his customers and to inspire a prophecy by William C. Whitney that, if he retained
his health, he would become one of the richest men

in the country.   Afterwards, when he knew him more intimately, Whitney elaborated this estimate by saying that Ryan was "the most adroit, suave, and noiseless man he had ever known." Ryan had two compelling traits that soon won for him these influential admirers.   First of all was his marvelous industry.   His genius was not spasmodic.   He worked steadily, regularly, never losing a moment, never getting excited, going, day after day, the same monotonous dog-trot, easily outdistancing scores of apparently stronger men.   He also had the indispensable faculty of silence.   He has always been the least talkative man in Wall Street, but, with all his reserve, he has remained the soul of courtesy and outward good nature.

Here, then, we have the characters of this great impending drama — Yerkes in Chicago, Widener and Elkins in Philadelphia, Whitney and Ryan in New York.   These five men did not invariably work as a unit.   Yerkes, though he had considerable interest in Philadelphia, which had been the scene of his earliest exploits, limited his activities largely to Chicago.   Widener and Elkins, however, not only dominated Philadelphia traction but participated in all of Yerkes's enterprises in Chicago and held an equal interest with Whitney and

Ryan in New York. The latter Metropolitan pair, though they confined their interest chiefly to their own city, at times transferred their attention to Chicago. Thus, for nearly thirty years, these five men found their oyster in the transit systems of America's three greatest cities — and, for that matter, in many others also.

An attempt to trace the convolutions of America's street railway and public lighting finance would involve a puzzling array of statistics and an inextricable complexity of stocks, bonds, leases, holding companies, operating companies, construction companies, reorganizations, and the like. Difficult and apparently impenetrable as is this financial morass, the essential facts still stand out plainly enough. As already indicated, the fundamental basis upon which the whole system rested was the control of municipal politics. The story of the Metropolitan's manipulation of the New York street railways starts with one of the most sordid episodes in the municipal annals of America's largest city. Somewhat more than thirty years ago, a group of New York city fathers acquired an international fame as the "boodle aldermen." These men had finally given way to the importunities of a certain Jacob Sharp, an eccentric

New York character, who had for many years operated New York City railways, and granted a franchise for the construction of a horse-car line on lower Broadway.   Soon after voting this franchise, regarded as perhaps the most valuable in the world, these same aldermen had begun to wear diamonds, to purchase real estate, and give other outward evidences of unexpected prosperity. Presently, however, these city fathers started a migration to Canada, Mexico, Spain, and other countries where the processes of extradition did not work smoothly. Sharp's enemies had succeeded in precipitating a legislative investigation under the very capable leadership of Roscoe Conkling, who had little difficulty in showing that Sharp had purchased his aldermen for $500,000 cash. In a short time, such of the aldermen as were accessible to the police were languishing in prison, and Sharp had been arrested on twenty-one indictments for bribery and sentenced to four years' hard labor — a sentence which he was saved from serving by his lonely and miserable death in Ludlow Street Jail. In the delirium preceding his dissolution Sharp raved constantly about his Broadway railroad and his enemies; it was apparently his belief that the investigation which had uncovered his rascality and the subsequent "persecutions" had been engineered by certain of his rivals, either to compel Sharp to disgorge his franchise or to produce the facts that would justify the legislature in annulling it on the ground of fraud.

Though the complete history of this transaction can never be written, we do possess certain facts that lend some color to this diagnosis. Up to the time that Sharp had captured this franchise, Ryan, Whitney, and the Philadelphians — not as partners, but as rivals — had competed with him for this prize. At the trial of Arthur J. McQuade in 1886, a fellow conspirator, who bore the somewhat suggestive name of Fullgraff, related certain details which, if true, would indicate that Sharp's methods differed from those of his rivals only in that they had proved more successful. Thirteen members of the Board of Aldermen, said Fullgraff, had formed a close corporation, elected a chairman, and adopted a policy of "business unity in all important matters," which meant that they proposed to keep together in order to secure the highest price for the Broadway franchise. The cable railroad, which was the one with which Mr. Ryan was identified, offered $750,000, half in bonds and half in cash.

Mr. Sharp, however, offered $500,000 all in cash. The aldermen voted in favor of Sharp because cash was not only a more valuable commodity than the bonds but, to use Alderman Fullgraff's own words — "less easily traced." That Whitney financed lawsuits against the validity of Sharp's franchise appears upon the record, and that Ryan was actively promoting the Conkling investigation, is likewise a matter of evidence. Sharp's victory had the great result of bringing together the three forces — Ryan, Whitney, and the Philadelphians — who had hitherto combated one another as rivals; that is, it caused the organization of the famous Whitney-Ryan-Widener-Elkins syndicate. If these men had inspired all those attacks on Sharp, their maneuver proved successful; for when the investigation had attained its climax and public indignation against Sharp had reached its most furious stage, that venerable corruptionist, worn down by ill health, and almost crazed by the popular outcry, sold his Broadway railroad to Peter A. B. Widener, William L. Elkins, and William H. Kemble. Thomas F. Ryan became secretary of the new corporation, and William C. Whitney an active participant in its affairs.

This Broadway franchise formed the vertebral

column of the New York transit system; with it
as a basis, the operators formed the Metropolitan Street Railway Company in 1893, commonly
known as the "Metropolitan." They organized
also the Metropolitan Traction Company, an organization which enjoys an historic position as the
first "holding company" ever created in this country. Its peculiar attribute was that it did not construct and operate street railways itself, but merely
owned other corporations that did so. Its only
assets, that is, were paper securities representing
the ownership and control of other companies.
This "holding company," which has since become
almost a standardized form of corporation control
in this country, was the invention of Mr. Francis
Lynde Stetson, one of America's greatest corporation lawyers. "Mr. Stetson," Ryan is said to
have remarked, "do you know what you did when
you drew up the papers of the Metropolitan Traction Company? You made us a great big tin box."

The plan which Whitney and his associates now
followed was to obtain control, in various ways,
of all the surface railways in New York and place
them under the leadership of the Metropolitan.
Through their political influences they obtained
franchises of priceless value, organized subsidiary

street railway companies, and exchanged the stock of these subsidiary companies for that of the Metropolitan. A few illustrations will show the character of these transactions. They thus acquired, practically as a free gift, a franchise to build a cable railroad on Lexington Avenue. At an extremely liberal estimate, this line cost perhaps $2,500,000 to construct, yet the syndicate turned this over to the Metropolitan for $10,000,000 of Metropolitan securities. They similarly acquired a franchise for a line on Columbus Avenue, spending perhaps $500,000 in construction, and handing the completed property over to the Metropolitan for $6,-000,000. In exchange for these two properties, representing a real investment, it has been maintained, of $3,000,000, the inside syndicates received securities which had a face value of $16,000,000 and which, as will appear subsequently, had a market cash value of not far from $25,000,000. They purchased an old horse-car line on Fulton Street, a line whose assets consisted of one-third of a mile of tracks, ten little box cars, thirty horses, and an operating deficit of $40,000 a year. At auction, its visible assets might have brought $15,000; yet the syndicate turned this over to the Metropolitan for $1,000,000. They spent $50,000

in constructing and equipping a horse railroad on
Twenty-eighth and Twenty-ninth Streets and
turned this over to the Metropolitan for $3,000,000.
For two and a half miles of railroad on Thirty-
fourth Street, which represented a cash expenditure of perhaps $100,000, they received $2,000,000
of Metropolitan stock.   But it is hardly necessary
to catalogue more instances; the plan of operations
must now be fairly evident.   It was for the members of the syndicate, as individuals, to collect all
the properties and new franchises that were available and to transfer them to the Metropolitan at
enormously inflated values.   So far, all these deals
were purely stock transactions — no cash had yet
changed hands. When the amalgamation was complete, the insiders found themselves in possession
of large amounts of Metropolitan stock.   Their
scheme for transforming this paper into more tan-
gible property forms the concluding chapter of this
Metropolitan story. [1]

Nearly all the properties actually purchased and
transferred in the manner described above, had
little earning capacity, and therefore little value;
they were decrepit horse-car lines in unprofitable

---

[1] In 1897 the Traction Company dissolved, after distributing
$6,000.000 as "a voluntary dividend" among its stockholders.

territory. The really valuable roads were those that traversed the great north and south thoroughfares — Lenox, Third, Fourth, Sixth, Eighth, and Ninth Avenues. Many old New York families and estates had held these properties for years and had collected large annual dividends from them. Naturally they had no desire to sell, yet their acquisition was essential to the monopoly which the Whitney-Ryan syndicate aspired to construct. They finally leased all these roads, under agreements which guaranteed large annual rentals. In practically all these cases the Metropolitan, in order to secure physical possession, agreed to pay rentals that far exceeded the earning capacity of the road. What is the explanation of such insane finance? We do not have the precise facts in the matter of the New York railways; but similar operations in Chicago, which have been officially made public, shed the utmost light upon the situation. In order to get possession of a single road in Chicago, Widener and Elkins guaranteed a thirty-five per cent dividend; to get one Philadelphia line, they guaranteed $65\frac{1}{2}$ per cent on capital paid in. This, of course, was not business; the motives actuating the syndicate were purely speculative. In Chicago, Widener and Elkins quietly made large purchases of the stock in these roads before they leased them to the parent company. The exceedingly profitable lease naturally gave such stocks a high value, in case they preferred to sell; if they held them, they reaped huge rewards from the leases which they had themselves decreed. Perhaps their most remarkable exploit was the lease of the West Division Railway Company of Chicago to the West Chicago Street Railroad. Widener and Elkins controlled the West Division Railway; their partner, Charles T. Yerkes, controlled the latter corporation. The negotiation of a lease, therefore, was a purely informal matter; the partners were merely dealing with one another; yet Widener and Elkins received a fee of $5,000,000 as personal compensation for negotiating this lease!

But this whole leasing system, both in New York and Chicago, entailed scandals perhaps even more reprehensible. All these leased properties, when taken over, were horse-car lines, and their transformation into electrically propelled systems involved reconstruction operations on an extensive scale. It seems perfectly clear that the chief motive which inspired these extravagant leases was the determination of the individuals who made up the syndicate to obtain physical possession and to make huge profits on construction. The "construction accounts" of the Metropolitan in New York form the most mysterious and incredible chapter in its history. The Metropolitan reports show that they spent anywhere from $500,000 to $600,000 a mile building underground trolley lines which, at their own extravagant estimate, should have cost only $150,000. In a few years untold millions, wasted in this way, disappeared from the Metropolitan treasury. In 1907 the Public Service Commission of New York began investigating these "construction accounts," but it had not proceeded far when the discovery was made that all the Metropolitan books containing the information desired had been destroyed. All the ledgers, journals, checks, and vouchers containing the financial history of the Metropolitan since its organization in 1893 had been sold for $117 to a junkman, who had agreed in writing to grind them into pulp, so that they would be safe from "prying eyes." We shall therefore never know precisely how this money was spent. But here again the Chicago transactions help us to an understanding. In 1898 Charles T. Yerkes, with that cynical frankness which some people have regarded as a redeeming trait in his character, opened his books for the preceding twenty-five years to the Civic Federation of Chicago. These books disclosed that Mr. Yerkes and his associates, Widener and Elkins, had made many millions in reconstructing the Chicago lines at prices which represented gross overcharges to the stockholders. For this purpose Yerkes, Widener, and Elkins organized the United States Construction Company and made contracts for installing the new electric systems on the lines which they controlled by lease or stock ownership. It seems a not unnatural suspicion that the vanished Metropolitan books would have disclosed similar performances in New York.

The concluding chapter of this tragedy has its setting in the Stock Exchange. These inside gentlemen, as already said, received no cash as their profits from these manipulations — only stock. But in the eyes of the public this stock represented an enormous value. Metropolitan securities, for example, represented the control and ownership of all the surface transit business in the city of New York. Naturally, it had a great investment value. When it began to pay regularly seven per cent dividends, the public appetite for Metropolitan became insatiable. The eager purchasers did not know, what we know now, that the Metropolitan did not earn these dividends and never could have earned them. The mere fact that it was paying, as rentals on its leased lines, annual sums far in excess of their earning capacity, necessarily prevented anything in the nature of profitable operation. The unpleasant fact is that these dividends were paid with borrowed money merely to make the stock marketable. It is not unlikely that the padded construction accounts, already described, may have concealed large disbursements of money for unearned dividends. When the Metropolitan was listed in 1897, it immediately went beyond par. The excitement that followed forms one of the most memorable chapters in the history of Wall Street. The investing public, egged on by daring and skillful stock manipulators, simply went mad and purchased not only Metropolitan but street railway shares that were then even more speculative. It was in these bubble days that Brooklyn Rapid Transit soared to heights from which it subsequently descended precipitately. Under this stimulus, Metropolitan stock ultimately sold at $269 a share. While the whole investing public was scrambling for Metropolitan, the members of the exploiting syndicate found ample opportunity to sell. The real situation became apparent when William

C. Whitney died in 1904 leaving an estate valued at
$40,000,000. Not a single share of Metropolitan
was found among his assets! The final crash came
in 1907, when the Metropolitan, a wrecked and
plundered shell, confessed insolvency and went into a receivership. Those who had purchased its
stock found their holdings as worthless as the traditional western gold mine. The story of the Chicago
and Philadelphia systems, as well as that of numerous other cities, had been essentially the same.
The transit facilities of millions of Americans had
merely become the instruments of a group of specu-
lators who had made huge personal fortunes and had
left, as a monument of their labors, street railway
lines whose gross overcapitalization was apparent
to all and whose physical dilapidation in many
cases revealed the character of their management.

It seems perhaps an exaggeration to say that the
enterprises which have resulted in equipping our
American cities and suburbs with trolley lines and
electric lighting facilities have followed the plan
of campaign sketched above. Perhaps not all
have repeated the worst excesses of the syndicate
that so remorselessly exploited New York, Chicago,
and Philadelphia. Yet in most cases these elaborate undertakings have been largely speculative in

character.   Huge issues of fictitious stock, created purely for the benefit of inner rings, have been almost the prevailing rule.   Stock speculation and municipal corruption have constantly gone hand in hand everywhere with the development of the public utilities.   The relation of franchise corporations to municipalities is probably the thing which has chiefly opened the eyes of Americans to certain glaring defects in their democratic organization. The popular agitation which has resulted has led to great political reforms.   The one satisfaction which we can derive from such a relation as that given above is that, after all, it is representative of a past era in our political and economic life.   No new "Metropolitan syndicate" can ever repeat the operations of its predecessors.   Practically every State now has utility commissions which regulate the granting of franchises, the issue of securities, the details of construction and equipment and service.   An awakened public conscience has effectively ended the alliance between politics and franchise corporations and the type of syndicate described in the foregoing pages belongs as much to our American past as that rude frontier civilization with which, after all, it had many characteristics in common.

CHAPTER VI

THE Civil War in America did more than free the negro slave: it freed the white man as well. In the Civil War agriculture, for the first time in history, ceased to be exclusively a manual art. Up to that time the typical agricultural laborer had been a bent figure, tending his fields and garnering his crops with his own hands. Before the war had ended the American farmer had assumed an erect position; the sickle and the scythe had given way to a strange red chariot, which, with practically no expenditure of human labor, easily did the work of a dozen men. Many as have been America's contributions to civilization, hardly any have exerted greater influence in promoting human welfare than her gift of agricultural machinery. It seems astounding that, until McCormick invented his reaper, in 1831, agricultural methods, in both the New and the Old World, differed little from those that had prevailed in the days of the Babylonians. The New England farmer sowed his fields and reaped his crops with almost identically the same instruments as those which had been used by the Roman farmer in the time of the Gracchi. Only a comparatively few used the scythe; the great majority, with crooked backs and bended knees, cut the grain with little hand sickles precisely like those which are now dug up in Etruscan and Egyptian tombs.

Though McCormick had invented his reaper in 1831, and though many rival machines had appeared in the twenty years preceding the Civil War, only the farmers on the great western plains had used the new machinery to any considerable extent. The agricultural papers and agricultural fairs had not succeeded in popularizing these great labor-saving devices. Labor was so abundant and so cheap that the farmer had no need of them. But the Civil War took one man in three for the armies, and it was under this pressure that the farmers really discovered the value of machinery. A small boy or girl could mount a McCormick reaper and cut a dozen acres of grain in a day. This circumstance made it possible to place millions of soldiers in the field and to feed the armies from farms on which mature men did very little work. But the reaper promoted the Northern cause in other ways. Its use extended so in the early years of the war that the products of the farms increased on an enormous scale, and the surplus, exported to Europe, furnished the liquid capital that made possible the financing of the war. Europe gazed in astonishment at a new spectacle in history; that of a nation fighting the greatest war which had been known up to that time, employing the greater part of her young and vigorous men in the armies, and yet growing infinitely richer in the process. The Civil War produced many new implements of warfare, such as the machine gun and the revolving turret for battleships, but, so far as determining the result was concerned, perhaps the most important was the reaper.

Extensive as the use of agricultural machinery became in the Civil War, that period only faintly foreshadowed the development that has taken place since. The American farm is today like a huge factory; the use of the hands has almost entirely disappeared; there are only a few operations of husbandry that are not performed automatically. In Civil War days the reaper merely cut the grain; now machinery rakes it up and binds it into sheaves and threshes it. Similar mechanisms bind corn and rice. Machinery is now used to plant potatoes; grain, cotton, and other farm products are sown automatically. The husking bees that formed one of our social diversions in Civil War days have disappeared, for particular machines now rip the husks off the ears. Horse hay-forks and horse hay-rakes have supplanted manual labor. The mere names of scores of modern instruments of farming, all unknown in Civil War days — hay carriers, hay loaders, hay stackers, manure spreaders, horse corn planters, corn drills, disk harrows, disk ploughs, steam ploughs, tractors, and the like — give some suggestion of the extent to which America has made mechanical the most ancient of occupations. In thus transforming agriculture, we have developed not only our own Western plains, but we have created new countries. Argentina could hardly exist today except for American agricultural machinery. Ex-President Loubet declared, a few years ago, that France would starve to death except for the farming machines that were turned out in Chicago. There is practically no part of the world where our self-binders are not used. In many places America is not known as the land of freedom and opportunity, but merely as "the place from which the reapers come." The traveler suddenly comes upon these familiar agents in every European country, in South America, in Egypt, China, Algiers, Siberia, India, Burma, and Australia. For agricultural machinery remains today, what it has always been, almost exclusively an American manufacture. It is practically the only native American product that our European competitors have not been able to imitate. Tariff walls, bounty systems, and all the other artificial aids to manufacturing have not developed this industry in foreign lands, and today the United States produces four-fifths of all the agricultural machinery used in the world. The International Harvester Company has its salesmen in more than fifty countries, and has established large American factories in many nations of Europe.

One day, a few years before his death, Prince Bismarck was driving on his estate, closely following a self-binder that had recently been put to work. The venerable statesman, bent and feeble, seemed to find a deep melancholy interest in the operation.

"Show me the thing that ties the knot," he said. It was taken to pieces and explained to him in detail.

"Can these machines be made in Germany?" he asked.

"No, your Excellency," came the reply. "They can be made only in America."

The old man gave a sigh. "Those Yankees are ingenious fellows," he said. "This is a wonderful machine."

In this story of American success, four names stand out preëminently. The men who made the greatest contributions were Cyrus H. McCormick, C. W. Marsh, Charles B. Withington, and John F. Appleby. The name that stands foremost, of course, is that of McCormick, but each of the others made additions to his invention that have produced the present finished machine. It seems like the stroke of an ironical fate which decreed that since it was the invention of a Northerner, Eli Whitney, that made inevitable the Civil War, so it was the invention of a Southerner, Cyrus McCormick, that made inevitable the ending of that war in favor of the North.

McCormick was born in Rockbridge County, Virginia, on a farm about eighteen miles from Staunton. He was a child of that pioneering Scotch-Irish race which contributed so greatly to the settlement of this region and which afterward made such inestimable additions to American citizenship. The country in which he grew up was rough and, so far as the conventionalities go, uncivilized; the family homestead was little more than a log cabin; and existence meant a continual struggle with a not particularly fruitful soil. The most remarkable figure in the McCormick home circle, and the one whose every-day life exerted the greatest influence on the boy, was his father. The older McCormick had one obsessing idea that made him the favorite butt of the local humorists. He believed that the labor spent in reaping grain was a useless expenditure of human effort and that machinery might be made to do the work. Other men, in this country and in Europe, had nourished similar notions. Several Englishmen had invented reaping machines, all of which had had only a single defect — they would not reap. An ingenious English actor had developed a contrivance which would cut imitation wheat on the stage, but no one had developed a machine that would work satisfactorily in real life. Robert McCormick spent the larger part of his days and nights tinkering at a practical machine. He finally produced a horrific contrivance, made up of whirling sickles, knives, and revolving rods, pushed from behind by two horses; when he tried this upon a grain-field, however, it made a humiliating failure.

Evidently Robert McCormick had ambitions far beyond his powers; yet without his absurd experiments the development of American agriculture might have waited many years. They became the favorite topics of conversation in the evening gatherings that took place about the family log fire. Robert McCormick had several sons, and one manifested a particular interest in his repeated failures. From the time he was seven years old Cyrus Hall McCormick became his father's closest companion. Others might ridicule and revile, but this chubby, bright-eyed, intelligent little boy was always the keenest listener, the one comfort which the father had against his jeering neighbors. He also became his father's constant associate in his rough workshop. Soon, however, the older man noticed a change in their relations. The boy was becoming the teacher, and the father was taught. By the time Cyrus was eighteen, indeed, he had advanced so far beyond his father that the latter had become merely a proud observer. Young McCormick threw into the discard all his father's ideas and struck out on entirely new lines. By the time he had reached his twenty-second birthday he had constructed a machine which, in all its essential details, is the one which we have today. He had introduced seven principles, all of which are an indispensable part of every reaper constructed now. One afternoon he drove his unlovely contraption upon his father's farm, with no witnesses except his own family. This group now witnessed the first successful attempt ever made to reap with machinery. A few days later young McCormick gave a public exhibition at Steele's Tavern, cutting six acres of oats in an afternoon. The popular ridicule soon changed into acclaim; the new invention was exhibited in a public square and Cyrus McCormick became a local celebrity. Perhaps the words that pleased him most, however, were those spoken by his father. "I am proud," said the old man, "to have a son who can do what I failed to do."

This McCormick reaper dates from 1831; but it represented merely the beginnings of the modern machine. It performed only a single function; it simply cut the crop. When its sliding blade had performed this task, the grain fell back upon a platform, and a farm hand, walking alongside, raked this off upon the ground. A number of human harvesters followed, picked up the bundles, and tied a few strips of grain around them, making the sheaf. The work was exceedingly wearying and particularly hard upon the women who were frequently impressed into service as farm-hands. About 1858 two farmers named Marsh, who lived near De Kalb, Illinois, solved this problem. They attached to their McCormick reaper a moving platform upon which the cut grain was deposited. A footboard was fixed to the machine upon which two men stood. As the grain came upon this moving platform these men seized it, bound it into sheaves, and threw it upon the field. Simple as this procedure seemed it really worked a revolution in agriculture; for the first time since the pronouncement of the primal curse, the farmer abandoned his hunchback attitude and did his work standing erect. Yet this device also had its disqualifications, the chief one being that it converted the human sheaf-binder into a sweat-shop worker. It was necessary to bind the grain as rapidly as the platform brought it up; the worker was therefore kept in constant motion; and the consequences were frequently distressing and nerve racking. Yet this "Marsh Harvester" remained the great favorite with farmers from about 1860 to 1874.

All this time, however, there was a growing

feeling that even the Marsh harvester did not represent the final solution of the problem; the air was full of talk and prophecies about self-binders, something that would take the loose wheat from the platform and transform it into sheaves. Hundreds of attempts failed until, in 1874, Charles B. Withington of Janesville, Wisconsin, brought to McCormick a mechanism composed of two steel arms which seized the grain, twisted a wire around it, cut the wire, and tossed the completed sheaf to the earth. In actual practice this contrivance worked with the utmost precision. Finally American farmers had a machine that cut the grain, raked it up, and bound it into sheaves ready for the mill. Human labor had apparently lost its usefulness; a solitary man or woman, perched upon a seat and driving a pair of horses, now performed all these operations of husbandry.

By this time, scores of manufacturers had entered the field in opposition to McCormick, but his acquisition of Withington's invention had apparently made his position secure. Indeed, for the next ten years he had everything his own way. Then suddenly an ex-keeper of a dry-goods store in Maine crossed his path. This was William Deering, a character quite as energetic, forceful, and

pugnacious as was McCormick himself. Though
McCormick had made and sold thousands of his
self-binders, farmers were already showing signs
of discontent. The wire proved a continual annoyance. It mingled with the straw and killed
the cattle — at least so the farmers complained; it
cut their hands and even found its way, with dis-
astrous results, into the flour mills. Deering now
appeared as the owner of a startling invention by
John F. Appleby. This did all that the Withington machine did and did it better and quicker;
and it had the great advantage that it bound with
twine instead of wire. The new machine immediately swept aside all competitors; McCormick,
to save his reaper from disaster, presently perfected a twine binder of his own. The appearance
of Appleby's improvement in 1884 completes the
cycle of the McCormick reaper on its mechanical
side The harvesting machine of fifty nations to-
day is the one to which Appleby put the final
touches in 1884. Since then nothing of any great
importance has been added.

This outline of invention, however, comprises
only part of the story. The development of the
reaper business presents a narrative quite as adventurous as that of the reaper itself. Cyrus

McCormick was not only a great inventor; he was also a great business man.   So great was his ability in this direction, indeed, that there has been a tendency to discredit his achievements as a creative genius and to attribute his success to his talents as an organizer and driver of industry.   "I may make a million dollars from this reaper," said McCormick, in the full tide of enthusiasm over his invention; and these words indicate an indispensable part of his program.   He had no miserly instinct but he had one overpowering ambition.   It was McCormick's conviction, almost religious in its fervor, that the harvester business of the world belonged to him.   As already indicated, plenty of other hardy spirits, many of them almost as commanding personalities as himself, disputed the empire.   Not far from 12,000 patents on harvesting machines were granted in this country in the fifty years following McCormick's invention, and more than two hundred companies were formed to compete for the market.   McCormick always regarded these competitors as highwaymen who had invaded a field which had been almost divinely set apart for himself.   A man of covenanting antecedents, heroic in his physical proportions, with a massive, Jove-like head and beard, tirelessly devoted to his work, watching every detail with a microscopic eye, marshaling a huge force of workers who were as possessed by this one overruling idea as was McCormick himself, he certainly presented an almost unassailable battlefront to his antagonists.

The competition that raged between McCormick and the makers of rival machines was probably the fiercest that has prevailed in any American industry. For marketing his machine McCormick developed a system almost as ingenious as the machine itself. The popularization of so ungainly and expensive a contrivance as the harvester proved a slow and difficult task. McCormick at first attempted to build his product on his Virginia farm and for many years it was known as the Virginia Reaper. Nearly ten years passed, however, before he sold his first machine. The farmer first refused to take it seriously. "It's a great invention," he would say, "but I'm running a farm, not a circus." About 1847 McCormick decided that the Western prairies offered the finest field for its activities, and established his factory at Chicago, then an ugly little town on the borders of a swamp. This selection proved to be a stroke of genius, for it placed the harvesting factory right at the door of its largest market.

The price of the harvester, however, seemed an insurmountable obstacle to its extensive use. The early settlers of the Western plains had little more than their brawny hands as capital, and the homestead law furnished them their land practically free. In the eyes of a large-seeing pioneer like McCormick this was capital enough. He determined that his reaper should develop this extensive domain, and that the crops themselves should pay the cost. Selling expensive articles on the installment plan now seems a commonplace of business, but in those days it was practically unknown. McCormick was the first to see its possibilities. He established an agent, usually the general storekeeper, in every agricultural center. Any farmer who had a modicum of cash and who bore a reputation for thrift and honesty could purchase a reaper. In payment he gave a series of notes, so timed that they fell due at the end of harvesting seasons. Thus, as the money came in from successive harvests, the pioneer paid off the notes, taking two, three, or four years in the process. In the sixties and seventies immigrants from the Eastern States and from Europe poured into the Mississippi Valley by the hundreds of thousands. Almost the first person who greeted the astonished Dane, German, or Swede was an agent of the harvester company, offering to let him have one of these strange machines on these terms. Thus the harvester, under McCormick's comprehensive selling plans, did as much as the homestead act in opening up this great farming region.

McCormick covered the whole agricultural United States with these agents. In this his numerous competitors followed suit, and the liveliest times ensued. From that day to this the agents of harvesting implements have lent much animation and color to rural life in this country. Half a dozen men were usually tugging away at one farmer at the same time. The mere fact that the farmer had closed a contract did not end his troubles, for "busting up competitors' sales" was part of the agent's business. The situation frequently reached a point where there was only one way to settle rival claims and that was by a field contest. At a stated time two or three or four rival harvesters would suddenly appear on the farmer's soil, each prepared to show, by actual test, its superiority over the enemy. Farmers and idlers for miles around would gather to witness the Homeric struggle. At a given signal the small army of machines would spring savagely at a field of wheat. The one that could cut the allotted area in the shortest time was regarded as the winner. The harvester would rush on all kinds of fields, flat and hilly, dry and wet, and would cut all kinds of crops, and even stubble. All manner of tests were devised to prove one machine stronger than its rival; a favorite idea was to chain two back to back, and have them pulled apart by frantic careering horses; the one that suffered the fewest breakdowns would be generally acclaimed from town to town. Sometimes these field tests were the most exciting and spectacular events at country fairs.

Thus the harvesting machine "pushed the frontier westward at the rate of thirty miles a year," according to William H. Seward. It made American and Canadian agriculture the most efficient in the world. The German brags that his agriculture is superior to American, quoting as proof the more bushels of wheat or potatoes he grows to an acre. But the comparison is fallacious. The real test of efficiency is, not the crops that are grown per acre, but the crops that are grown per man employed. German efficiency gets its results by impressing women as cultivators — depressing bent figures that are in themselves a sufficient criticism upon any civilization. America gets its results by using a minimum of human labor and letting machinery do the work. Thus America's methods are superior not only from the standpoint of economics but of social progress. All nations, including Germany, use our machinery, but none to the extent that prevails on the North American Continent.

Perhaps McCormick's greatest achievement is that his machine has banished famine wherever it is extensively used, at least in peace times. Before the reaper appeared existence, even in the United States, was primarily a primitive struggle for bread. The greatest service of the harvester has been that it has freed the world — unless it is a world distracted by disintegrating war — from a constant anxiety concerning its food supply. The hundreds of thousands of binders, active in the fields of every country, have made it certain that humankind shall not want for its daily bread. When McCormick exhibited his harvester at the London Exposition of 1851, the *London Times* ridiculed it as "a cross between an Astley chariot, a wheel barrow, and a flying machine." Yet this same grotesque object, widely used in Canada, Argentina, Australia, South Africa, and India, becomes an engine that really holds the British Empire together.

For the forty years succeeding the Civil War the manufacture of harvesting machinery was a business in which many engaged, but in which few survived. The wildest competition ruthlessly destroyed all but half a dozen powerful firms. Cyrus McCormick died in 1884, but his sons proved worthy successors; the McCormick factory still headed the list, manufacturing, in 1900, one-third of all the self-binders used in the world. The William Deering Company came next and then D. M. Osborne, J. J. Glessner, and W. H. Jones, established factories that made existence exceedingly uncomfortable for the pioneers. Whatever one may think of the motives which caused so many combinations in the early years of the twentieth century, there is no question that irresistible economic forces compelled these great harvester companies to get together. Quick profits in the shape of watered stock had nothing to do with the formation of the International Harvester Company. All the men who controlled these enterprises were individualists, with a natural loathing for trusts, combinations, and pools. They wished for nothing better than to continue fighting the Spartan battle that had made existence such an exciting pastime for more than half a century. But the simple fact west that those several concerns were destroying one another. It was a question of joining hands, ending the competition that was eating so deeply into their financial resources, or reducing the whole business to chaos.   When Mr. George W. Perkins, of J. P. Morgan and Company, first attempted to combine these great companies, the antagonism which had been accumulated in many years of warfare constantly threatened to defeat his end.   He early discovered that the only way to bring these men together was to keep them apart.   The usual way of creating such combinations is to collect the representative leaders, place them around a table, and persuade them to talk the thing over.   Such an amicable situation, however, was impossible in the present instance.   Even when the four big men — McCormick, Deering, Glessner, and Jones — were finally brought for the final treaty of peace to J. P. Morgan's office, Mr. Perkins had to station them in four separate rooms and flit from one to another arranging terms.   Had these four men been brought face to face, the Harvester Company would probably never have been formed.

Having once signed their names, however, these once antagonistic interests had little difficulty in forming a strong combination.   The company thus brought together manufactured 85 per cent of all the farm machinery used in this country. It owned its own coal-fields and iron mines and its own forests, and it produces most of the implements used by 10,000,000 farmers. In 1847 Cyrus McCormick made 100 reapers and sold them for $10,000; by 1902 the annual production of the corporation amounted to hundreds of thousands of harvesters — besides an almost endless assortment of other agricultural tools, ploughs, drills, rakes, gasoline engines, tractors, threshers, cream separators, and the like — and the sales had grown to about $75,-000,000. This is merely the financial measure of progress; the genuine achievements of McCormick's invention are millions of acres of productive land and a farming population which is without parallel elsewhere for its prosperity, intelligence, manfulness, and general contentment.

CHAPTER VII

THE DEMOCRATIZATION OF THE AUTOMOBILE

In many manufacturing lines, American genius for organization and large scale production has developed mammoth industries. In nearly all the tendency to combination and concentration has exercised a predominating influence. In the early years of the twentieth century the public realized, for the first time, that one corporation, the American Sugar Refining Company, controlled ninety-eight per cent of the business of refining sugar. Six large interests — Armour, Swift, Morris, the National Packing Company, Cudahy, and Schwarzschild and Sulzberger — had so concentrated the packing business that, by 1905, they slaughtered practically all the cattle shipped to Western centers and furnished most of the beef consumed in the large cities east of Pittsburgh. The "Tobacco Trust" had largely monopolized both the wholesale and retail trade in this article of luxury and had also made

extensive inroads into the English market.   The
textile industry had not only transformed great
centers of New England into an American Lanca-
shire, but the Southern States, recovering from the
demoralization of the Civil War, had begun to spin
their own cotton and to send the finished product
to all parts of the world.   American shoe manufacturers had developed their art to a point where
"American shoes" had acquired a distinctive standing in practically every European country.

It is hardly necessary to describe in detail each
of these industries.   In their broad outlines they
merely repeat the story of steel, of oil, of agricultural machinery; they are the product of the same
methods, the same initiative.   There is one branch
of American manufacture, however, that merits
more detailed attention.   If we scan the manufacturing statistics of 1917, one amazing fact stares us
in the face.   There are only three American industries whose product has attained the billion mark;
one of these is steel, the other food products, while
the third is an industry that was practically unknown in the United States fifteen years ago.
Superlatives come naturally to mind in discussing
American progress, but hardly any extravagant
phrases could do justice to the development of

American automobiles.   In 1899 the United States produced 3700 motor vehicles; in 1916 we made 1,500,000.   The man who now makes a personal profit of not far from $50,000,000 a year in this industry was a puttering mechanic when the twentieth century came in.   If we capitalized Henry Ford's income, he is probably a richer man than Rockefeller; yet, as recently as 1905 his possessions consisted of a little shed of a factory which employed a dozen workmen.   Dazzling as is this personal success, its really important aspects are the things for which it stands.   The American automobile has had its wild-cat days; for the larger part, however, its leaders have paid little attention to Wall Street, but have limited their activities exclusively to manufacturing.   Moreover, the automobile illustrates more completely than any other industry the technical qualities that so largely explain our industrial progress.   Above all, American manufacturing has developed three characteristics.   These are quantity production, standardization, and the use of labor-saving machinery.   It is because Ford and other manufacturers adapted these principles to making the automobile that the American motor industry has reached such gigantic proportions.

A few years ago an English manufacturer, seeking the explanation of America's ability to produce an excellent car so cheaply, made an interesting experiment. He obtained three American automobiles, all of the same "standardized" make, and gave them a long and racking tour over English highways. Workmen then took apart the three cars and threw the disjointed remains into a promiscuous heap. Every bolt, bar, gas tank, motor, wheel, and tire was taken from its accustomed place and piled up, a hideous mass of rubbish. Workmen then painstakingly put together three cars from these disordered elements. Three chauffeurs jumped on these cars, and they immediately started down the road and made a long journey just as acceptably as before. The Englishman had learned the secret of American success with automobiles. The one word "standardization" explained the mystery.

Yet when, a few years before, the English referred to the American automobile as a "glorified perambulator," the characterization was not unjust. This new method of transportation was slow in finding favor on our side of the Atlantic. America was sentimentally and practically devoted to the horse as the motive power for vehicles; and the fact that we had so few good roads also worked against the introduction of the automobile. Yet here, as in Europe, the mechanically propelled wagon made its appearance in early times. This vehicle, like the bicycle, is not essentially a modern invention; the reason any one can manufacture it is that practically all the basic ideas antedate 1840. Indeed, the automobile is really older than the railroad. In the twenties and thirties, steam stage coaches made regular trips between certain cities in England and occasionally a much resounding power-driven carriage would come careering through New York and Philadelphia, scaring all the horses and precipitating the intervention of the authorities. The hardy spirits who devised these engines, all of whose names are recorded in the encyclopedias, deservedly rank as the "fathers" of the automobile. The responsibility as the actual "inventor" can probably be no more definitely placed. However, had it not been for two developments, neither of them immediately related to the motor car, we should never have had this efficient method of transportation. The real "fathers" of the automobile are Gottlieb Daimler, the German who made the first successful gasoline engine, and Charles Goodyear, the American who discovered

the secret of vulcanized rubber. Without this engine to form the motive power and the pneu-
matic tire to give it four air cushions to run on, the
automobile would never have progressed beyond
the steam carriage stage. It is true that Charles
Baldwin Selden, of Rochester, has been pictured as
the "inventor of the modern automobile" because,
as long ago as 1879, he applied for a patent on the
idea of using a gasoline engine as motive power,
securing this basic patent in 1895, but this, it must
be admitted, forms a flimsy basis for such a preten-
tious claim.

The French apparently led all nations in the
manufacture of motor vehicles, and in the early
nineties their products began to make occasional
appearances on American roads. The type of
American who owned this imported machine was
the same that owned steam yachts and a box at the
opera. Hardly any new development has aroused
greater hostility. It not only frightened horses,
and so disturbed the popular traffic of the time,
but its speed, its glamour, its arrogance, and the
haughty behavior of its proprietor, had apparently
transformed it into a new badge of social cleavage.
It thus immediately took its place as a new gew-
gaw of the rich; that it had any other purpose to

serve had occurred to few people.   Yet the French
and English machines created an entirely different
reaction in the mind of an imaginative mechanic
in Detroit.   Probably American annals contain
no finer story than that of this simple American
workman.   Yet from the beginning it seemed inevitable that Henry Ford should play this appointed part in the world.   Born in Michigan in
1863, the son of an English farmer who had emi-
grated to Michigan and a Dutch mother, Ford had
always demonstrated an interest in things far removed from his farm.   Only mechanical devices
interested him.   He liked getting in the crops,
because McCormick harvesters did most of the
work; it was only the machinery of the dairy that
held him enthralled.   He developed destructive
tendencies as a boy; he had to take everything to
pieces.   He horrified a rich playmate by resolving
his new watch into its component parts — and
promptly quieted him by putting it together again.
"Every clock in the house shuddered when it saw
me coming," he recently said.   He constructed a
small working forge in his school-yard, and built a
small steam engine that could make ten miles an
hour.   He spent his winter evenings reading mechanical and scientific journals; he cared little for

general literature, but machinery in any form was almost a pathological obsession. Some boys run away from the farm to join the circus or to go to sea; Henry Ford at the age of sixteen ran away to get a job in a machine shop. Here one anomaly immediately impressed him. No two machines were made exactly alike; each was regarded as a separate job. With his savings from his weekly wage of $2.50, young Ford purchased a three dollar watch, and immediately dissected it. If several thousand of these watches could be made, each one exactly alike, they would cost only thirty-seven cents a piece. "Then," said Ford to himself, "everybody could have one." He had fairly elaborated his plans to start a factory on this basis when his father's illness called him back to the farm.

This was about 1880; Ford's next conspicuous appearance in Detroit was about 1892. This appearance was not only conspicuous; it was exceedingly noisy. Detroit now knew him as the pilot of a queer affair that whirled and lurched through her thoroughfares, making as much disturbance as a freight train. In reading his technical journals Ford had met many descriptions of horseless carriages; the consequence was that he had again broken away from the farm, taken a job at \$45 a month in a Detroit machine shop, and devoted his evenings to the production of a gasoline engine. His young wife was exceedingly concerned about his health; the neighbors' snap judgment was that he was insane. Only two other Americans, Charles B. Duryea and Ellwood Haynes, were attempting to construct an automobile at that time. Long before Ford was ready with his machine, others had begun to appear. Duryea turned out his first one in 1892; and foreign makes began to appear in considerable numbers. But the Detroit mechanic had a more comprehensive inspiration. He was not working to make one of the finely upholstered and beautifully painted vehicles that came from overseas. "Anything that isn't good for everybody is no good at all," he said. Precisely as it was Vail's ambition to make every American a user of the telephone and McCormick's to make every farmer a user of his harvester, so it was Ford's determination that every family should have an automobile. He was apparently the only man in those times who saw that this new machine was not primarily a luxury but a convenience. Yet all manufacturers, here and in Europe, laughed at his idea. Why not give every poor man a Fifth Avenue house? Frenchmen and Englishmen scouted the idea that any one could make a cheap automobile. Its machinery was particularly refined and called for the highest grade of steel; the clever Americans might use their labor-saving devices on many products, but only skillful hand work could turn out a motor car. European manufacturers regarded each car as a separate problem; they individualized its manufacture almost as scrupulously as a painter paints his portrait or a poet writes his poem. The result was that only a man with several thousand dollars could purchase one. But Henry Ford—and afterward other American makers—had quite a different conception.

Henry Ford's earliest banker was the proprietor of a quick-lunch wagon at which the inventor used to eat his midnight meal after his hard evening's work in the shed. "Coffee Jim," to whom Ford confided his hopes and aspirations on these occasions, was the only man with available cash who had any faith in his ideas. Capital in more substantial form, however, came in about 1902. With money advanced by "Coffee Jim," Ford had built a machine which he entered in the Grosse Point races that year. It was a hideous-looking affair, but it ran like the wind and outdistanced all competitors. From that day Ford's career has been an uninterrupted triumph. But he rejected the earliest offers of capital because the millionaires would not agree to his terms. They were looking for high prices and quick profits, while Ford's plans were for low prices, large sales, and use of profits to extend the business and reduce the cost of his machine. Henry Ford's greatness as a manufacturer consists in the tenacity with which he has clung to this conception. Contrary to general belief in the automobile industry he maintained that a high sale price was not necessary for large profits; indeed he declared that the lower the price, the larger the net earnings would be. Nor did he believe that low wages meant prosperity. The most efficient labor, no matter what the nominal cost might be, was the most economical. The secret of success was the rapid production of a serviceable article in large quantities. When Ford first talked of turning out 10,000 automobiles a year, his associates asked him where he was going to sell them. Ford's answer was that that was no problem at all; the machines would sell themselves. He called attention to the fact that there were millions of people in this country whose incomes exceeded $1800 a year; all in that class would become prospective purchasers of a low-priced auto-

mobile.   There were **6,000,000 farmers**; what more
receptive market could one ask?   His only problem
was the technical one — how to produce his machine in sufficient quantities.

The bicycle business in this country had passed
through a similar experience.   When first placed
on the market bicycles were expensive; it took
$100 or $150 to buy one.   In a few years, however,
an excellent machine was selling for $25 or $30.
What explained this drop in price?   The answer is
that the manufacturers learned to standardize their
product.   Bicycle factories became not so much
places where the articles were manufactured as
assembling rooms for putting them together.   The
several parts were made in different places, each
establishment specializing in a particular part; they
were then shipped to centers where they were transformed into completed machines.   The result was
that the United States, despite the high wages
paid here, led the world in bicycle making and
flooded all countries with this utilitarian article.
Our great locomotive factories had developed on
similar lines.   Europeans had always marveled
that Americans could build these costly articles
so cheaply that they could undersell European
makers.   When they obtained a glimpse of an

American locomotive factory, the reason became plain.   In Europe each locomotive was a separate problem; no two, even in the same shop, were exactly alike.   But here locomotives are built in parts, all duplicates of one another; the parts are then sent by machinery to assembling rooms and rapidly put together.   American harvesting machines are built in the same way; whenever a farmer loses a part, he can go to the country store and buy its duplicate, for the parts of the same machine do not vary to the thousandth of an inch. The same principle applies to hundreds of other articles.

Thus Henry Ford did not invent standardization; he merely applied this great American idea to a product to which, because of the delicate labor required, it seemed at first unadapted.   He soon found that it was cheaper to ship the parts of ten cars to a central point than to ship ten completed cars.   There would therefore be large savings in making his parts in particular factories and shipping them to assembling establishments.   In this way the completed cars would always be near their markets.   Large production would mean that he could purchase his raw materials at very low prices; high wages meant that he could get the efficient labor which was demanded by his rapid fire method of campaign. It was necessary to plan the making of every part to the minutest detail, to have each part machined to its exact size, and to have every screw, bolt, and bar precisely interchangeable. About the year 1907 the Ford factory was systematized on this basis. In that twelvemonth it produced 10,000 machines, each one the absolute counterpart of the other 9999. American manufacturers until then had been content with a few hundred a year! From that date the Ford production has rapidly increased; until, in 1916, there were nearly 4,000,000 automobiles in the United States — more than in all the rest of the world put together — of which one-sixth were the output of the Ford factories. Many other American manufacturers followed the Ford plan, with the result that American automobiles are duplicating the story of American bicycles; because of their cheapness and serviceability, they are rapidly dominating the markets of the world. In the Great War American machines have surpassed all in the work done under particularly exacting circumstances.

A glimpse of a Ford assembling room — and we can see the same process in other American factories — makes clear the reasons for this success.

In these rooms no fitting is done; the fragments of automobiles come in automatically and are simply bolted together. First of all the units are assembled in their several departments. The rear axles, the front axles, the frames, the radiators, and the motors are all put together with the same precision and exactness that marks the operation of the completed car. Thus the wheels come from one part of the factory and are rolled on an inclined plane to a particular spot. The tires are propelled by some mysterious force to the same spot; as the two elements coincide, workmen quickly put them together. In a long room the bodies are slowly advanced on moving platforms at the rate of about a foot per minute. At the side stand groups of men, each prepared to do his bit, their materials being delivered at convenient points by chutes. As the tops pass by these men quickly bolt them into place, and the completed body is sent to a place where it awaits the chassis. This important section, comprising all the machinery, starts at one end of a moving platform as a front and rear axle bolted together with the frame. As this slowly advances, it passes under a bridge containing a gasoline tank, which is quickly adjusted. Farther on the motor is swung over by a small hoist and lowered into position on the frame.   Presently the dash slides down and is placed in position behind the motor. As the rapidly accumulating mechanism passes on, different workmen adjust the mufflers, exhaust pipes, the radiator, and the wheels which, as already indicated, arrive on the scene completely tired. Then a workman seats himself on the gasoline tank, which contains a small quantity of its indispensable fuel, starts the engine, and the thing moves out the door under its own power. It stops for a moment outside; the completed body drops down from the second floor, and a few bolts quickly put it securely in place. The workman drives the now finished Ford to a loading platform, it is stored away in a box car, and is started on its way to market. At the present time about 2000 cars are daily turned out in this fashion. The nation demands them at a more rapid rate than they can be made.

Herein we have what is probably America's greatest manufacturing exploit. And this democratization of the automobile comprises more than the acme of efficiency in the manufacturing art. The career of Henry Ford has a symbolic significance as well. It may be taken as signalizing the new ideals that have gained the upper hand in

American industry. We began this review of American business with Cornelius Vanderbilt as the typical figure. It is a happy augury that it closes with Henry Ford in the foreground. Vanderbilt, valuable as were many of his achievements, represented that spirit of egotism that was rampant for the larger part of the fifty years following the war. He was always seeking his own advantage, and he never regarded the public interest as anything worth a moment's consideration. With Ford, however, the spirit of service has been the predominating motive. His earnings have been immeasurably greater than Vanderbilt's; his income for two years amounts to nearly Vanderbilt's total fortune at his death; but the piling up of riches has been by no means his exclusive purpose. He has recognized that his workmen are his partners and has liberally shared with them his increasing profits. His money is not the product of speculation; Ford is a stranger to Wall Street and has built his business independently of the great banking interest. He has enjoyed no monopoly, as have the Rockefellers; there are more than three hundred makers of automobiles in the United States alone. He has spurned all solicitations to join combinations. Far from asking tariff favors he has entered European markets and undersold English, French, and German makers on their own ground. Instead of taking advantage of a great public demand to increase his prices, Ford has continuously lowered them. Though his idealism may have led him into an occasional personal absurdity, as a business man he may be taken as the full flower of American manufacturing genius. Possibly America, as a consequence of universal war, is advancing to a higher state of industrial organization; but an economic system is not entirely evil that produces such an industry as that which has made the automobile the servant of millions of Americans.

BIBLIOGRAPHICAL NOTE

THE materials are abundant for the history of American industry in the last fifty years. They exist largely in the form of official documents. Any one ambitious of studying this subject in great detail should consult, first of all, the catalogs issued by that very valuable institution, the Government Printing Office. The Bureau of Corporations has published elaborate reports on such industries as petroleum (Standard Oil Company), beef, tobacco, steel, and harvesting machinery, which are indispensable in studying these great basic enterprises. The American habit of legislative investigation and trust-fighting in the courts, whatever its public value may have been, has at least had the result of piling up mountains of material for the historian of American industry. For one single corporation, the Standard Oil Company, a great library of such literature exists. The nearly twenty volumes of testimony, exhibits, and briefs assembled in the course of the Federal suit which led to its dissolution is the ultimate source of material on America's greatest trust. As most of our other great corporations — the Steel Trust, the Harvester Company, the Tobacco Company, and the like — have passed through similar ordeals, all the information the student could ask concerning them exists in the same form. The archives of such bodies as the Interstate Commerce

Commission and Public Utility Commissions of the States are also bulging with documentary evidence. Thus all the material contained in this volume — and much more — concerning the New York traction situation will be found in the investigation conducted in 1907 by the Public Service Commission of New York, Second District.

American business has also developed a great talent for publicity. Nearly all our big corporations have assembled much material about their own history, all of which is public property. Thus the American Telephone and Telegraph Company can furnish detailed information on every phase of its business and history. Indeed, one's respect for the achievements of American industry is increased by the praiseworthy curiosity which it displays about its own past and the readiness with which it makes such material accessible to the public. Despite the abundance of data, there is not a great amount of popular writing on these subjects that has much fascination as literature or much value as history. The only book that is really important is Miss Ida M. Tarbell's *History of the Standard Oil Company*, 2 vols. (new edition 1911). Of other popular volumes the present writer has found most useful Herbert N. Casson's *Romance of Steel* (1907), *History of the Telephone* (1910), and *Cyrus Hall McCormick: His Life and Work* (1909); J. H. Bridge's *Inside History of the Carnegie Steel Company* (1903); *Henry Ford's Own Story* as told to Rose Wildes Lane (1917).

For Chapter V, the author has drawn from articles contributed by him in 1907–8 to *McClure's Magazine* on *Great American Fortunes and their Making;* and for Chapter IV, from an article contributed to the same magazine in 1914, on *Telephones for the Millions.*

INDEX

Helena M. James
December 1928

WAD

Jeremy

HUGH WALPOLE

JEREMY

HUGH WALPOLE

The SUN DIAL Library

GARDEN CITY PUBLISHING COMPANY, INC.

GARDEN CITY, NEW YORK

BRUCE

FROM

HIS LOVING UNCLE

> "*It is due to him to say that he was an obedient boy and a boy whose word could be depended on.. . . .*"
>
> Jackanapes

CONTENTS

JEREMY

JEREMY

CHAPTER I

THE BIRTHDAY

ABOUT thirty years ago there was at the top of the right-hand side of Orange Street, in Polchester, a large stone house. I say "was"; the shell of it is still there, and the people who now live in it are quite unaware, I suppose, that anything has happened to the inside of it, except that they are certainly assured that their furniture is vastly superior to the furniture of their predecessors. They have a gramophone, a pianola, and a lift to bring the plates from the kitchen into the dining-room, and a small motor garage at the back where the old pump used to be, and a very modern rock-garden where once was the pond with the fountain that never worked. Let them cherish their satisfaction. No one grudges it to them. The Coles were, by modern standards, old-fashioned people, and the Stone House was an old-fashioned house.

Young Jeremy Cole was born there in the year 1884, very early in the morning of December 8th. He was still there very early in the morning of December 8th, 1892.

He was sitting up in bed. The cuckoo clock had just struck five, and he was aware that he was, at this very moment, for the first time in his life, eight years old. He had gone to bed at eight o'clock on the preceding evening with the choking consciousness that he would awake in the morning a different creature. Although he had slept, there had permeated the texture of his dreams that same choking excitement, and now, wide awake, as though he had asked the cuckoo to call him in order that he might not be late for the great occasion, he stared into the black distance of his bedroom and reflected, with a beating heart, upon the great event. He was eight years old, and he had as much right now to the nursery arm-chair with a hole in it as Helen had.

That was his first definite realisation of approaching triumph. Throughout the whole of his seventh year he had fought with Helen, who was most unjustly a year older than he and persistently proud of that injustice, as to his right to use the wicker arm-chair whensoever it pleased him. So destructive of the general peace of the house had these incessant battles been, so unavailing the suggestions of elderly relations that gentlemen always yielded to ladies, that a compromise had been arrived at. When Jeremy was eight he should have equal rights with Helen. Well and good. Jeremy had yielded to that. It was the only decent chair in the nursery. Into the place where the wicker, yielding to rude and impulsive pressure, had fallen away, one's body might be most happily fitted. It was of exactly the right height; it made the handsomest creaking noises when one rocked in it—and, in any case, Helen was only a girl.

But the sense of his triumph had not yet fully descended upon him. As he sat up in bed, yawning, with a tickle in the middle of his back and his throat very dry, he was disappointingly aware that he was still the same Jeremy of yesterday. He did not know what it was exactly that he had expected, but he did not feel at present that confident proud glory for which he had been prepared. Perhaps it was too early.

He turned round, curled his head into his arm, and with a half-muttered, half-dreamt statement about the wicker chair, he was once again asleep.

II

He awoke to the customary sound of the bath water running into the bath. His room was flooded with sunshine, and old Jampot, the nurse (her name was Mrs. Preston and her shape was Jampot), was saying as usual: "Now, Master Jeremy, eight o'clock; no lying in bed—out —you get—bath—ready."

He stared at her, blinking.

"You should say 'Many Happy Returns of the Day, Master Jeremy,'" he remarked. Then suddenly, with a leap, he was out of bed, had crossed the floor, pushed back the nursery door, and was sitting in the wicker arm-chair, his naked feet kicking a triumphant dance.

"Helen! Helen!" he called. "I'm in the chair."

No sound.

"I'm eight," he shouted, "and I'm in the chair."

Mrs. Preston, breathless and exclaiming, hurried across to him.

"Oh, you naughty boy . . . death of cold . . . in your nightshirt."

"I'm eight," he said, looking at her scornfully, "and I can sit here as long as I please."

Helen, her pigtails flapping on either shoulder, her nose
red, as it always was early in the morning, appeared at the
opposite end of the nursery.

"Nurse, he mustn't, must he? Tell him not to. I don't
care how old you are. It's my chair. Mother said——"

"No, she didn't. Mother said——"

"Yes, she did. Mother said——"

"Mother said that when——"

"Oh, you story. You know that Mother said——"
Then suddenly a new, stiffening, trusting dignity filled
him, as though he had with a turn of the head discovered
himself in golden armour.

He was above this vulgar wrangling now. That was for
girls. He was superior to them all. He got down from the
chair and stood, his head up, on the old Turkey rug (red
with yellow cockatoos) in front of the roaring fire.

"You may have your old chair," he said to Helen. "I'm
eight now, and I don't want it any more . . . although
if I *do* want it I shall have it," he added.

He was a small, square boy with a pug-nosed face. His
hair was light brown, thin and stiff, so that it was difficult
to brush, and although you watered it, stood up in unexpected places and stared at you. His eyes were good, dark
brown and large, but he was in no way handsome; his neck,
his nose ridiculous. His mouth was too large, and his chin
stuck out like a hammer.

He was, plainly, obstinate and possibly sulky, although
when he smiled his whole face was lighted with humour.
Helen was the only beautiful Cole child, and she was abun-
dantly aware of that fact. The Coles had never been a
good-looking family.

He stood in front of the fireplace now as he had seen his

father do, his short legs apart, his head up, and his hands behind his back.

"Now, Master Jeremy," the Jampot continued, "you may be eight years old, but it isn't a reason for disobedience the very first minute, and, of course, your bath is ready and you catching your death with naked feet, which you've always been told to put your slippers on and not to keep the bath waiting, when there's Miss Helen and Miss Mary, as you very well know, and breakfast coming in five minutes, which there's sausages this morning, because it's your birthday, and them all getting cold——"

"Sausages!"

He was across the floor in a moment, had thrown off his nightshirt and was in his bath. Sausages! He was translated into a world of excitement and splendour. They had sausages so seldom, not always even on birthdays, and to-day, on a cold morning, with a crackling fire and marmalade, perhaps—and then all the presents.

Oh, he was happy. As he rubbed his back with the towel a wonderful glowing Christian charity spread from his head to his toes and tingled through every inch of him. Helen should sit in the chair when she pleased; Mary should be allowed to dress and undress the large woollen dog, known as "Sulks," his own especial and beloved property, so often as she wished; Jampot should poke the twisted end of the towel in his ears and brush his hair with the hard brushes, and he would not say a word. Aunt Mary should kiss him (as, of course, she would want to do), and he would not shiver; he would (bravest deed of all) allow Mary to read "Alice in Wonderland" in her sing-sing voice so long as ever she wanted. . . . Sausages! Sausages!

In his shirt and his short blue trousers, his hair on end, tugging at his braces, he stood in the doorway and shouted:

"Helen, there are sausages—because it's my birthday. Aren't you glad?"

And even when the only response to his joyous invitation was Helen's voice crossly admonishing the Jampot: "Oh, you do pull so; you're hurting!"—his charity was not checked.

Then when he stood clothed and of a cheerful mind once more in front of the fire a shyness stole over him. He knew that the moment for Presents was approaching; he knew that very shortly he would have to kiss and be kissed by a multitude of persons, that he would have to say again and again, "Oh, thank you, thank you so much!" that he would have his usual consciousness of his inability to thank anybody at all in the way that they expected to be thanked. Helen and Mary never worried about such things. They delighted in kissing and hugging and multitudes of words. If only he might have had his presents by himself and then stolen out and said "Thank you" to the lot of them and have done with it.

He watched the breakfast-table with increasing satisfaction—the large teapot with the red roses, the dark blue porridge plates, the glass jar with the marmalade a rich yellow inside it, the huge loaf with the soft pieces bursting out between the crusty pieces, the solid square of butter, so beautiful a colour and marked with a large cow and a tree on the top (he had seen once in the kitchen the wooden shape with which the cook made this handsome thing). There were also his own silver mug, given him at his christening by Canon Trenchard, his godfather, and his silver spoon, given him on the same occasion by Uncle Samuel.

All these things glittered and glowed in the firelight, and a kettle was singing on the hob and Martha the canary was singing in her cage in the window. (No one really knew whether the canary were a lady or a gentleman, but the name had been Martha after a beloved housemaid, now married to the gardener, and the sex had followed the name.)

There were also all the other familiar nursery things. The hole in the Turkey carpet near the bookcase, the rocking-horse, very shiny where you sit and very Christmas-tree-like as to its tail; the doll's house, now deserted, because Helen was too old and Mary too clever; the pictures of "Church on Christmas Morning" (everyone with their mouths very wide open, singing a Christmas hymn, with holly), "Dignity and Impudence," after Landseer, "The Shepherds and the Angels," and "The Charge of the Light Brigade." So packed was the nursery with history for Jeremy that it would have taken quite a week to relate it all. There was the spot where he had bitten the Jampot's fingers, for which deed he had afterwards been slippered by his father; there the corner where they stood for punishment (he knew exactly how many ships with sails, how many ridges of waves, and how many setting suns there were on that especial piece of corner wallpaper—three ships, twelve ridges, two and a half suns) ; there was the place where he had broken the ink-bottle over his shoes and the carpet, there by the window, where Mary had read to him once when he had toothache, and he had not known whether her reading or the toothache agonised him the more; and so on, an endless sequence of sensational history.

His reminiscences were cut short by the appearance of Gladys with the porridge. Gladys, who was only the be-

tween-maid, but was nevertheless stout, breathless from her climb and the sentiment of the occasion, produced from a deep pocket a dirty envelope, which she laid upon the table.

"Many 'appy returns, Master Jeremy." Giggle . . . giggle. . . . "Lord save us if I 'aven't gone and forgotten they spunes," and she vanished. The present-giving had begun.

He had an instant's struggle as to whether it were better to wait until all the presents had accumulated, or whether he would take them separately as they arrived. The dirty envelope lured him. He advanced towards it and seized it. He could not read very easily the sprawling writing on the cover, but he guessed that it said "From Gladys to Master Jeremy." Within was a marvellous card, tied together with glistening cord and shining with all the colours of the rainbow. It was apparently a survival from last Christmas, as there was a church in snow and a peal of bells; he was, nevertheless, very happy to have it.

After his introduction events moved swiftly. First Helen and Mary appeared, their faces shining and solemn and mysterious—Helen self-conscious and Mary staring through her spectacles like a profound owl.

Because Jeremy had known Mary ever since he could remember, he was unaware that there was anything very peculiar about her. But in truth she was a strange-looking child. Very thin, she had a large head, with big outstanding ears, spectacles, and yellow hair pulled back and "stringy." Her large hands were always red, and her forehead was freckled. She was as plain a child as you were ever likely to see, but there was character in her mouth and eyes, and although she was only seven years old.

she could read quite difficult books (she was engaged at this particular time upon "Ivanhoe"), and she was a genius at sums.

The passion of her life, as the family were all aware, was Jeremy, but it was an unfortunate and uncomfortable passion. She bothered and worried him, she was insanely jealous; she would sulk for days did he ever seem to prefer Helen to herself. No one understood her; she was considered a "difficult child," quite unlike any other member of the family, except possibly Samuel, Mr. Cole's brother-in-law, who was an unsuccessful painter and therefore "odd."

As Mary was at present only seven years of age it would be too much to say that the family was afraid of her. Aunt Amy's attitude was: "Well, after all, she's sure to be clever when she grows up, poor chi " and although the parishioners of Mary's father alwa alluded to her as "the ludicrous Cole child," they told ed little stories about the infant's mental capacities, and included comfortably, "I'm glad Alice (or Jane or Mar or Anabel) isn't clever like that. They overwork when th are young, and then when they grow up——"

Meanwhile Mary led her private life. She attached herself to no one but Jeremy; she was delicate and suffered from perpetual colds; she therefore spent much of her time in the nursery reading, her huge spectacles close to the page, her thin legs like black sticks stuck up on the fender in front of the fire or curled up under her on the window-seat.

Very different was Helen. Helen had a mass of dark black hair, big black eyes with thick eye-lashes, a thin white neck, little feet, and already an eye to "effects" in dress.

She was charming to strangers, to the queer curates who haunted the family hall, to poor people and rich people, to old people and young people. She was warm-hearted but not impulsive, intelligent but not clever, sympathetic but not sentimental, impatient but never uncontrolled. She liked almost everyone and almost everything, but no one and nothing mattered to her very deeply; she liked going to church, always learnt her Collect first on Sunday, and gave half her pocket-money to the morning collection. She was generous but never extravagant, enjoyed food but was not greedy. She was quite aware that she was pretty and might one day be beautiful, and she was glad of that, but she was never silly about her looks.

When Aunt Amy, who was always silly about everything, said in her presence to visitors, "Isn't Helen the loveliest thing you ever saw?" she managed by her shy self-confidence to suggest that she *was* pretty, that Aunt Amy *was* a fool, and life was altogether very agreeable, but that none of these things was of any great importance. She was very good friends with Jeremy, but she played no part in his life at all. At the same time she often fought with him, simply from her real deep consciousness of her superiority to him. She valued her authority and asserted it incessantly. That authority had until last year been unchallenged, but Jeremy now was growing. She had, although she did not as yet realise it, a difficult time before her.

Helen and Mary advanced with their presents, laid them on the breakfast-table, and then retreated to watch the effect of it all.

"Shall I now?" asked Jeremy.

"Yes, now," said Helen and Mary.

There were three parcels, one large and "shoppy," two small and bound with family paper, tied by family hands with family string. He grasped immediately the situation. The shoppy parcel was bought with mother's money and only "pretended" to be from his sisters; the two small parcels were the very handiwork of the ladies themselves, the same having been seen by all eyes at work for the last six months, sometimes, indeed, under the cloak of attempted secrecy, but more often—because weariness or ill-temper made them careless—in the full light of day.

His interest was centred almost entirely in the "shoppy" parcel, which by its shape might be "soldiers"; but he knew the rules of the game, and disregarding the large, ostentatious brown-papered thing, he went magnificently for the two small incoherent bundles.

He opened them. A flat green table-centre with a red pattern of roses, a thick table-napkin ring worked in yellow worsted, these were revealed.

"Oh!" he cried, "just what I wanted." (Father always said that on *his* birthday.)

"Is it?" said Mary and Helen.

"Mine's the ring," said Mary. "It's dirty rather, but it would have got dirty, anyway, afterwards." She watched anxiously to see whether he preferred Helen's.

He watched them nervously, lest he should be expected to kiss them. He wiped his mouth with his hand instead, and began rapidly to talk:

"Jampot will know now which mine is. She's always giving me the wrong one. I'll have it always, and the green thing too."

"It's for the middle of a table," Helen interrupted.

"Yes, I know," said Jeremy hurriedly. "I'll always

have it too—like Mary's—when I'm grown up and all. . . . I say, shall I open the other one now?"

"Yes, you can," said Helen and Mary, ceasing to take the central place in the ceremony, spectators now and eagerly excited.

But Mary had a last word.

"You do like mine, don't you?"

"Of course, like anything."

She wanted to say "Better than Helen's?" but restrained herself.

"I was ever so long doing it; I thought I wouldn't finish it in time."

He saw with terror that she meditated a descent upon him; a kiss was in the air. She moved forward; then, to his extreme relief, the door opened and the elders arriving saved him.

There were Father and Mother, Uncle Samuel and Aunt Amy, all with presents, faces of birthday tolerance and "do-as-you-please-to-day, dear" expressions.

The Rev. Herbert Cole was forty years of age, rector of St. James's, Polchester, during the last ten years, and marked out for greater preferment in the near future. To be a rector at thirty is unusual, but he had great religious gifts, preached an admirable "as-man-to-man" sermon, and did not believe in thinking about more than he could see. He was an excellent father in the abstract sense, but the parish absorbed too much of his time to allow of intimacies with anyone.

Mrs. Cole was the most placid lady in Europe. She had a comfortable figure, but was not stout, here a dimple and there a dimple. Nothing could disturb her. Children, servants, her husband's sermons, district visiting, her Tuesday "at homes," the butcher, the dean's wife, the wives of the canons, the Polchester climate, bills, clothes, other women's clothes—over all these rocks of peril in the sea of daily life her barque happily floated. Some ill-natured people thought her stupid, but in her younger days she had liked Trollope's novels in the *Cornhill,* disapproved placidly of "Jane Eyre," and admired Tennyson, so that she could not be considered unliterary.

She was economical, warm-hearted, loved her children, talked only the gentlest scandal, and was a completely happy woman—all this in the placidest way in the world.

Miss Amy Trefusis, her sister, was very different, being thin both in her figure and her emotions. She skirted tempestuously over the surface of things, was the most sentimental of human beings, was often in tears over reminiscences of books or the weather, was deeply religious in a superficial way, and really—although she would have been entirely astonished had you told her so—cared for no one in the world but herself. She was dressed always in dark colours, with the high shoulders of the day, elegant bonnets and little chains that jingled as she moved. In her soul she feared and distrusted children, but she did not know this. She did know, however, that she feared and distrusted her brother Samuel.

Her brother Samuel was all that the Trefusis family, as a conservative body who believed in tradition, had least reason for understanding. He had been a failure from the first moment of his entry into the Grammar School in Polchester thirty-five years before this story. He had continued a failure at Winchester and at Christ Church, Oxford. He had desired to be a painter; he had broken from the family and gone to study Art in Paris. He had starved and starved, was at death's door, was dragged home, and there suddenly had relapsed into Polchester, lived first on his father, then on his brother-in-law, painted about the town, painted, made cynical remarks about the Polcastrians, painted, made blasphemous remarks about the bishop, the dean and all the canons, painted, and refused to leave his brother-in-law's house. He was a scandal, of course; he was fat, untidy, wore a blue tam-o'-shanter when he was "out," and sometimes went down Orange Street in carpet slippers.

He was a scandal, but what are you to do if a relative is obstinate and refuses to go? At least make him shave, say the wives of the canons. But no one had ever made Samuel Trefusis do anything that he did not want to do. He was sometimes not shaved for three whole days and nights. At any rate, there he is. It is of no use saying that he does not exist, as many of the Close ladies try to do. And at least he does not paint strange women; he prefers flowers and cows and the Polchester woods, although anything less like cows, flowers and woods, Mrs. Sampson, wife of the Dean, who once had a water-colour in the Academy, says she has never seen. Samuel Trefusis is a failure, and, what is truly awful, he does not mind; nobody buys his pictures and he does not care; and, worst taste of all, he laughs at his relations, although he lives on them. Nothing further need be said.

To Helen, Mary and Jeremy he had always been a fascinating object, although they realised, with that sharp worldly wisdom to be found in all infants of tender years, that he was a failure, a dirty man, and disliked children. He very rarely spoke to them; was once quite wildly enraged when Mary was discovered licking his paints. (It was the paints he seemed anxious about, not in the least the poor little thing's health, as his sister Amy said), and had publicly been heard to say that his brother-in-law had only got the children he deserved.

Nevertheless Jeremy had always been interested in him. He liked his fat round shape, his rough, untidy grey hair, his scarlet slippers, his blue tam-o'-shanter, the smudges of paint sometimes to be discovered on his cheeks, and the jingling noises he made in his pocket with his money. He was certainly more fun than Aunt Amy.

There, then, they all were with their presents and their birthday faces.

"Shall I undo them for you, darling?" of course said Aunt Amy. Jeremy shook his head (he did not say what he thought of her) and continued to tug at the string. He was given a large pair of scissors. He received (from Father) a silver watch, (from Mother) a paint-box, a dark blue and gold prayer book with a thick squashy leather cover (from Aunt Amy).

He was in an ecstasy. How he had longed for a watch, just such a turnip-shaped one, and a paint-box. What colours he could make! Even Aunt Amy's prayer book was something, with its squashy cover and silk marker (only why did Aunt Amy never give him anything sensible?).

He stood there, his face flushed, his eyes sparkling, the watch in one hand and the paint-box in the other.

Remarks were heard like: "You mustn't poke it with your finger, Jerry darling, or you'll break the hands off"; and "I thought he'd better have the square sort, and not the tubes. They're *so* squashy"; and "You'll be able to learn your Collect so easily with that big print, Jerry dear. Very kind of you, Amy."

Meanwhile he was aware that Uncle Samuel had given him nothing. There was a little thick catch of disappointment in his throat, not because he wanted a present, but because he liked Uncle Samuel. Suddenly, from somewhere behind him his uncle said: "Shut your eyes, Jerry. Don't open them until I tell you"—then rather crossly, "No, Amy, leave me alone. I know what I'm about, thank you."

Jeremy shut his eyes tight. He closed them so that the eyelids seemed to turn right inwards and red lights flashed. He stood there for at least a century, all in darkness, no one saying anything save that once Mary cried "Oh!" and clapped her hands, which same cry excited him to such a pitch that he would have dug his nails into his hands had he not so consistently in the past bitten them that there were no nails with which to dig. He waited. He waited. He waited. He was not eight, he was eighty when at last Uncle Samuel said, "Now you may look."

He opened his eyes and turned; for a moment the nursery, too, rocked in the unfamiliar light. Then he saw. On the middle of the nursery carpet was a village, a real village, six houses with red roofs, green windows and white porches, a church with a tower and a tiny bell, an orchard with flowers on the fruit trees, a green lawn, a street with a butcher's shop, a post office, and a grocer's. Villager Noah, Mrs. Noah and the little Noahs, a field with cows, horses, dogs, a farm with chickens and even two pigs. . . .

He stood, he stared, he drew a deep breath.

"It comes all the way from Germany," said Aunt Amy, who always made things uninteresting if she possibly could.

There was much delighted talk. Jeremy said nothing. But Uncle Samuel understood.

"Glad you like it," he said, and left the room.

"Aren't you pleased?" said Helen.

Jeremy still said nothing.

"Sausages. Sausages!" cried Mary, as Gladys, grinning, entered with a dish of a lovely and pleasant smell.

But Jeremy did not turn. He simply stood there— staring.

III

It is of the essence of birthdays that they cannot maintain throughout a long day the glorious character of their early dawning. In Polchester thirty years ago there were no cinematographs, no theatre save for an occasional amateur performance at the Assembly Rooms and, once and again, a magic-lantern show. On this particular day, moreover, Mr. and Mrs. Cole were immensely busied with preparations for some parochial tea. Miss Trefusis had calls to make, and, of course, Uncle Samuel was invisible. The Birthday then suddenly became no longer a birthday but an ordinary day—with an extraordinary standard. This is why so many birthdays end in tears.

But Jeremy, as was usual with him, took everything quietly. He might cry aloud about such an affair as the conquest of the wicker chair because that did not deeply matter to him, but about the real things he was silent. The village was one of the real things; during all the morning he remained shut up in his soul with it, the wide world closed off from them by many muffled doors. How had Uncle Samuel known that he had deep in his own inside, so deep that he had not mentioned it even to himself,

wanted something just like this? Thirty years ago there
were none of the presents that there are for children now—
no wonderful railways that run round the nursery from
Monte Carlo to Paris with all the stations marked; no
dolls that are so like fashionable women that you are given
a manicure set with them to keep their nails tidy; no
miniature motor-cars that run of themselves and go for
miles round the floor without being wound up. Jeremy
knew none of these things, and was the happier that he
did not. To such a boy such a village was a miracle.
. . . It had not come from Germany, as Aunt Amy
said, but from heaven. But it was even more of Uncle
Samuel than the village that he was thinking. When they
started—Helen, Mary and he in charge of the Jampot—
upon their afternoon walk, he was still asking himself the
same questions. How had Uncle Samuel known so exactly? Had it been a great trouble to bring from so far
away? Had Uncle Samuel thought it bad of him not to
thank him?

He was lost in such considerations when the Jampot
inquired of him the way that their walk should take—it
was his choice because it was his Birthday. He had no
choice. There was one walk that far exceeded all others
in glory, straight down Orange Street, straight again
through the Market, past the Assembly Rooms and the
Town Hall, past the flower and fruit stalls, and the old
banana woman under the green umbrella and the toy stall
with coloured balloons, the china dogs and the nodding
donkeys, up the High Street, into the cobble-stones of the
Close, whence one could look down, between the houses on
to the orchards, round the Cathedral with the meadows,

Pol Meads sloping down to the river, so through Orchard Lane into Orange Street once again.

Such a walk combined every magic and delight known to the heart of man, but it was not generally allowed, because Jeremy would drag past the shops, the stalls in the Market Place and the walk behind the Cathedral, whence one might sometimes see boats on the river, sheep and cows in the meads, and, in their proper season, delight of delights—lambs.

They set out. . . .

Thirty years ago the winter weather in Polchester was wonderful. Now, of course, there are no hard winters, no frost, no snow, no waits, no snowmen, and no skating on the Pol. Then there were all those things. To-day was of a hard, glittering frost; the sun, like a round, red lacquer tray, fell heavily, slowly through a faint pale sky that was not strong enough to sustain it. The air had the cold, sweet twang of peppermints in the throat. Polchester was a painted town upon a blue screen, the Cathedral towers purple against the sky; the air was scented with burning leaves, and cries from the town rose up clear and hard, lingering and falling like notes of music. Somewhere they were playing football, and the shouting was distant and regular like the tramp of armed men. "Three" struck the Cathedral clock, as though it were calling "Open Sesame." Other lesser clocks repeated the challenge cry through the town. "Woppley—Woppley—Why!" sung the man who was selling skins down Orange Street. The sky, turning slowly from blue to gold, shone mysteriously through the glass of the street lamps, and the sun began to wrap itself in tints of purple and crocus and iris.

"Woppley—Woppley—Why!" screamed the skin-man suddenly appearing at the top of the street.

"Now 'urry, Master Jeremy," said the Jampot, "or we
shall never get 'ome this night, and I might have known
you'd choose the longest walk possible. Come along, Miss
Mary, now—none of that dawdling."

Jeremy, in his H.M.S. *Adventure's* cap and rough blue
navy coat, felt himself superior to the Jampot, so he only
said, "Oh, don't bother, Nurse," and then in the same
breath, "I'll run you down the hill, Mary," and before
anyone could say a word there they were at the bottom
of Orange Street, as though they had fallen into a well.
The sun was gone, the golden horizon was gone—only
the purple lights began to gather about their feet and
climb slowly the high black houses.

Mary liked this, because she now had Jeremy to herself.
She began hurriedly, so that she should lose no time:

"Shall I tell you a story, Jeremy? I've got a new one.
Once upon a time there were three little boys, and they
lived in a wood, and an old witch ate them, and the Princess who had heaps of jewellery and a white horse and a
lovely gold dress came, and it was snowing and the
witch——"

This was always Mary's way. She loved to tell Jeremy
interesting stories, and he did not mind because he did
not listen and could meanwhile think his own thoughts.

His chief decision arrived at as he marched along was
that he would keep the village to himself; no one else
should put their fingers into it, arrange the orchard with
the coloured trees, decide upon the names of the Noah
family, settle the village street in its final order, ring the
bell of the church, or milk the cows. He alone would do

all these things. And, so considering, he seemed to himself very like God. God, he supposed, could pull Polchester about, root out a house here, another there, knock the Assembly Rooms down and send a thunderbolt on to the apple woman's umbrella. Well, then—so could he with his village. He walked swollen with pride. He arrived at the first Island of Circe, namely, the window of Mr. Thompson, the jeweller in Market Street, pressed his nose to the pane, and refused to listen when the Jampot suggested that he should move forward.

He could see the diamonds like drops of water in the sun, and the pearls like drops of milk, and the rubies like drops of blood, but it was not of diamonds, pearls or rubies that he was thinking—he thought only of his village. He would ring the church bell, and then all the Noah family should start out of the door, down the garden, up the village street. . . . It did not matter if one of the younger Noahs should be lazy and wish to stay at home beneath the flowering trees of the orchard. She would not be allowed. . . . He was as God. . . . He was as God. . . . The butcher should go (if he was not stuck to his shop), and even some of his cows might go. . . . He was as God. . . .

He heard Mary's voice in his ear.

"And after that they all ate chocolates with white cream and red cream, and they sucked it off pins, and there were hard bits and soft bits, and the Princess (she was a frog now. You remember, don't you, Jeremy? The witch turned her) hotted the oven like cook has, with black doors, and hotted it and hotted it, but suddenly there was a noise——"

And, on the other side, the Jampot's voice: "You

naughty boy, stoppin' 'ere for everyone to see, just because it's your birthday, which I wish there wasn't no birthdays, nor there wouldn't be if I had my way."

Jeremy turned from Mr. Thompson's window, a scornful smile on his face:

"I'm bigger'n you, Nurse," he said. "If I said out loud, 'I won't go,' I wouldn't go, and no one could make me."

"Well, come along, then," said Nurse.

"Don't be so stupid, Jerry," said Helen calmly. "If a policeman came and said you had to go home you'd have to go."

"No I wouldn't," said Jeremy.

"Then they'd put you in prison."

"They could."

"They'd hang you, perhaps."

"They could," replied Jeremy.

Farther than this argument cannot go, so Helen shrugged her shoulders and said: "You *are* silly."

And they all moved forward.

He found then that this new sense of God-like power detracted a little from the excitements of the Market Place, although the flower-stall was dazzling with flowers; there was a new kind of pig that lifted its tail and lowered it again on the toy stall, and the apple-woman was as fat as ever and had thick clumps of yellow bananas hanging most richly around her head. They ascended the High Street and reached the Close. It was half-past three, and the Cathedral bells had begun to ring for evensong. All the houses in the Close were painted with a pale yellow light; across the long green Cathedral lawn thin black shadows like the fingers of giants pointed to the Cathedral door.

All was so silent here that the bells danced against the houses and back again, the echoes lingering in the high elms and mingling with the placid cooing of the rooks.

"There's Mrs. Sampson," said Jeremy. "Aunt Amy says she's a wicked woman. Do you think she's a wicked woman, Nurse?" He gazed at the stout figure with interest. If he were truly God he would turn her into a rabbit. This thought amused him, and he began to laugh.

"You naughty boy; now come along, do," said the Jampot, who distrusted laughter in Jerry.

"I'll ring the bells when I grow up," he said, "and I'll ring them in the middle of the night, so that everyone will have to go to church when they don't want to. I'll be able to do what I like when I grow up."

"No, you won't," said Helen. "Father and Mother can't do what they like."

"Yes they can," said Jeremy.

"No they can't," answered Helen, "or they would."

"So they do," said Jeremy—"silly."

"Silly yourself," said Helen very calmly, because she knew very well that she was not silly.

"Now, children, stop it, do," said the Jampot.

Jeremy's sense of newly received power reached its climax when they walked round the Close and reached the back of the Cathedral. I know that now, both for Jeremy and me, that prospect has dwindled into its proper grown-up proportions, but how can a man, be he come to three-score and ten and more, ever forget the size, the splendour, the stupendous extravagance of that early vision?

Jeremy saw that day the old fragment of castle wall, the green expanse falling like a sheeted waterfall from the Cathedral heights, the blue line of river flashing in the evening sun between the bare-boughed trees, the long spaces of black shadow spreading slowly over the colour, as though it were all being rolled up and laid away for another day; the brown frosty path of the Rope Walk, the farther bank climbing into fields and hedges, ending in the ridge of wood, black against the golden sky. And all so still! As the children stood there they could catch nestlings' faint cries, stirrings of dead leaves and twigs, as birds and beasts moved to their homes; the cooing of the rooks about the black branches seemed to promise that this world should be for ever tranquil, for ever cloistered and removed; the sun, red and flaming above the dark wood, flung white mists hither and thither to veil its departure. The silence deepened, the last light flamed on the river and died upon the hill.

"Now, children, come along do," said the Jampot who had been held in spite of herself, and would pay for it, she knew, in rheumatism to-morrow. It was then that Jeremy's God-flung sense of power, born from that moment early in the day when he had sat in the wicker chair, reached its climax. He stood there, his legs apart, looking upon the darkening world and felt that he could do anything—anything. . . .

At any rate, there was one thing that he could do, disobey the Jampot.

"I'm not coming," he said, "till I choose."

"You wicked boy!" she cried, her temper rising with the evening chills, her desire for a cup of hot tea, and an aching longing for a comfortable chair. "When everyone's been so good to you to-day and the things you've been given and all—why, it's a wicked shame."

The Jampot, who was a woman happily without imagination, saw a naughty small boy spoiled and needing the slipper.

A rook, taking a last look at the world before retiring to rest, watching from his leafless bough, saw a mortal spirit defying the universe, and sympathised with it.

"I shall tell your mother," said the Jampot. "Now come, Master Jeremy, be a good boy."

"Oh, don't bother, Nurse," he answered impatiently. "You're such a fuss."

She realised in that moment that he was suddenly beyond her power, that he would never be within it again. She had nursed him for eight years, she had loved him in her own way; she, dull perhaps in the ways of the world, but wise in the ways of nurses, ways that are built up of surrender and surrender, gave him, then and there, to the larger life. . . .

"You may behave as you like, Master Jeremy," she said. "It won't be for long that I'll have the dealing with you, praise be. You'll be going to school next September, and then we'll see what'll happen to your wicked pride."

"School!" he turned upon her, his eyes wide and staring.

"School!" he stared at them all.

The world tumbled from him. In his soul was a confusion of triumph and dismay, of excitement and loneliness, of the sudden falling from him of all old standards old horizons, of pride and humility. . . . How little now was the Village to him. He looked at them to see whether they could understand. They could not.

Very quietly he followed them home. His birthday had achieved its climax. . . .

CHAPTER II

THE FAMILY DOG

I

THAT winter of Jeremy's eighth birthday was famous for its snow. Glebeshire has never yielded to the wishes of its children in the matter of snowy Christmases, and Polchester has the reputation of muggy warmth and foggy mists, but here was a year when traditions were fulfilled in the most reckless manner, and all the 1892 babies were treated to a present of snow on so fine a scale that certainly for the rest of their days they will go about saying: "Ah, you should see the winters we used to have when we were children. . . ."

The snow began on the very day after Jeremy's birthday, coming down doubtfully, slowly, little grey flakes against a grey sky, then sparkling white, then vanishing flashes of moisture on a wet, unsympathetic soil. That day the snow did not lie; and for a week it did not come again; then with a whirl it seized the land, and for two days and nights did not loosen its grip. From the nursery windows the children watched it, their noses making little rings on the window-pane, their delighted eyes snatching fascinating glimpses of figures tossed through the storm, cabs beating their way, the rabbit-skin man, the milkman, the postman, brave adventurers all, fighting, as it seemed, for their very lives.

For two days the children did not leave the house, and the natural result of that was that on the second afternoon tempers were, like so many dogs, straining, tugging, pulling at their chains.

It could not be denied that Jeremy had been tiresome to everyone since the afternoon when he had heard the news of his going to school next September. It had seemed to him a tremendous event, the Beginning of the End. To the others, who lived in the immediate present, it was a crisis so remote as scarcely to count at all. Mary would have liked to be sentimental about it, but from this she was sternly prevented. There was then nothing more to be said. . . .

Jeremy was suddenly isolated from them all. His destiny was peculiar. They were girls, he was a boy. They understood neither his fears nor his ambitions; he needed terribly a companion. The snow, shutting them in, laughed at their struggles against monotony. The nursery clock struck three and they realised that two whole hours must pass before the next meal. Mary, her nose red from pressing on the window-pane, her eyes gazing through her huge spectacles wistfully at Jeremy, longed to suggest that she should read aloud to him. She knew that he hated it; she pretended to herself that she did not know.

Jeremy stared desperately at Helen who was sitting, dignified and collected, in the wicker chair hemming a minute handkerchief.

"We might play Pirates," Jeremy said with a little cough, the better to secure her attention. There was no answer.

"Or there's the hut in the wood—if anyone likes it better," he added politely. He did not know what was the matter. Had the Jampot not told him about school he would at this very moment be playing most happily with his village. It spread out there before him on the nursery floor, the Noah family engaged upon tea in the orchard, the butcher staring with fixed gaze from the door of his shop, three cows and a sheep absorbed in the architecture of the church.

He sighed, then said again: "Perhaps Pirates would be better."

Still Helen did not reply. He abandoned the attempted control of his passions.

"It's very rude," he said, "not to answer when gentlemen speak to you."

"I don't see any gentlemen," answered Helen quietly, without raising her eyes, which was, as she knew, a provoking habit.

"Yes, you do," almost screamed Jeremy. "I'm one."

"You're not," continued Helen; "you're only eight. Gentlemen must be over twenty like Father or Mr. Jellybrand."

"I hate Mr. Jellybrand and I hate you," replied Jeremy.

"I don't care," said Helen.

"Yes, you do," said Jeremy, then suddenly, as though even a good quarrel were not worth while on this heavily burdened afternoon, he said gently: "You might play Pirates, Helen. You can be Sir Roger."

"I've got this to finish."

"It's a dirty old thing," continued Jeremy, pursuing an argument, "and it'll be dirtier soon, and the Jampot says you do all the stitches wrong. I wish I was at school."

"I wish you were," said Helen.

There was a pause after this. Jeremy went sadly back
to his window-seat. Mary felt that her moment had arrived. Sniffing, as was her habit when she wanted something very badly, she said in a voice that was little more
than a whisper:

"It would be fun, wouldn't it, perhaps if I read something, Jeremy?"

Jeremy *was* a gentleman, although he was only eight.
He looked at her and saw behind the spectacles eyes beseeching his permission.

"Well, it wouldn't be *much* fun," he said, "but it's all
beastly this afternoon, anyway."

"Can I sit on the window too?" asked Mary.

"Not too close, because it tickles my ear, but you can
if you like."

She hurried across to the bookshelf. "There's 'Stumps'
and 'Rags and Tatters,' and 'Engel the Fearless,' and
'Herr Baby' and 'Alice' and——"

" 'Alice' is best," said Jeremy, sighing. "You know it
better than the others." He curled himself into a corner
of the window-seat. From his position there he had a fine
view. Immediately below him was the garden, white and
grey under the grey sky, the broken fountain standing up
like a snow man in the middle of it. The snow had ceased
to fall and a great stillness held the world.

Beyond the little iron gate of the garden that always
sneezed "Tishoo" when you closed it, was the top of Orange
Street; then down the hill on the right was the tower of
his father's church; exactly opposite the gate was the road
that led to the Orchards, and on the right of that was the
Polchester High School for Young Ladies, held in great
contempt by Jeremy, the more that Helen would shortly

be a day-boarder there, would scream with the other girls, and, worst of all, would soon be seen walking with her arm round another girl's neck, chattering and eating sweets. . . .

The whole world seemed deserted. No colour, no movement, no sound. He sighed once more—"I'd like to eat jam and jam—lots of it," he thought. "It would be fun to be sick."

Mary arrived and swung herself up on to the window-seat.

"It's the 'Looking Glass' one. I hope you don't mind," she said apprehensively.

"Oh, it's all right," he allowed. He flung a glance back to the lighted nursery. It seemed by contrast with that grey world outside to blaze with colour; the red-painted ships on the wallpaper, the bright lights and shadows of "The Charge of the Light Brigade," the salmon fronts of the doll's house, the green and red of the village on the floor with the flowery trees, the blue table-cloth, the shining brass coal-scuttle all alive and sparkling in the flames and shadows of the fire, caught and held by the fine gold of the higher fender. Beyond that dead white—soon it would be dark, the curtains would be drawn, and still there would be nothing to do. He sighed again.

"It's a nice bit about the shop," said Mary. Jeremy said nothing, so she began. She started at a run:

" 'She looked at the Queen, who seemed to have' "—sniff, sniff—" 'sud-den-ly suddenly wra-wra-w-r-a-p-p-e-d wrapped——' "

"Wrapped ?" asked Jeremy.

"I don't know," said Mary, rubbing her nose, "what it means, but perhaps we'll see presently, 'herself up in w-o-o-l wool. Alice rubbed her eyes and looked again she couldn't——' "

" 'Looked again she couldn't'?" asked Jeremy. "It should be, 'she couldn't look again.' "

"Oh, there's a stop," said Mary. "I didn't see. After 'again' there's a stop. 'She couldn't make out what had happened at all——' "

"I can't either," said Jeremy crossly. "It would be better perhaps if I read it myself."

"It will be all right in a minute," said Mary confidently. " 'Was she in a shop? And was that really—was it really a ship that was sitting on the counter?' " she finished with a run.

"A what?" asked Jeremy.

"A ship——"

"A ship! How could it sit on a counter?" he asked.

"Oh no, it's a sheep. How silly I am!" Mary exclaimed.

"You *do* read badly," he agreed frankly. "I never can understand nothing." And it was at that very moment that he saw the Dog.

II

He had been staring down into the garden with a gaze half abstracted, half speculative, listening with one ear to Mary, with the other to the stir of the fire, the heavy beat of the clock and the rustlings of Martha the canary.

He watched the snowy expanse of garden, the black gate, the road beyond. A vast wave of pale grey light, the herald of approaching dusk, swept the horizon, the snowy roofs, the streets, and Jeremy felt some contact with the strange air, the mysterious omens that the first snows of the winter spread about the land. He watched as though he were waiting for something to happen.

The creature came up very slowly over the crest of Orange Street. No one else was in sight, no cart, no horse, no weather-beaten wayfarer. At first the dog was only a little black smudge against the snow; then, as he arrived at the Coles' garden-gate, Jeremy could see him very distinctly. He was, it appeared, quite alone; he had been, it was evident, badly beaten by the storm. Intended by nature to be a rough and hairy dog, he now appeared before God and men a shivering battered creature, dripping and wind-tossed, bedraggled and bewildered. And yet, even in that first distant glimpse, Jeremy discerned a fine independence. He was a short stumpy dog, in no way designed for dignified attitudes and patronising superiority; nevertheless, as he now wandered slowly up the street, his nose was in the air and he said to the whole world: "The storm may have done its best to defeat me—it has failed. I am as I was. I ask charity of no man. I know what is due to me."

It was this that attracted Jeremy; he had himself felt thus after a slippering from his father, or idiotic punishments from the Jampot, and the uninvited consolations of Mary or Helen upon such occasions had been resented with so fierce a bitterness that his reputation for sulkiness had been soundly established with all his circle.

Mary was reading . . . ! " 'an old Sheep, sitting in an arm-chair, knitting, and every now and then leaving off to look at her through a great pair of spec-t-a-c-les spectacles!' "

He touched her arm and whispered:

"I say, Mary, stop a minute—look at that dog down there."

They both stared down into the garden. The dog had stopped at the gate; it sniffed at the bars, sniffed at the wall beyond, then very slowly but with real dignity continued its way up the road.

"Poor thing," said Jeremy. "It *is* in a mess." Then to their astonishment the dog turned back and, sauntering down the road again as though it had nothing all day to do but to wander about, and as though it were not wet, shivering and hungry, it once more smelt the gate.

"Oh," said Mary and Jeremy together.

"It's like Mother," said Jeremy, "when she's going to see someone and isn't sure whether it's the right house."

Then, most marvellous of unexpected climaxes, the dog suddenly began to squeeze itself between the bottom bar of the gate and the ground. The interval was fortunately a large one; a moment later the animal was in the Coles' garden.

The motives that led Jeremy to behave as he did are uncertain. It may have been something to do with the general boredom of the afternoon, it may have been that he felt pity for the bedraggled aspect of the animal—most probable reason of all, was that devil-may-care independence flung up from the road, as it were, expressly at himself.

The dog obviously did not feel any great respect for the Cole household. He wandered about the garden, sniffing and smelling exactly as though the whole place belonged to him, and a ridiculous stump of tail, unsubdued by the weather, gave him the ludicrous dignity of a Malvolio.

"I'm going down," whispered Jeremy, flinging a cautious glance at Helen who was absorbed in her sewing.

Mary's eyes grew wide with horror and admiration. "You're not going out," she whispered. "In the snow. Oh, Jeremy. They *will* be angry."

"I don't care," whispered Jeremy back again. "They can be."

Indeed, before Mary's frightened whisper he had not intended to do more than creep down into the pantry and watch the dog at close range; now it was as though Mary had challenged him. He knew that it was the most wicked thing that he could do—to go out into the snow without a coat and in his slippers. He might even, according to Aunt Amy, die of it, but as death at present meant no more to him than a position of importance and a quantity of redcurrant jelly and chicken, *that* prospect did not deter him. He left the room so quietly that Helen did not even lift her eyes.

Then upon the landing he waited and listened. The house had all the lighted trembling dusk of the snowy afternoon; there was no sound save the ticking of the clocks. He might come upon the Jampot at any moment, but this was just the hour when she liked to drink her cup of tea in the kitchen; he knew from deep and constant study every movement of her day. Fortune favoured him. He reached without trouble the little dark corkscrew servants' staircase. Down this he crept, and found himself beside the little gardener's door. Although here there was only snow-lit dusk, he felt for the handle of the lock, found it, turned it, and was, at once, over the steps, into the garden.

Here, with a vengeance, he felt the full romance and

danger of his enterprise. It was horribly cold; he had been in the nursery for two whole days, wrapped up and warm, and now the snowy world seemed to leap up at him and drag him down as though into an icy well. Mysterious shadows hovered over the garden; the fountain pointed darkly against the sky, and he could feel from the feathery touches upon his face that the snow had begun to fall again.

He moved forward a few steps; the house was so dark behind him, the world so dim and uncertain in front of him, that for a moment his heart failed him. He might have to search the whole garden for the dog.

Then he heard a sniff, felt something wet against his leg—he had almost stepped upon the animal. He bent down and stroked its wet coat. The dog stood quite still, then moved forward towards the house, sniffed at the steps, at last walked calmly through the open door as though the house belonged to him. Jeremy followed, closed the door behind him; then there they were in the little dark passage with the boy's heart beating like a drum, his teeth chattering, and a terrible temptation to sneeze hovering around him. Let him reach the nursery and establish the animal there and all might be well, but let them be discovered, cold and shivering, in the passage, and out the dog would be flung. He knew so exactly what would happen. He could hear the voices in the kitchen. He knew that they were sitting warm there by the fire, but that at any moment Jampot might think good to climb the stairs and see "what mischief they children were up to." Everything depended upon the dog. Did he bark or whine, out into the night he must go again, probably to die in the cold. But Jeremy, the least sentimental of that most sentimental race the English, was too intent upon his threatened sneeze to pay much attention to these awful possibilities.

He took off his slippers and began to climb the stairs, the dog close behind him, very grave and dignified, in spite of the little trail of snow and water that he left in his track. The nursery door was reached, pushed softly open, and the startled gaze of Mary and Helen fell wide-eyed upon the adventurer and his prize.

III

The dog went directly to the fire; there, sitting in the very middle of the golden cockatoos on the Turkey rug, he began to lick himself. He did this by sitting very square on three legs and spreading out the fourth stiff and erect, as though it had been not a leg at all but something of wood or iron. The melted snow poured off him, making a fine little pool about the golden cockatoos. He must have been a strange-looking animal at any time, being built quite square like a toy dog, with a great deal of hair, very short legs, and a thick stubborn neck; his eyes were brown, and now could be seen very clearly because the hair that usually covered them was plastered about his face by the snow. In his normal day his eyes gleamed behind his hair like sunlight in a thick wood. He wore a little pointed beard that could only be considered an affectation; in one word, if you imagine a ridiculously small sheep-dog with no legs, a French beard and a stump of a tail, you have him. And if you want to know more than that I can only refer you to the description of his great-great-great-grandson "Jacob," described in the Chronicles of the Beaminster Family.

The children meanwhile gazed, and for a long time no one said a word. Then Helen said: "Father *will* be angry."

But she did not mean it. The three were, by the entrance of the dog, instantly united into an offensive and defensive alliance. They knew well that shortly an attack from the Outside World must be delivered, and without a word spoken or a look exchanged they were agreed to defend both themselves and the dog with all the strength in their power. They had always wanted a dog; they had been prevented by the stupid and selfish arguments of uncomprehending elders.

Now this dog was here; they would keep him.

"Oh, he's perfectly sweet," suddenly said Helen.

The dog paused for a moment from his ablutions, raised his eyes, and regarded her with a look of cold contempt, then returned to his task.

"Don't be so silly," said Jeremy. "You know you always hate it when Aunt Amy says things like that about you."

"Did Nurse see?" asked Mary.

"No, she didn't," said Jeremy; "but she'll be up in a minute."

"What are you going to do?" asked Mary, her mouth wide open.

"Do? Keep him, of course," said Jeremy stoutly; at the same time his heart a little failed him as he saw the pool of water slowly spreading and embracing one cockatoo after another in its ruinous flood.

"We ought to wipe him with a towel," said Jeremy; "if we could get him dry before Nurse comes up she mightn't say so much."

But alas, it was too late for any towel; the door opened, and the Jampot entered, humming a hymn, very cheerful and rosy from the kitchen fire and an abundant series of chronicles of human failings and misfortunes. The hymn ceased abruptly. She stayed there where she was, "frozen into an image," as she afterwards described it. She also said: "You could 'ave knocked me down with a feather."

The dog did not look at her, but crocked under him the leg that had been stiff like a ramrod and spread out another. The children did not speak.

"Well!" For a moment words failed her; then she began, her hands spread out as though she was addressing a Suffragette meeting in Trafalgar Square. (She knew, happy woman, nothing of Suffragettes.) "Of all the things, and it's you, Master Jeremy, that 'as done it, as anyone might have guessed by the way you've been be-'aving this last fortnight, and what's come over you is more nor I nor anyone else can tell, which I was saying only yesterday to your mother that it's more than one body and pair of hands is up to the managing of now you've got so wild and wicked; and wherever from did you get the dirty animal dropping water all over the nursery carpet and smelling awful, I'll be bound, which anyone can see that's got eyes, and you'd know what your father will do to you when he knows of it, and so he shall, as sure as my name is Lizzie Preston. . . . Go on out, you ugly, dirty animal—ough, you 'orrible creature you. I'll——"

But her advance was stopped. Jeremy stopped it. Standing in front of the dog, his short thick legs spread defiantly apart, his fists clenched, he almost shouted:

"You shan't touch him. . . . No, you shan't. I don't

care. He shan't go out again and die. You're a cruel, wicked woman."

The Jampot gasped. Never, no, never in all her long nursing experience had she been so defied, so insulted.

Her teeth clicked as always when her temper was roused, the reason being that thirty years ago the arts and accomplishments of dentistry had not reached so fine a perfection as to-day can show.

She had, moreover, bought a cheap set. Her teeth clicked. She began: "The moment your mother comes I give her notice. To think that all these years I've slaved and slaved only to be told such things by a boy as——"

Then a very dramatic thing occurred. The door opened, just as it might in the third act of a play by M. Sardou, and revealed the smiling faces of Mrs. Cole, Miss Amy Trefusis and the Rev. William Jellybrand, Senior Curate of St. James's, Orange Street.

Mr. Jellybrand had arrived, as he very often did, to tea. He had expressed a desire, as he very often did, to see the "dear children." Mrs. Cole, liking to show her children to visitors, even to such regular and ordinary ones as Mr. Jellybrand, at once was eager to gratify his desire.

"We'll catch them just before their tea," she said happily.

There is an unfortunate tendency on the part of our Press and stage to caricature our curates; this tendency I would willingly avoid. It should be easy enough to do, as I am writing about Polchester, a town that simply abounds—and also abounded thirty years ago—in curates of the most splendid and manly type. But, unfortunately,

Mr. Jellybrand was not one of these. I, myself, remember him very well, and can see him now flinging his thin, black, and—as it seemed to me then—gigantic figure up Orange Street, his coat flapping behind him, his enormous boots flapping in front of him, and his huge hands flapping on each side of him like a huge gesticulating crow.

He had, the Polchester people who liked him said, "a rich voice." The others who did not like him called him "an affected ass." He ran up and down the scale like this:

		Mrs.
	dear	
My		
		Cole.

and his blue cheeks looked colder than any iceberg. But then I must confess that I am prejudiced. I did not like him; no children did.

The Cole children hated him. Jeremy because he had damp hands, Helen because he never looked at her, Mary because he once said to her, "Little girls must play as well as work, you know." He always talked down to us as though we were beings of another and inferior planet. He called it, "Getting on with the little ones." No, he was not popular with us.

He stood on this particular and dramatic occasion in front of the group in the doorway and stared—as well he might. Unfortunately the situation, already bad enough, was aggravated by this dark prominence of Mr. Jellybrand. It cannot be found in any chronicles that Mr. Jellybrand and the dog had met before; it is simply a fact that the dog, raising his eyes at the opening of the door and catching sight of the black-coated figure, forgot instantly his toilet, rose dripping from his rug, and advanced growling, his lips back, his ears out, his tail erect, towards the door. Then everything happened together. Mr. Jellybrand, who had been afraid of dogs ever since, as an infant, he had been mistaken for a bone by a large retriever, stepped back upon Aunt Amy, who uttered a shrill cry. Mrs. Cole, although she did not forsake her accustomed placidity, said: "Nurse . . . Nurse . . ." Jeremy cried: "It's all right, he wouldn't touch anything, he's only friendly." Mary and Helen together moved forward as though to protect Jeremy, and the Jampot could be heard in a confused wail: "Not me, Mum. . . . Wickedest boy . . . better give notice . . . as never listens . . . dog . . . dog . . ."

The animal, however, showed himself now, as at that first earlier view of him, indifferent to his surroundings. He continued his advance and then, being only a fraction of an inch from Mr. Jellybrand's tempting gleaming black trousers, he stopped, crouched like a tiger, and with teeth still bared continued his kettle-like reverberations. Aunt Amy, who hated dogs, loved Mr. Jellybrand, and was not in the least sentimental when her personal safety was in danger, cried in a shrill voice: "But take it away. Take it away. Alice, tell him. It's going to bite Mr. Jellybrand."

The dog raised one eye from his dreamy contemplation of the trousers and glanced at Aunt Amy; from that moment may be dated a feud which death only concluded. This dog was not a forgetful dog.

Jeremy advanced. "It's all right," he cried scornfully.

"He wouldn't bite anything." He bent down, took the
animal by the scruff of the neck, and proceeded to lead
it back to the fire. The animal went without a moment's
hesitation; it would be too much to say that it exchanged
a wink with Jeremy, but something certainly passed
between them. Back again on the Turkey rug he became
master of the situation. He did the only thing possible:
he disregarded entirely the general company and addressed
himself to the only person of ultimate importance—namely,
Mrs. Cole. He lay down on all fours, looked up directly
into her face, bared his teeth this time in a smile and not
in a growl, and wagged his farcical tail.

Mrs. Cole's psychology was of the simplest: if you were
nice to her she would do anything for you, but in spite of
all her placidity she was sometimes hurt in her most
sensitive places. These wounds she never displayed, and
no one ever knew of them, and indeed they passed very
quickly—but there they occasionally were. Now on what
slender circumstances do the fates of dogs and mortals
hang. Only that afternoon Mr. Jellybrand, in the innocent self-confidence of his heart, had agreed with Miss
Maple, an elderly and bitter spinster, that the next sewing
meeting of the Dorcas Sisterhood should be held in her
house and not at the Rectory. He had told Mrs. Cole of
this on his way upstairs to the nursery. Now Mrs. Cole
liked the Dorcas meetings at the Rectory; she liked the
cheerful chatter, the hospitality, the gentle scandal and
her own position as hostess.

She did not like—she never liked—Miss Maple, who
was always pushing herself forward, criticising and back-
biting. Mr. Jellybrand should not have settled this without
consulting her. He had taken it for granted that she

would agree. He had said: "I agreed with Miss Maple that it would be better to have it at her house. I'm sure you will think as I do." Why should he be sure? Was he not forgetting his position a little? . . .

Kindest woman in the world, she had seen with a strange un-Christian pleasure the dog's advance upon the black trousers. Then Mr. Jellybrand had been obviously afraid. He fancied, perhaps, that she too had been afraid. He fancied, perhaps, that she was not mistress in her house, that she could be browbeaten by her sister and her nurse.

She smiled at him. "There's no reason to be afraid, Mr. Jellybrand. . . . He's such a little dog."

Then the dog smiled at her.

"Poor little thing," she said. "He must have nearly died in the snow."

Thus Miss Maple, bitterest of spinsters, influenced, all unwitting, the lives not only of a dog and a curate, but of the entire Cole family, and through them, of endless generations both of dogs and men as yet unborn. Miss Maple, sitting in her little yellow-curtained parlour drinking, in jaundiced contentment, her afternoon's cup of tea, was, of course, unaware of this. A good thing that she was unaware—she was quite conceited enough already.

IV

After that smiling judgment of Mrs. Cole's, affairs were quickly settled.

"Of course it can only be for the night, children. Father will arrange something in the morning. Poor little thing. Where did you find him?"

"We saw him from the window," said Jeremy quickly, "and he was shivering like anything, so we called him in to warm him."

"My dear Alice, you surely don't mean——" began Aunt Amy, and the Jampot said: "I really think, Mum——," and Mr. Jellybrand, in his rich voice, murmured: "Is it quite wise, dear Mrs. Cole, do you think?"

With thoughts of Miss Maple she smiled upon them all.

"Oh, for one night, I think we can manage. He seems a clean little dog, and really we can't turn him out into the snow at once. It would be *too* cruel. But mind, children, it's only for one night. He looks a good little dog."

When the "quality" had departed, Jeremy's mind was in a confused condition of horror and delight. Such a victory as he had won over the Jampot, a victory that was a further stage in the fight for independence begun on his birthday, might have very awful qualities. There would begin now one of the Jampot's sulks—moods well known to the Cole family, and lasting from a day to a week, according to the gravity of the offence. Yes, they had already begun. There she sat in her chair by the fire, sewing, sewing, her fat, roly-poly face carved into a parody of deep displeasure. Life would be very unpleasant now. No tops of eggs, no marmalade on toast, no skins of milk, no stories of "when I was a young girl," no sitting up five minutes "later," no stopping in the market-place for a talk with the banana woman—only stern insistence on every detail of daily life; swift judgment were anything left undone or done wrong.

Jeremy sighed; yes, it would be horrid and, for the

sake of the world in general, which meant Mary and
Helen, he must see what a little diplomacy would do.
Kneeling down by the dog, he looked up into her face
with the gaze of ingenuous innocence.

"You wouldn't have wanted the poor little dog to have
died in the snow, would you, Nurse? . . . It might, you
know. It won't be any trouble, I expect——"

There was no reply. He could hear Mary and Helen
drawing in their breaths with excited attention.

"Father always said we might have a dog one day when
we were older—and we are older now."

Still no word.

"We'll be extra good, Nurse, if you don't mind. Don't
you remember once you said you had a dog when you
were a little girl, and how you cried when it had its ear
bitten off by a nasty big dog, and how your mother said
she wouldn't have it fighting round the house, and sent
it away, and you cried, and cried, and cried, and how
you said that p'r'aps we'll have one one day?—and now
we've got one."

He ended triumphantly. She raised her eyes for one
moment, stared at them all, bit off a piece of thread, and
said in deep, sepulchral tones:

"Either *it* goes, or I go."

The three stared at one another. The Jampot go?
Really go? . . . They could hear their hearts thumping
one after another. The Jampot go?

"Oh, Nurse, would you really?" whispered Mary. This
innocent remark of Mary's conveyed in the tone of it more
pleased anticipation than was, perhaps, polite. Certainly
the Jampot felt this; a flood of colour rose into her face.
Her mouth opened. But what she would have said is

uncertain, for at that very moment the drama was further developed by the slow movement of the door, and the revelation of half of Uncle Samuel's body, clothed in its stained blue painting smock, and his ugly fat face clothed in its usual sarcastic smile.

"Excuse me one moment," he said; "I hear you have a dog."

The Jampot rose, as good manners demanded, but said nothing.

"Where is the creature?" he asked.

The new addition to the Cole family had finished his washing; the blazing fire had almost dried him, and his hair stuck out now from his body in little stiff prickles, hedgehog fashion, giving him a truly original appearance. His beard afforded him the air of an ambassador, and his grave, melancholy eyes the absorbed introspection of a Spanish hidalgo; his tail, however, in its upright, stumpy jocularity, betrayed his dignity.

"There he is," said Jeremy, with a glance half of terror, half of delight, at the Jampot. "Isn't he lovely?"

"Lovely. My word!" Uncle Samuel's smile broadened. "He's about the most hideous mongrel it's ever been my lot to set eyes on. But he has his points. He despises you all, I'm glad to see."

Jeremy, as usual with Uncle Samuel, was uncertain as to his sincerity.

"He looks a bit funny just now," he explained. "He's been drying on the rug. He'll be all right soon. He wanted to bite Mr. Jellybrand. It *was* funny. Mr. Jellybrand was frightened as anything."

"Yes, that must have been delightful," agreed Uncle Samuel. "What's his name?"

"We haven't given him one yet. Wouldn't you think of one, Uncle Samuel?"

The uncle considered the dog. The dog, with grave and scornful eyes, considered the uncle.

"Well, if you really ask me," said that gentleman, "if you name him by his character I should say Hamlet would be as good as anything."

"What's Hamlet?" asked Jeremy.

"He isn't anything just now. But he was a prince who was unhappy because he thought so much about himself."

"Hamlet'll do," said Jeremy comfortably. "I've never heard of a dog called that, but it's easy to say."

"Well, I must go," said Uncle Samuel, making one of his usual sudden departures. "Glad to have seen the animal. Good-bye."

He vanished.

"Hamlet," repeated Jeremy thoughtfully. "I wonder whether he'll like that——"

His attention, however, was caught by the Jampot's sudden outburst.

"All of them," she cried, "supporting you in your wickedness and disobedience. I won't 'ave it nor endure it not a minute longer. They can 'ave my notice this moment, and I won't take it back, not if they ask me on their bended knees—no, I won't—and that's straight."

For an instant she frowned upon them all—then she was gone, the door banging after her.

They gazed at one another.

There was a dreadful silence. Once Mary whispered: "Suppose she really does."

Hamlet only was unmoved.

Ten minutes later, Rose, the housemaid, entered with

the tea-things. For a little she was silent. Then the
three faces raised to hers compelled her confidence.

"Nurse has been and given notice," she said, "and the
Missis has taken it. She's going at the end of the month.
She's crying now in the kitchen."

They were alone again. Mary and Helen looked at
Jeremy as though waiting to follow his lead. He did
not know what to say. There was Tragedy, there was
Victory, there was Remorse, there was Triumph. He was
sorry, he was glad. His eyes fell upon Hamlet, who was
now stretched out upon the rug, his nose between his paws,
fast asleep.

Then he looked at his sisters.

"Well," he said slowly, "it's awfully nice to have a dog
—anyway."

Such is the true and faithful account of Hamlet's
entrance into the train of the Coles.

CHAPTER III

I

I AM sometimes inclined to wonder whether, in very truth, those Polchester Christmases of nearly thirty years ago were so marvellous as now in retrospect they seem. I can give details of those splendours, facts and figures, that to the onlooker are less than nothing at all— a sugar elephant in a stocking, a box of pencils on a Christmas tree, "Hark, the Herald Angels . . ." at three in the morning below one's window, a lighted plum- pudding, a postman four hours late, his back bent with bursting parcels. And it is something further—behind the sugar cherries and the paper caps and the lighted tree —that remains to give magic to those days; a sense of expectancy, a sense of richness, a sense of worship, a visit from the Three Kings who have so seldom come to visit one since.

That Christmas of Jeremy's ninth year was one of the best that he ever had; it was perhaps the last of the *magical* Christmases. After this he was to know too much, was to see Father Christmas vanish before a sum in arith- metic, and a stocking change into something that "boys who go to school never have"—the last of the Christ- mases of divine magic, when the snow fell and the waits sang and the stockings were filled and the turkey fattened and the candles blazed and the holly crackled by the will of God rather than the power of man. It would be many years before he would realise that, after all, in those early days he had been right. . . .

A very fat book could be written about all that had happened during that wonderful Christmas, how Hamlet the Dog caught a rat to his own immense surprise; how the Coles' Christmas dinner was followed by a play acted with complete success by the junior members of the family, and it was only Mr. Jellybrand the curate who disapproved; how Aunt Amy had a new dress in which, by general consent, she looked ridiculous; how Mary, owing to the foolish kindness of Mrs. Bartholomew, the Precentor's wife, was introduced to the works of Charlotte Mary Yonge and became quite impossible in consequence; how Miss Maple had a children's party at which there was nothing to eat, so that all the children cried with disappointment, and one small boy (the youngest son of the Precentor) actually bit Miss Maple; how for two whole days it really seemed that there would be skating on The Pool, and everyone bought skates, and then, of course, the ice broke, and so on, and so on . . . there is no end to the dramatic incidents of that great sensational time.

The theme that I sing, however, is Jeremy's Progress, and although even Hamlet's catching of a rat influenced his development, there was one incident of this Christmas that stands out and away from all the others, an affair that he will never all his days forget, and that even now, at this distance of time and experience, causes his heart to beat roughly with the remembered excitement and pleasure.

Several weeks before Christmas there appeared upon the town walls and hoardings the pictured announcements of the approaching visit to Polchester of Denny's Great Christmas Pantomime "Dick Whittington." Boxing Night was to see the first performance at our Assembly Rooms, and during every afternoon and evening of the next three weeks this performance was to be repeated.

A pantomime had, I believe, never visited our town before; there had, of course, for many years been the Great Christmas Pantomime at the Theatre Royal, Drymouth, but in those days trains were not easy, and if you wished to attend an afternoon performance at the Drymouth Theatre you must rise very early in the morning by the candle-light and return late in the evening, with the cab forgetting to meet you at the station as commanded, and the long walk up Orange Street, and a headache and a bad temper next day.

It happened naturally then that the majority of the Polchester children had never set their inquisitive noses within the doors of a theatre, and although the two eldest daughters of the Dean, aged ten and eleven, had been once to London and to Drury Lane Theatre, their sense of glory and distinction so clouded their powers of accuracy and clarity that we were no nearer, by their help and authority, to the understanding of what a pantomime might really be.

I can myself recall the glory of those "Dick Whittington" pictures. Just above Martin's the pastry-cook's (where they sold lemon biscuits), near the Cathedral, there was a big wooden hoarding, and on to this was pasted a marvellous representation of Dick and his Cat dining with the King of the Zanzibar Islands. The King, a Mulatto, sat with his court in a hall with golden pillars, and the rats were to be seen flying in a confused flood towards the golden gates, whilst Dick, in red plush and diamond buckles, stood in dignified majesty, the Cat at his side. There was another wonderful picture of Dick asleep at the Cross Roads, fairies watching over him, and London Town in a lighted purple distance—and another of the streets of Old London with a comic fat serving man, diamond-paned windows, cobblestones and high pointing eaves to the houses.

Jeremy saw these pictures for the first time during one of his afternoon walks, and returned home in such a state of choking excitement that he could not drink his tea. As was ever his way he was silent and controlled about the matter, asked very few questions, and although he talked to himself a little did not disturb the general peace of the nursery. On Mary and Helen the effect of the posters had been less. Mary was following the adventures of the May family in "The Daisy Chain," and Helen was making necklaces for herself out of a box of beads that had been given her.

When Jeremy said once, "Who was the man in the red trousers with gold on them?" no one paid any attention save Hamlet, who wagged his tail, looked wise and growled a little.

Who indeed could tell how he ached and longed and desired? He had a very vague idea as to the nature of a play; they had often dressed up at home and pretended to be different things and people, and, of course, he knew by heart the whole history of Dick Whittington, but this knowledge and experience did not in the least force him to realise that this performance of Mr. Denny's was simply a larger, more developed "dressing up" and pretending. In some mysterious but nevertheless direct fashion Dick Whittington was coming to Polchester. It was just as he had heard for a long time of the existence of Aunt Emily who lived in Manchester—and then one day she appeared in a black bonnet and a shawl, and gave them wet kisses and sixpence apiece.

Dick Whittington was coming, having perhaps heard that Polchester was a very jolly place. So might come any day Jack of the Beanstalk, Cinderella, Queen Victoria, and God.

There were questions meanwhile that he would like to ask, but he was already a victim to that properly English fear of making a fool of himself, so he asked nothing. He dragged out his toy village and tried to make it a bridge in his imagination between the nursery and Whittington's world. As the village opened a door from the nursery, so might Whittington open a door from the village.

He considered Hamlet and wondered whether he knew anything about it. Hamlet, in spite of his mongrel appearance, was a very clever dog. He had his especial corners in the garden, the kitchen and the nursery. He never misbehaved, was never in the way, and was able to amuse himself for hours together. Although he attached himself quite deliberately to Jeremy, he did this in no sentimental fashion, and in his animosities towards the Jampot, Aunt Amy and the boy who helped with the boots and the knives, he was always restrained and courteous. He did indeed growl at Aunt Amy, but always with such a sense of humour that everyone (except Aunt Amy) was charmed, and he never actually supported the children in their rebellions against the Jampot, although you could

see that he liked and approved of such things. The Jampot
hated him with a passion that caused the nursery to quiver
with emotion. Was he not the cause of her approaching
departure, his first appearance having led her into a
tempest of passion that had caused her to offer a "notice"
that she had never for an instant imagined would be
accepted? Was he not a devilish dog who, with his quiet
movements and sly expressions, was more than human?
"Mark my words," she said in the kitchen, "there's a
devil in that there animal, and so they'll find before they're
many years older—'Amlet indeed—a 'eathenish name and
a 'eathenish beast."

Her enemy had discovered that in one corner of the
nursery there were signs and symbols that witnessed to
something in the nature of a mouse or a rat. That nursery
corner became the centre of all his more adventurous
instincts. It happened to be just the corner where the
Jampot kept her sewing machine, and you would think, if
you came to the nursery as a stranger, and saw him sitting,
his eyes fixed beamingly upon the machine, his tail erect,
and his body here and there quivering a little, that from
duties of manly devotion he was protecting the Jampot's
property. She knew better; she regarded, in some un-
defined way, this continued contemplation by him of her
possessions as an ironical insult. She did everything
possible to drive him from the corner; he inevitably
returned, and as he always delicately stepped aside when
she approached, it could not be said that he was in her
way. Once she struck him; he looked at her in such a
fashion that "her flesh crept." . . . She never struck him
again.

For Jeremy he became more and more of a delight. He

understood so much. He sympathised, he congratulated, he sported, always at the right moment. He would sit gravely at Jeremy's feet, his body pressed against Jeremy's leg, one leg stuck out square, his eyes fixed inquisitively upon the nursery scene. He would be motionless; then suddenly some thought would electrify him—his ears would cock, his eyes shine, his nose quiver, his tail tumble. The crisis would pass; he would be composed once more. He would slide down to the floor, his whole body collapsing; his head would rest upon Jeremy's foot; he would dream of cats, of rats, of birds, of the Jampot, of beef and gravy, of sugar, of being washed, of the dogs' Valhalla, of fire and warmth, of Jeremy, of walks when every piece of flying paper was a challenge, of dogs, dogs that he had known of when he was a puppy, of doing things he shouldn't, of punishment and wisdom, pride and anger, of love-affairs of his youth, of battle, of settling-down, of love-affairs in the future, again of cats and beef, and smells— smells—smells, again of Jeremy, whom he loved. And Jeremy, watching him now, thus sleeping, and thinking of Dick Whittington, wondered why it was that a dog would understand so easily, without explanations, the thoughts and desires he had, and that all grown-up people would not understand, and would demand so many explanations, and would laugh at one, and pity one, and despise one. Why was it? he asked himself.

"I know," he suddenly cried, turning upon Helen; "it can be your birthday treat!"

"What can?" she asked.

"Why, going to Dick Whittington—all of us."

Helen had, most unfortunately for herself, a birthday only a week after Christmas, the result being that, in her

own opinion at any rate, she never received "proper presents" on either of those two great present-giving occasions.
She was always allowed, however, a "treat"; her requests
were generally in the nature of food; once of a ride in the
train; once even a visit to the Polchester Museum. . . .
It was difficult in those days to find "treats" in Polchester.

"Oh, do you think they'd let us?" she said, her eyes
wide.

"We can try," said Jeremy. "I heard Aunt Amy say
the other day that she didn't think it was right for children
to see acting, and Mother always does the opposite to
what Aunt Amy says, so p'r'aps it will be all right. I
wish Hamlet could go," he added.

"Don't be silly!" said Helen.

"It isn't silly," Jeremy said indignantly. "It's all about
a cat, anyway, and he'd love to see all the rats and things.
He wouldn't bark if we told him not to, and I held his
collar."

"If Aunt Amy sat next him he would," said Mary.

"Oh, bother Aunt Amy," said Jeremy.

After this Helen needed a great deal of urging; but
she heard that Lucy and Angela, the aforesaid daughters
of the Dean, were going, and the spirit of rivalry drove
her forward.

It happened that the Dean himself one day said something to Mr. Cole about "supporting a very praiseworthy
effort. They are presenting, I understand, the proceeds
of the first performance to the Cathedral Orphanage."

Helen was surprised at the readiness with which her
request was granted.

"We'll all go," said Mr. Cole, in his genial, pastoral

fashion. "Good for us . . . good for us . . . to see the little ones laugh . . . good for us all."

Only Uncle Samuel said "that nothing would induce him——"

II

I pass swiftly over Christmas Eve, Christmas Day, and the day after, although I should like to linger upon these sumptuous dates. Jeremy had a sumptuous time; Hamlet had a sumptuous time (a whole sugar rat, plates and plates of bones, and a shoe of Aunt Amy's); Mary and Helen had sumptuous times in their own feminine fashion.

Upon the evening of Christmas Eve, when the earth was snow-lit, and the street-lamps sparkled with crystals, and the rime on the doorsteps crackled beneath one's feet, Jeremy accompanied his mother on a present-leaving expedition. The excitement of that! The wonderful shapes and sizes of the parcels, the mysterious streets, the door-handles and the door-bells, the glittering stars, the maid-servants, the sense of the lighted house, as though you opened a box full of excitements and then hurriedly shut the lid down again. Jeremy trembled and shook, not with cold, but with exalting, completely satisfying happiness.

There followed the Stocking, the Waits, the Carols, the Turkey, the Christmas Cake, the *Tree,* the Presents, Snapdragon, Bed. . . . There followed Headache, Ill-temper, Smacking of Mary, Afternoon Walk, Good Temper again, Complete Weariness, Hamlet sick on the Golden Cockatoos, Hamlet Beaten, Five minutes with Mother downstairs, Bed. . . . Christmas was over.

From that moment of the passing of Boxing Day it was simply the counting of the minutes to "Dick Whittington."

Six days from Boxing Day. Say you slept from eight to seven—eleven hours; that left thirteen hours; six thirteen hours was, so Helen said, seventy-eight. Seventy-eight hours, and Sunday twice as long as the other days, and that made thirteen more; ninety-one, said Helen, her nose in the air.

The week dragged along, very difficult work for everybody, and even Hamlet felt the excitement and watched his corner with the Jampot's sewing machine in it with more quivering intensity than ever. The Day Before The Day arrived, the evening before The Day, the last supper before The Day, the last bed before The Day. . . . Suddenly, like a Jack-in-the-Box, The Day itself.

Then the awful thing happened.

Jeremy awoke to the consciousness that something terrific was about to occur. He lay for a minute thinking —then he was up, running about the nursery floor as though he were a young man in Mr. Rossetti's poetry shouting: "Helen! Mary! Mary! Helen! . . . It's Dick Whittington! Dick Whittington!"

On such occasions he lost entirely his natural reserve and caution. He dressed with immense speed, as though that would hasten the coming of the evening. He ran into the nursery, carrying the black tie that went under his sailor-collar.

He held it out to the Jampot, who eyed him with disfavour. She was leaving them all in a week and was a strange confusion of sentiment and bad temper, love and hatred, wounded pride and injured dignity.

"Nurse. Please. Fasten it," he said impatiently.

"And that's not the way to speak, Master Jeremy, and

well you know it," she said. "'Ave you cleaned your teeth?"

"Yes," he answered without hesitation. It was not until the word was spoken that he realised that he had not. He flushed. The Jampot eyed him with a sudden sharp suspicion. He was then and ever afterwards a very bad hand at a lie. . . .

He would have taken the word back, he wanted to take it back—but something held him as though a stronger than he had placed his hand over his mouth. His face flamed.

"You've truly cleaned them?" she said.

"Yes, truly," he answered, his eyes on the ground. Never was there a more obvious liar in all the world.

She said no more; he moved to the fireplace. His joy was gone. There was a cold clammy sensation about his heart. Slowly, very slowly, the consciousness stole upon him that he was a liar. He had not thought it a lie when he had first spoken, now he knew.

Still there was time. Had he turned round and spoken, all might still have been well. But now obstinacy held him. He was not going to give the Jampot an opportunity for triumphing over him. After all, he *would* clean them so soon as she went to brush Helen's hair. In a moment what he had said would be true.

But he was miserable. Hamlet came up from the nether regions where he had spent the night, showing his teeth, wagging his tail, and even rolling on the cockatoos. Jeremy paid no attention. The weight in his heart grew heavier and heavier. He watched, from under his eyelids, the Jampot. In a moment she must go into Helen's room. But she did not. She stayed for a little arranging the things on the breakfast-table—then suddenly, without a word, she turned into Jeremy's bedchamber. His heart began to hammer. There was an awful pause; he heard from miles away Mary's voice: "Do do that button, Helen, I can't get it!" and Helen's "Oh, bother!"

Then, like Judgment, the Jampot appeared again. She stood in the doorway, looking across at him.

"You 'ave *not* cleaned your teeth, Master Jeremy," she said. "The glass isn't touched, nor your toothbrush. . . . You wicked, wicked boy. So it's a liar you've become, added on to all your other wickedness."

"I forgot," he muttered sullenly. "I thought I had."

She smiled the smile of approaching triumph.

"No, you did not," she said. "You knew you'd told a lie. It was in your face. All of a piece—all of a piece."

The way she said this, like a pirate counting over his captured treasure, was enraging. Jeremy could feel the wild fury at imself, at her, at the stupid blunder of the whole business rising to his throat.

"If you think I'm going to let this pass you're making a mighty mistake," she continued, "which I wouldn't do not if you paid me all the gold in the kingdom. I mayn't be good enough to keep my place and look after such as you, but anyways I'm able to stop your lying for another week or two. I know my duty even though there's them as thinks I don't."

She positively snorted, and the excitement of her own vindication and the just condemnation of Jeremy was such that her hands trembled.

"I don't care what you do," Jeremy shouted. "You can tell anyone you like. I don't care what you do. You're a beastly woman."

She turned upon him, her face purple. "That's enough, Master Jeremy," she said, her voice low and trembling. "I'm not here to be called names by such as you. You'll be sorry for this before you're much older. . . . You see."

There was then an awful and sickly pause. Jeremy seemed to himself to be sinking lower and lower into a damp clammy depth of degradation. What must this world be that it could change itself so instantly from a place of gay and happy pleasure into a dim groping room of punishment and dismay?

His feelings were utterly confused. He supposed that he was terribly wicked. But he did not feel wicked. He only felt miserable, sick and defiant. Mary and Helen came in, their eyes open to a crisis, their bodies tuned sympathetically to the atmosphere of sin and crime that they discerned around them.

Then Mr. Cole came in as was his daily habit—for a moment before his breakfast.

"Well, here are you all," he cried. "Ready for to-night? No breakfast yet? Why, now . . . ?"

Then perceiving, as all practised fathers instantly must, that the atmosphere was sinful, he changed his voice to that of the Children's Sunday Afternoon Service—a voice well known in his family.

"Please, sir," began the Jampot, "I'm sorry to 'ave to tell you, sir, that Master Jeremy's not been at all good this morning."

"Well, Jeremy," he said, turning to his son, "what is it?"

Jeremy's face, raised to his father's, was hard and set and sullen.

"I've told a lie," he said; "I said I'd cleaned my teeth when I hadn't. Nurse went and looked, and then I called her a beastly woman."

The Jampot's face expressed a grieved and at the same time triumphant confirmation of this.

"You told a lie?" Mr. Cole's voice was full of a lingering sorrow.

"Yes," said Jeremy.

"Are you sorry?"

"I'm sorry that I told a lie, but I'm not sorry I called Nurse a beastly woman."

"Jeremy!"

"No, I'm not. She *is* a beastly woman."

Mr. Cole was always at a loss when anyone defied him, even though it were only a small boy of eight. He took refuge now in his ecclesiastical and parental authority.

"I'm very distressed—very distressed indeed. I hope that punishment, Jeremy, will show you how wrong you have been. I'm afraid you cannot come with us to the Pantomime to-night."

At that judgment a quiver for an instant held Jeremy's face, turning it, for that moment, into something shapeless and old. His heart had given a wild leap of terror and dismay. But he showed no further sign. He simply stood there waiting.

Mr. Cole was baffled, as he always was by Jeremy's moods, so he continued:

"And until you've apologised to Nurse for your rudeness you must remain by yourself. I shall forbid your sisters to speak to you. Mary and Helen, you are not to speak to your brother until he has apologised to Nurse."

"Yes, Father," said Helen.

"Oh, Father, mayn't he come to-night?" said Mary.

"No, Mary, I'm afraid not."

A tear rolled down her cheek. "It won't be any fun without Jeremy," she said. She wished to make the further sacrifice of saying that she would not go unless Jeremy did, but some natural caution restrained her.

Mr. Cole, his face heavy with sorrow, departed.

At the dumb misery of Jeremy's face the Jampot's heart—in reality a kind and even sentimental heart—repented her.

"There, Master Jeremy, you be a good boy all day, and I dare say your father will take you, after all; and we won't think no more about what you said to me in the 'eat of the moment."

But Jeremy answered nothing; nor did he respond to the smell of bacon, nor the advances of Hamlet, nor the flood of sunlight that poured into the room from the frosty world outside.

A complete catastrophe. They none of them had wanted to see this thing with the urgent excitement that he had felt. They had not dreamt of it for days and nights and nights and days, as he had done. Their whole future existence did not depend upon their witnessing this, as did his.

During that morning he was a desperate creature, like something caged and tortured. Do happy middle-aged philosophers assure us that children are light-hearted and unfeeling animals? Let them realise something of the agony which Jeremy suffered that day. His whole world had gone.

He was wicked, an outcast; his word could never be trusted again; he would be pointed at as the boy who had told a lie. . . . And he would not meet Dick Whittington.

The eternity of his punishment hung around his neck like an iron chain. Childhood's tragedies are terrible tragedies, because a child has no sense of time; a moment's dismay is eternal; a careless word from an elder is a lasting judgment; an instant's folly is a lifetime's mistake.

The day dragged its weary length along, and he scarcely moved from his corner by the fire. He did not attempt conversation with anyone. Once or twice the Jampot tried to penetrate behind that little mask of anger and dismay.

"Come, now, things aren't so bad as all that. You be a good boy, and go and tell your father you're sorry. . . ." or "Well, then, Master Jeremy, there'll be another time, I dare say, you can go to the the-ayter. . . ."

But she found no response. If there was one thing that she hated, it was sulks. Here they were, sulks of the worst—and so, like many wiser than herself, she covered up with a word a situation that she did not understand, and left it at that.

The evening came on; the curtains were drawn. Tea arrived; still Jeremy sat there, not speaking, not raising his eyes, a condemned creature. Mary and Helen and Hamlet had had a wretched day. They all sympathised with him.

The girls went to dress. Seven o'clock struck. They were taken downstairs by Nurse, who had her evening out. Rose, the housemaid, would sit with Master Jeremy.

Doors closed, doors opened, voices echoed, carriage-wheels were heard.

Jeremy and Hamlet were left to themselves. . . .

III

The last door had closed, and the sudden sense that everyone had gone and that he might behave now as he pleased, removed the armour in which all day he had encased himself.

He raised his head, looked about the deserted nursery, and then, with the sudden consciousness of that other lighted and busied place where Whittington was pursuing his adventures, he burst into tears. He sobbed, his head down upon his arms, and his body squeezed together so that his knees were close to his nose and his hair in his boots. Hamlet restored him to himself. Instead of assisting his master's grief, as a sentimental dog would have done, by sighing or sniffing or howling, he yawned, stretched himself, and rolled on the carpet. He did not believe in giving way to feelings, and he was surprised, and perhaps disappointed, at Jeremy's lack of restraint.

Jeremy felt this, and in a little while sobs came very slowly, and at last were only little shudders, rather pleasant and healthy. He looked about him, rubbed his red nose with a hideously dirty handkerchief, and felt immensely sleepy.

No, he would not cry any more. Rose would shortly appear, and he did not intend to cry before housemaids. Nevertheless, his desolation was supreme. He was a liar. He had told lies before, but they had not been discovered, and so they were scarcely lies. . . . Now, in some strange way, the publication of his lie had shown him what truly impossible things lies were. He had witnessed this effect upon the general public; he had not believed that he was so wicked. He did not even now feel really wicked, but he saw quite clearly that there was one world for liars and one for truthful men. He wanted, terribly badly, someone to tell him that he was still in the right world. . . .

And then, on the other side, the thought that Mary and Helen were at this very moment witnessing the coloured history of Dick Whittington, the history that he had pursued ceaselessly during all these days and nights—that picture of them all in the lighted theatre—once more nearly overcame him. But he pulled himself together.

He sniffed, left his dirty handkerchief, and went slowly and sorrowfully to drag out his toy village from its corner and see whether anything could be done with it. . . . After all, he was going to school in September. His punishment could not be quite limitless. Hamlet had just shown his approval of this manly conduct by strolling up and sniffing at the Noah family, who were, as usual, on their way to church, when the door suddenly opened, and in came Uncle Samuel.

Jeremy had forgotten his uncle, and now blinked up at him from the floor, where he was squatting, rather ashamed of his swollen eyes and red nose.

Uncle Samuel, however, had no time for details; he was apparently in a hurry. He did not wear his blue painting-smock, but was in a comparatively clean black suit, and on the back of his head was a squashy brown hat.

"Come on," he said, "or we shall be too late."

Jeremy choked. "Too late?" he repeated.

"You're coming, aren't you—to the Pantomime? They sent me back for you."

The room suddenly got on to its legs, like the food and the families during Alice's feast in the "Looking Glass," and swung round, lurching from side to side, and causing the fire to run into the gas and the gas to fly out of the window.

"I—don't—understand," Jeremy stammered.

"Well, if you don't understand in half a shake," said Uncle Samuel, "you won't see any of the show at all. Go on. Wash your face. There are streaks of dirt all down it as though you were a painted Indian; stick on your cap and coat and boots and come along."

Exactly as one moves in sleep so Jeremy now moved. He had once had a wonderful dream, in which he had been at a meal that included everything that he had most loved—fish-cakes, sausages, ices, strawberry jam, sponge-cake, chocolates, and scrambled eggs—and he had been able to eat, and eat, and had never been satisfied, and had never felt sick—a lovely dream.

He often thought of it. And now in the same bewildering fashion he found his boots and cap and coat and then, deliberately keeping from him the thought of the Pantomime lest he should suddenly wake up, he said:

"I'm ready, Uncle."

Samuel Trefusis looked at him.

"You're a strange kid," he said; "you take everything so quietly—but, thank God, I don't understand children."

"There's Hamlet," said Jeremy, wondering whether perhaps the dream would extend to his friend. "I suppose he can't come too."

"No, he certainly can't," said Uncle Samuel grimly.

"And there's Rose. She'll wonder where I've gone."

"I've told her. Don't you worry. What a conscientious infant you are. Just like your father. Anything else?"

"No," said Jeremy breathlessly, and nearly murdered himself going downstairs because he shut his eyes in

order to continue the dream so long as it was possible.
Then in the cold night air, grasping his uncle's hand with
a feverish hold, he stammered:

"Is it really true? Are we going—really?"

"Of course we're going. Come on—step out or you'll
miss the Giant."

"But—but—oh!" he drew a deep breath. "Then they
don't think me a liar any more?"

"They—who?"

"Father and Mother and everyone."

"Don't you think about them. You'd better enjoy
yourself."

"But you said you wouldn't go to the Pantomime—not
for anything?"

"Well, I've changed my mind. Don't talk so much.
You know I hate you children chattering. Always got
something to say."

So Jeremy was silent. They raced down Orange Street,
Jeremy being almost carried off his feet. This was exactly
like a dream. This rushing movement and the way that
the lamp-posts ran up to you as though they were going
to knock you down, and the way that the stars crackled and
sputtered and trembled overhead. But Uncle Samuel's
hand was flesh and blood, and the heel of Jeremy's right
shoe hurt him and he felt the tickle of his sailor-collar at
the back of his neck, just as he did when he was awake.

Then there they were at the Assembly Rooms door,
Jeremy having become so breathless that Uncle Samuel
had to hold him up for a moment or he'd have fallen.

"Bit too fast for you, was it? Well, you shouldn't be
so fat. You eat too much. Now we're not going to sit
with your father and mother—there isn't room for you

there. So don't you go calling out to them or anything. We're sitting in the back and you'd better be quiet or they'll turn you out."

"I'll be quiet," gasped Jeremy.

Uncle Samuel paused at a lighted hole in the wall and spoke to a large lady in black silk who was drinking a cup of tea. Jeremy caught the jingle of money. Then they moved forward, stumbling in the dark up a number of stone steps, pushing at a heavy black curtain, then suddenly bathed in a bewildering glow of light and scent and colour.

Jeremy's first impression, as he fell into this new world, was of an ugly, harsh, but funny voice crying out very loudly indeed: "Oh, my great aunt! Oh, my great aunt! Oh, my great aunt!" A roar of laughter rose about him, almost lifting him off his feet, and close to his ear a Glebeshire voice sobbed: "Eh, my dear. Poor worm! Poor worm!"

He was aware then of a strong smell of oranges, of Uncle Samuel pushing him forward, of stumbling over boots, knees, and large hands that were clapping in his very nose, of falling into a seat and then clinging to it as though it was his only hope in this strange puzzling world. The high funny voice rose again: "Oh, my great aunt! Oh, my great aunt!" And again it was followed by the rough roar of delighted laughter.

He was aware then that about him on every side gas was sizzling, and then, as he recovered slowly his breath, his gaze was drawn to the great blaze of light in the distance, against which figures were dimly moving, and from the heart of which the strange voice came. He heard a woman's voice, then several voices together; then sud-

denly the whole scene shifted into focus, his eyes were
tied to the light; the oranges and the gas and the smell
of clothes and heated bodies slipped back into distance—
he was caught into the world where he had longed to be.

He saw that it was a shop—and he loved shops. His
heart beat thickly as his eyes travelled up and up and up
over the rows and rows of shelves; here were bales of
cloth, red and green and blue; carpets from the East,
table-covers, sheets and blankets. Behind the long yellow
counters young men in strange clothes were standing. In
the middle of the scene was a funny old woman, her hat
tumbling off her head, her shabby skirt dragging, large
boots, and a red nose. It was from this strange creature
that the deep ugly voice proceeded. She had, this old
woman, a number of bales of cloth under her arms, and she
tried to carry them all, but one slipped, and then another,
and then another; she bent to pick them up and her hat
fell off; she turned for her hat and all the bales tumbled
together. Jeremy began to laugh—everyone laughed; the
strange voice came again and again, lamenting, bewailing,
she had secured one bale, a smile of cautious triumph began
to spread over her ugly face, then the bales all fell again,
and once more she was on her knees. It was then that
her voice or some movement brought to Jeremy's eyes so
vividly the figure of their old gardener, Jordan, that he
turned round to Uncle Samuel, and suddenly grasping
that gentleman's fat thigh, exclaimed convulsively: "Why,
she's a man!"

What a strange topsy-turvy world this was in which
women were men, and shops turned (as with a sudden
creaking and darkness and clattering did this one) into
gardens by the sea. Jeremy drew his breath deeply and

held on. His mouth was open and his hair on end. . . .

It is impossible to define exactly Jeremy's ultimate impression as the entertainment proceeded. Perhaps he had no ultimate impression. It cannot in reality have been a very wonderful Pantomime. Even at Drury Lane thirty years back there were many things that they did not know, and it is not likely that a touring company fitted into so inadequate an old building as our Assembly Rooms would have provided anything very fine. But Jeremy will never again discover so complete a realisation for his illusions. Whatever failures in the presentation there were, he himself made good.

As a finale to the first half of the entertainment there was given Dick's dream at the Cross-Roads. He lay on the hard ground, his head upon his bundle, the cat as large as he watching sympathetically beside him. In the distance were the lights of London, and then, out of the half dusk, fairies glittering with stars and silver danced up and down the dusky road whilst all the London bells rang out "Turn again, Whittington, Lord Mayor of London."

Had Jeremy been of the age and wisdom of Uncle Samuel he would have discovered that Dick was a stout lady and probably the mother of a growing family; that the fairies knew as much about dancing as the Glebeshire wives sitting on the bench behind; that the London bells were two hand instruments worked by a youth in shirt sleeves behind the scenes so energetically that the High Road and the painted London blew backwards and forwards in sympathy with his movements. Jeremy, happily, was not so worldly wise as his uncle. This scene created for him then a tradition of imperishable beauty that would never fade again. The world after that night would be a more magical place than it had ever been before. "Turn again, Whittington" continued the education that the Toy Village and Hamlet had already advanced.

When the gas rose once again, sizzling like crackling bacon, he was white with excitement. The only remark that he made was: "It's much better than the pictures outside Martin's, isn't it, Uncle Samuel?" to which Uncle Samuel, who had been railing for weeks at the deflowering of Polchester by those abominable posters, could truthfully reply, "Much better." Little by little he withdrew himself from the other world and realised his own. He could see that he and his uncle were certainly not amongst the Quality. Large ladies, their dresses tucked up over their knees, sucked oranges. Country farmers with huge knobbly looking sticks were there, and even some sailors, on their way probably to Drymouth. He recognised the lady who kept charge of the small Orange Street post-office, and waved to her with delighted excitement. The atmosphere was thick with gas and oranges, and I'm afraid that Uncle Samuel must have suffered a great deal. I can only put it on record that he, the most selfish of human beings, never breathed a word of complaint.

They were all packed very closely together up there in the gallery, where seventy years before an orchestra straight from Jane Austen's novels had played to the dancing of the contemporaries of Elizabeth Bennett, Emma Woodhouse, and the dear lady of "Persuasion." Another thirty-two years and that same gallery would be listening to recruiting appeals and echoing the drums and fifes of a martial band. The best times are always the old times.

The huge lady in the seat next to Jeremy almost

swallowed him up, so that he peered out from under her thick arm, and heard every crunch and crackle of the peppermints that she was enjoying. He grew hotter and hotter, so that at last he seemed, as once he had read in some warning tract about a greedy boy that Aunt Amy had given him, "to swim in his own fat." But he did not mind. Discomfort only emphasised his happiness. Then, peering forward beneath that stout black arm, he suddenly perceived, far below in the swimming distance, the back of his mother, the tops of the heads of Mary and Helen, the stiff white collar of his father, and the well-known coral necklace of Aunt Amy. For a moment dismay seized him, the morning's lie which he had entirely forgotten suddenly jumping up and facing him. But they had forgiven him.

"Shall I wave to them?" he asked excitedly of Uncle Samuel.

"No, no," said his uncle very hurriedly. "Nonsense. They wouldn't see you if you did. Leave them alone."

He felt immensely superior to them up where he was, and he wouldn't have changed places with them for anything. He gave a little sigh of satisfaction. "I could drop an orange on to Aunt Amy's head," he said. "Wouldn't she jump!"

"You must keep quiet," said Uncle Samuel. "You're good enough as you are."

"I'd rather be here," said Jeremy. "It's beautifully hot here and there's a *lovely* smell."

"There is," said Uncle Samuel.

Then the gas went down, and the curtain went up, and Dick, now in a suit of red silk with golden buttons, continued his adventures. I have not space here to describe in detail the further events of his life—how, receiving a telegram from the King of the Zanzibars about the plague of rats, he took ship with his cat and Alderman Fitzwarren and his wife, how they were all swallowed by a whale, cast up by a most lucky chance on the Zanzibars, nearly cooked by the natives, and rescued by the King of the Zanzibars' beautiful daughter, killed all the rats, were given a huge feast, with dance and song, and finally Dick, although tempted by the dusky Princess, refused a large fortune and returned to Alice of Eastcheap, the true lady of his heart. There were, of course, many other things, such as the aspirations and misadventures of Mrs. Fitzwarren, the deep-voiced lady who had already so greatly amused Jeremy. And then there was a Transformation Scene, in which roses turned into tulips and tulips into the Hall of Gold, down whose blazing steps marched stout representatives of all the nations.

It was in the middle of this last thrilling spectacle, when Jeremy's heart was in his mouth and he was so deeply excited that he did not know whether it were he or the lady next to him who was eating peppermints, that his uncle plucked him by the sleeve and said in his ear: "Come on. It's close on the end. We must go."

Jeremy very reluctantly got up, and stumbled out over knees and legs and exclamations like:

"There's Japan!" "No, it ain't; it's Chiney!" "Yon's a fine, hearty young woman!" and so on. He was dragged through the black curtain, down the stone steps, and into the street.

"But it wasn't the end," he said.

"It will be in one minute," said his uncle. "And I want us to get home first."

"Why?" said Jeremy.

"Never you mind. Come on; we'll race it."

They arrived home breathless, and then, once again in the old familiar hall, Uncle Samuel said:

"Now you nip up to the nursery, and then they'll never know you've been out at all."

"Never know?" said Jeremy. "But you said they'd sent for me."

"Well," said Uncle Samuel, "that wasn't exactly true. As a matter of fact, they don't know you were there."

"Oh!" said Jeremy, the corner of his mouth turning down. "Then I've told a lie again!"

"Nonsense!" said Uncle Samuel impatiently. "It wasn't you; it was I."

"And doesn't it matter your telling lies?" asked Jeremy.

The answer to this difficult question was, happily for Uncle Samuel, interrupted by the arrival of the household, who had careened up Orange Street in a cab.

When Mr. and Mrs. Cole saw Jeremy standing in the hall, his great coat still on and his muffler round his neck, there was a fine scene of wonder and amazement.

Uncle Samuel explained. "It was my fault. I told him you'd forgiven him and sent for him to come, after all. He's in an awful state now that you shouldn't forgive him."

Whatever they thought of Uncle Samuel, this was obviously neither the time nor the place to speak out. Mrs. Cole looked at her son. His body defiant, sleepy, excited. His mouth was obstinate, but his eyes appealed to her on the scene of the common marvellous experience that they had just enjoyed.

She hugged him.

"And you won't tell a lie again, will you, Jeremy, dear?"

"Oh, no!" And then, hurrying on: "And when the old woman tumbled down the steps, Mother, wasn't it lovely? And the fairies in Dick Whittington's sleep, and when the furniture all fell all over the place——"

He went slowly upstairs to the nursery, the happiest boy in the kingdom. But through all his happiness there was this puzzle: Uncle Samuel had told a lie, and no one had thought that it mattered. There were good lies and bad ones then. Or was it that grown-up people could tell lies and children mustn't? . . .

He tumbled into the warm, lighted nursery half asleep. There was Hamlet watching in front of the Jampot's sewing machine.

He would have things to think about for years and years and years. . . .

There was the Jampot.

"I'm sorry I called you a beastly woman," he said.

She sniffed.

"Well, I hope you'll be a good boy now," she said.

"Oh, I'll be good," he smiled. "But, Nurse, are there some people can tell lies and others mustn't?"

"All them that tell lies goes to Hell," said the Jampot. "And now, Master Jeremy, come along and take your things off. It's past eleven, and what you'll be like to-morrow——"

CHAPTER IV

MISS JONES

I

THE coming of the new year meant the going of the Jampot, and the going of the Jampot meant the breaking of a life-time's traditions. The departure was depressing and unsettling; the weather was—as it always is during January in Glebeshire—at its worst, and the Jampot, feeling it all very deeply, maintained a terrible Spartan composure, which was meant to show indifference and a sense of injustice. She had to the very last believed it incredible that she should really go. She had been in the old Orange Street house for eight years, and had intended to be there until she died. She was forced to admit that Master Jeremy was going beyond her; but in September he would go to school, and then she could help with the sewing and other things about the house. The real truth of the matter was that she had never been a very good servant, having too much of the Glebeshire pride and independence and too little of the Glebeshire fidelity.

Mrs. Cole had been glad of the opportunity that Hamlet's arrival in the family had given her. The Jampot, only a week before the date of her departure, came to her mistress and begged, with floods of tears, to be allowed to continue in her service. But Mrs. Cole, with all her placidity, was firm. The Jampot had to go.

I would like to paint a pleasant picture of the sentiment of the Cole children on this touching occasion; something, perhaps, in the vein of tragi-comedy with which Mr. Kenneth Graham embroiders a similar occasion in his famous masterpiece—but in this case there was very little sentiment and no tragedy at all. They did not think of the event beforehand, and then when it suddenly occurred there was all the excitement of being looked after by Rose, the housemaid, of having a longer time with their mother in the evening, and, best of all, a delightful walk with Aunt Amy, whose virginal peace of mind they attacked from every possible quarter.

The Jampot left in a high state of sulks, declaring to the kitchen that no woman had ever been so unfairly treated; that her married sister Sarah Francis, of Rafiel, with whom she was now to live, should be told all about it, and that the citizens of Rafiel should be compelled to sympathise. The children were not unfeeling, but they hated the Jampot's sulks, and while she waited in the nursery, longing for a word or movement of affection, but wearing a face of stony disapproval, they stood awkwardly beholding her, and aching for her to go. She was the more unapproachable in that she wore her Sunday silks and a heavy black bonnet with shiny rattling globes of some dark metal that nodded and becked and bowed like live things. Hamlet, who had, of course, always hated the Jampot, barked at this bonnet furiously, and would have bitten at it had it been within his reach. She had meant to leave them all with little sentences about life and morals; but the noise of the dog, the indifference of the children, and the general air of impatience for her departure strangled her aphorisms. Poor Jampot! She was de-

parting to a married sister who did not want her, and
would often tell her so; her prospects in life were not
bright, and it is sad to think that no inhabitant of the
Orange Street house felt any sorrow at the sight of the
last gesticulating wave of her black bonnet as she stepped
into the old mouldy Polchester cab.

"The King is dead—long live the King!" The Jampot
as a power in the Cole family has ceased to be.

The day following the Jampot's departure offered up
the news that, for the first time in the history of the Coles,
there was to be a governess. The word "governess"
had an awful sound, and the children trembled with a
mixture of delight and terror. Jeremy pretended indifference.

"It's only another woman," he said. "She'll be like
the Jampot—only, a lady, so she won't be able to punish
us as the Jampot could."

I expect that Mr. and Mrs. Cole had great difficulty
in finding anyone who would do. Thirty years ago governesses were an incapable race, and belonged too closely
either to the Becky Sharp or the Amelia type to be very
satisfactory. It was then that the New Woman was
bursting upon the scene, but she was not to be found
amongst the governesses. No one in Polchester had learnt
yet to cycle in rational costume, it was several years
before the publication of "The Heavenly Twins," and
Mr. Trollope's Lilys and Lucys were still considered
the ideal of England's maidenhood. Mrs. Cole, therefore,
had to choose between idiotic young women and crabbed
old maids, and she finally chose an old maid. I don't
think that Miss Jones was the very best choice that she
could have made, but time was short. Jeremy, aided by

Hamlet, was growing terribly independent, and Mr. Cole had neither the humour nor the courage to deal with him. No, Miss Jones was not ideal, but the Dean had strongly recommended her. It is true that the Dean had never seen her, but her brother, with whom she had lived for many years, had once been the Dean's curate. It was true that he had been a failure as a curate, but that made the Dean the more anxious to be kind now to his memory, he—Mr. Jones—having just died of general bad-temper and selfishness.

Miss Jones, buried during the last twenty years in the green depths of a Glebeshire valley, found herself now, at the age of fifty, without friends, without money, without relations. She thought that she would be a governess.

The Dean recommended her, Mrs. Cole approved of her birth, education and sobriety, Mr. Cole liked the severity of her countenance when she came to call, and she was engaged.

"Jeremy needs a tight hand," said Mr. Cole. "It's no use having a young girl."

"Miss Jones easily escapes that charge," said Uncle Samuel, who had met her in the hall.

The children were prepared to be good. Jeremy felt that it was time to take life seriously. He put away his toy village, scolded Hamlet for eating Mary's pincushion, and dragged out his dirty exercise-book in which he did sums.

"I do hate sums!" he said, with a sigh, regarding the hideous smudges of thumbs and tears that scored the page. "I shall never understand anything about them."

"I'll help you," said Mary, who was greatly excited at the thought of a governess. "We'll do them together."

"No we won't," said Jeremy, who hated to be dependent. "I'll learn it myself—if only the paper didn't get dirty so quickly."

"Mother says," remarked Helen, "that she's had a very hard life, and no one's ever been kind to her. 'She wants affection,' Mother says."

"I'll give her my napkin-ring that you gave me last Christmas, Mary," said Jeremy. "You don't mind, do you? It's all dirty now. I hope Hamlet won't bark at her."

Hamlet was worrying Mary's pincushion at the moment, holding it between his paws, his body stretched out in quivering excitement, his short, "snappy" tail, as Uncle Samuel called it, standing up straight in air. He stopped for an instant when he heard his name, and shook one ear.

"Mother says," continued Helen, "that she lived with a brother who never gave her enough to eat."

Jeremy opened his eyes. This seemed to him a horrible thing.

"She shall have my porridge, if she likes," he said; "I don't like it very much. And I'll give her that chocolate that Mr. Jellybrand sent us. There's still some, although it's rather damp now, I expect."

"How silly you are!" said Helen scornfully. "Of course, Mother will give her anything she wants."

"It isn't silly," said Jeremy. "Perhaps she'll want more than she really wants. I often do."

"Oh, you!" said Helen.

"And if for ever so long," said Jeremy, "she hasn't had enough to eat, she'll want twice as big meals now as other people—to make up."

"Mother says we've got to remember she's a lady," said Helen.

"What's the difference," asked Jeremy, "between a lady and not a lady?"

"Oh, you are!" said Helen. "Why, Aunt Amy's a lady, and Rose isn't."

"Rose is nicer," said Jeremy.

Miss Jones had, I am sorry to say, lied to Mrs. Cole in one particular. She had told her that "she had had to do with children all her life," the fact being that on several occasions some little cousins had come to stay with herself and her brother. On these occasions the little cousins had been so paralysed with terror that discipline had not been difficult. It was from these experiences that Miss Jones flattered herself that "she understood children."

So audacious a self-confidence is doomed to invite the scornful punishment of the gods.

Miss Jones arrived upon a wet January afternoon, one of those Glebeshire days when the town sinks into a bath of mud and mist and all the pipes run water and the eaves drip and horses splash and only ducks are happy. Out of a blurred lamp-lit dusk stumbled Miss Jones's cab, and out of a blurred unlit cab stumbled Miss Jones.

As she stood in the hall trying to look warm and amiable, Mrs. Cole's heart forsook her. On that earlier day of her visit Miss Jones had looked possible, sitting up in Mrs. Cole's drawing-room, smiling her brightest, because she so desperately needed the situation, and wearing her best dress. Now she was all in pieces; she had had to leave her little village early in the morning to catch the village bus; she had waited at wayside stations, as in Glebeshire

only one can wait; the world had dripped upon her head
and spattered upon her legs. She had neuralgia and a
pain in her back; she had worn her older dress because,
upon such a day, it would not do to travel in her best; and
then, as a climax to everything, she had left her umbrella
in the train. How she could do such a thing upon such a
day! Her memory was not her strongest point, poor lady,
and it was a good umbrella, and she could not afford to
buy another. Perhaps they would find it for her, but it
was very unlikely.

She had had it for a number of years.

She was a little woman, all skin and bone, with dried
withered cheeks, a large brown nose and protruding ears.
Her face had formed severe lines in self-defence against
her brother, but her eyes were mild, and when she smiled
her mouth was rather pleasantly pathetic.

"Oh, she'll never do," thought Mrs. Cole, as she looked
at her dripping in the hall.

"I can't think how I forgot it," said the poor lady, her
mind fixed upon her umbrella. "They said that perhaps
they would find it for me, but there was a man in my
carriage, I remember, who will most certainly have taken
it—and it was a nice one with a silver handle."

"Never mind," said Mrs. Cole cheerfully, "I'm sure
they'll find it. You must come up to the nursery—or the
schoolroom I suppose we must call it now; there's a lovely
fire there, and we'll both have tea with the children to-day,
so as to feel at home, all of us, as quickly as possible."

What Miss Jones wanted was to lie down on a bed in
a dark room and try and conquer her neuralgia. The
thought of a lighted nursery filled her with dismay. How-

ever, first impressions are so important. She pulled herself together.

The children had heard the arrival; they waited in a bunch by the fire, their eyes partly fixed on the door, partly on the strawberry jam that they were allowed to-day as a treat in the new governess's honour. Hamlet, his eyes and ears also upon the door, expecting perhaps a rat, perhaps Aunt Amy, sat in front of the group, its bodyguard.

"She's in the hall," said Helen, "and now Mother's saying: 'Do take off your things. You must be wet,' and now she's saying: 'You'll like to see the children, I expect,' and now——"

There they were, standing in the doorway, Mrs. Cole and Miss Jones. There followed a dismal pause. The children had not expected anyone so old and so ugly as Miss Jones. Hamlet did not bark—nothing occurred.

At last Mrs. Cole said: "Now, children, come and say, 'How do you do?' to Miss Jones. This is Helen, our eldest—this Mary—and this Jeremy."

Miss Jones did a dreadful thing. In her eagerness to be pleasant and friendly she kissed the girls, and then, before anyone could stop her, kissed Jeremy. He took it like a man, never turning his head nor wiping his mouth with his hand afterwards, but she might have seen in his eyes, had she looked, what he felt about it.

She said: "I hope we shall be happy together, dears."

The children said nothing, and presently they all sat down to tea.

II

It was unfortunate that there was so little precedent on both sides. Miss Jones had never been a governess before and the children had never had one. Of course, many mistakes were made. Miss Jones had had a true admiration for what she used to call "her brother's indomitable spirit," her name for his selfishness and bad temper. She was herself neither selfish nor bad-tempered, but she was ignorant, nervous, over-anxious, and desperately afraid of losing her situation. She had during so many years lived without affection that the wells of it had dried up within her, and now, without being at all a bad old lady, she was simply preoccupied with the business of managing her neuralgia, living on nothing a week, and building to her deceased brother's memory a monument of heroic character and self-sacrifice.

She was short-sighted and had a perpetual cold; she was forgetful and careless. She had, nevertheless, a real knowledge of many things, a warm heart somewhere could she be encouraged to look for it again, and a sense of humour buried deep beneath her cares and preoccupations. There were many worse persons in the world than Miss Jones. But, most unfortunately, her love for her brother's memory led her to resolve on what she called "firmness."

Mrs. Cole had told her that Jeremy was "getting too much" for his nurse; she approached Jeremy with exactly the tremors and quaking boldness that she would have summoned to her aid before a bull loose in a field. She really did look frightening with her large spectacles on the end of her large nose, her mouth firmly set, and a ruler in her hand.

"I insist on absolute obedience," was her motto. Jeremy looked at her but said no word.

It was made clear to them all that the new régime was to be far other than the earlier nursery one. There were to be regular lesson hours—nine to twelve and four to five. A neat piece of white paper was fastened to the wall with "Monday: Geography 9-10, Arithmetic 10-11," and so on. A careful graduation of punishments was instituted, copies to be written so many times, standing on a chair, three strokes on the hand with a ruler, and, worst of all, standing in the corner wearing a paper Dunce's cap. (This last she had read of in books.)

At first Jeremy had every intention of behaving well, in spite of that unfortunate embrace. He was proud of his advance in life; he was no longer a baby; the nursery was now a schoolroom; he stayed up an hour later at night; he was to be allowed twopence a week pocket-money; his whole social status had risen. He began to read for pleasure, and discovered that it was easier than he had expected, so that he passed quite quickly through "Lottie's Visit to Grandmama" into "Stumps" and out again in "Jackanapes." He heard some elder say that the road to a large fortune lay through "Sums," and, although this seemed to him an extremely mysterious statement, he determined to give the theory a chance. In fact, he sat down the first day at the schoolroom table, Mary and Helen on each side of him, and Miss Jones facing them, with fine resolves and high ambitions. Before him lay a pure white page, and at the head of this the noble words in a running hand:

"Slow and steady wins the race."

He grasped his pencil, and Miss Jones, eager to lose no time in asserting her authority, cried: "But that's not the way to hold your pencil, Jeremy, your thumb so, your finger so."

He scowled and found that lifting his thumb over the

pencil was as difficult as lifting Hamlet over a gate. He
made a bold attempt, but the pencil refused to move.

"Can't hold it that way," he said.

"You must never say 'can't,' Jeremy," remarked Miss
Jones. "There isn't such a word."

"Oh, yes," said Mary eagerly, "there is; I've seen it
in books."

"You musn't contradict, Mary," said Miss Jones. "I
only meant that you must behave as though there isn't,
because nothing is impossible to one who truly tries."

"My pencil waggles this way," said Jeremy politely.
"I think I'll hold it the old way, please."

"There's only one way of doing anything," said Miss
Jones, "and that's the right way."

"This is the right way for me," said Jeremy.

"If I say it's not the right way——"

"But it waggles," cried Jeremy.

The discussion was interrupted by a cry from Helen.

"Oh, do look, Miss Jones, Hamlet's got your spectacle-
case. He thinks it's a mouse."

There followed general confusion. Miss Jones jumped
up, and, with little cries of distress, pursued Hamlet, who
hastened into his favourite corner and began to worry the
spectacle-case, with one eye on Miss Jones and one on his
spoils.

Jeremy hurried up crying: "Put it down, Hamlet,
naughty dog, naughty dog," and Mary and Helen laughed
with frantic delight.

At last Miss Jones, her face red and her hair in dis-
order, rescued her property and returned to the table,
Hamlet meanwhile wagging his tail, panting and watching
for a further game.

"I can't possibly," said Miss Jones, "allow that dog in here during lesson hours. It's impossible."

"Oh, but Miss Jones——" began Jeremy.

"Not one word," said she, "let us have no more of this. Lead him from the room, Jeremy!"

"But, Miss Jones, he *must* be here. He's learning too. In a day or two he'll be as good as anything, really he will. He's *so* intelligent. He really thought it was his to play with, and he did give it up, didn't he, as soon as I said——"

"Enough," said Miss Jones, "I will listen to no more. I say he is not to remain——"

"But if I promise——" said Jeremy.

Then Miss Jones made a bad mistake. Wearied of the argument, wishing to continue the lesson, and hoping perhaps to please her tormentors, she said meekly:

"Well, if he really is good, perhaps——"

From that instant her doom was sealed. The children exchanged a glance of realisation. Jeremy smiled. The lesson was continued. What possessed Jeremy now? What possesses any child, naturally perhaps, of a kindly and even sentimental nature at the sight of something helpless and in its power? Is there any cruelty in after life like the cruelty of a small boy, and is there anything more powerful, more unreasoning, and more malicious than the calculating tortures that small children devise for those weaker than themselves? Jeremy was possessed with a new power.

It was something almost abstract in its manifestations it was something indecent, sinister, secret, foreign to his whole nature felt by him now for the first time, unanalysed, of course, but belonging, had he known it, to that world of which afterwards he was often to catch glimpses, that world of shining white faces in dark streets, of muffled cries from shuttered windows, of muttered exclamations, half caught, half understood. He was never again to be quite free from the neighbourhood of that half-world; he would never be quite sure of his dominance of it until he died.

He had never felt anything like this power before. With the Jampot his relations had been quite simple; he had been rebellious, naughty, disobedient, and had been punished, and there was an end. Now there was a game like tracking Red Indians in the prairie or tigers in the jungle.

He watched Miss Jones and discovered many things about her. He discovered that when she made mistakes in the things that she taught them she was afraid to confess to her mistakes, and so made them worse and worse. He discovered that she was very nervous, and that a sudden noise made her jump and turn white and put her hand to her heart. He discovered that she would punish him and then try to please him by saying he need not finish his punishment. He discovered that she would lose things, like her spectacles, her handkerchief, or her purse, and then be afraid to confess that she had lost them and endeavour to proceed without them. He discovered that she hated to hit him on the hand with a ruler (he scarcely felt the strokes). He discovered that when his mother or father was in the room she was terrified lest he should misbehave.

He discovered that she was despised by the servants, who quite openly insulted her.

All these things fed his sense of power. He did not consider her a human being at all; she was simply some-

thing upon which he could exercise his ingenuity and
cleverness. Mary followed him in whatever he did;
Helen pretended to be superior, but was not. Yes, Miss
Jones was in the hands of her tormentors, and there was
no escape for her.

Surely it must have been some outside power that drove
Jeremy on. The children called it "teasing Miss Jones,"
and the aboriginal savagery in their behaviour was as unconscious as their daily speech or fashion of eating their
food—some instinct inherited, perhaps, from the days
when the gentleman with the biggest muscles extracted for
his daily amusement the teeth and nails of his less happily
muscular friends.

There were many games to be played with Miss Jones.
She always began her morning with a fine show of authority, accumulated, perhaps, during hours of Spartan reso-
lution whilst the rest of the household slept. "To-morrow
I'll see that they do what I tell them——"

"Now, children," she would say, "I'm determined to
stand no nonsense this morning. Get out your copy books."
Five minutes later would begin: "Oh, Miss Jones, I can't
write with this pencil. May I find a better one?" Granted
permission, Mary's head and large spectacles would disappear inside the schoolroom cupboard. Soon Jeremy
would say very politely: "Miss Jones, I think I know
where it is. May I help her to find it?" Then Jeremy's
head would disappear. There would follow giggles, whispers, again giggles; then from the cupboard a book tum-
bles, then another, then another.

Then Miss Jones would say: "Now, Jeremy, come back
to the table. You've had quite enough time——" interrupted by a perfect avalanche of books. Mary crying:

"Oh, Jeremy!" Jeremy crying: "I didn't; it was you!"
Miss Jones: "Now, children——"

Then Jeremy, very politely:

"Please, Miss Jones, may I help Mary to pick the books
up? There are rather a lot." Then, both on their knees,
more whispers and giggles. Miss Jones, her voice trembling: "Children, I really insist——" And more books
dropped, and more whispers and more protests, and so on
ad infinitum. A beautiful game to be played all the morning.

Or there was the game of Not Hearing, Miss Jones
would say: "And twice two are four." Mary would repeat
loudly: "And twice two is five——"

"Four, Mary."

"Oh, I thought you said five."

And then a second later Jeremy would ask:

"Did you say four or five, Miss Jones?"

"I told Mary I said four——"

"Oh, I've written five—and now it's all wrong. Didn't
you write five, Mary?"

"Yes, I've written five. You did say four, didn't you,
Miss Jones?"

"Yes—yes. And three makes——"

"What did you say made five?" asked Jeremy.

"I didn't say five. I said four. Twice two."

"Is that as well as 'add three,' Miss Jones? I've got
twice two, and then add three, and then twice two——"

"No, no. I was only telling Jeremy——"

"Please, Miss Jones, would you mind beginning
again——"

This is a very unpleasant game for a lady with neuralgia.

Or there is the game of Making a Noise. At this game, without any earlier training or practice, Jeremy was a perfect master. The three children would be sitting there very, very quiet, learning the first verse of "Tiger, Tiger, burning bright——" A very gentle creaking sound would break the stillness—a creaking sound that can be made, if you are clever, by rubbing a boot against a boot. It would not come regularly, but once, twice, thrice, a pause, and then once, twice and another pause.

"Who's making a noise?"

Dead silence. A very long pause, and then it would begin again.

"That noise must cease, I say. Jeremy, what are you doing?"

He would lift to her then eyes full of meekness and love.

"Nothing, Miss Jones."

Soon it would begin again. Miss Jones would be silent this time, and then Mary would speak.

"Please, would you ask Jeremy not to rub his boots together? I can't learn my verse——"

"I didn't know I was," says Jeremy.

Then it would begin again. Jeremy would say:

"Please, may I take my boots off?"

"Take your boots off? Why?"

"They will rub together, and I can't stop them, because I don't know when I do it, and it is hard for Mary——"

"Of course not! I never heard of such a thing! Next time you do it you must stand on your chair."

Soon Jeremy is standing on his chair. Soon his poetry book drops with a terrible crash to the ground, and five million pins stab Miss Jones's heart. With white face and trembling hands, she says:

"Go and stand in the corner, Jeremy! I shall have to speak to your mother!"

He goes, grinning at Mary, and stands there knowing that his victim is watching the door in an agony lest Mrs. Cole should suddenly come in and inquire what Jeremy had done, and that so the whole story of his insubordination be revealed and Miss Jones lose her situation for incapacity.

How did he discover this final weakness of Miss Jones? No one told him; but he knew, and, as the days passed, rejoiced in his power and his might and his glory.

Then came the climax. The children were not perfectly sure whether, after all, Miss Jones might not tell their mother. They did not wish this to happen, and so long as this calamity was possible they were not complete masters of the poor lady. Then came a morning when they had been extremely naughty, when every game had been played and every triumph scored. Miss Jones, almost in tears, had threatened four times that the Powers Above should be informed. Suddenly Mrs. Cole entered.

"Well, Miss Jones, how have the children been this morning? If they've been good I have a little treat to propose."

The children waited, their eyes upon their governess. Her eyes stared back upon her tormentors. Her hands worked together. She struggled. Why not call in Mrs. Cole's authority to her aid? No; she knew what it would mean—"I'm very sorry, Miss Jones, but I think a younger governess, perhaps——"

Her throat moved.

"They've been very good this morning, Mrs. Cole."

The eyes of Mary and of Jeremy were alight with triumph.

They had won their final victory.

III

I know what Miss Jones suffered during those weeks. She was not an old lady of very great power of resistance, and it must have positively terrified her that these small children should so vindictively hate her. She could not have seen it as anything but hatred, being entirely ignorant of children and the strange forces to whose power they are subject, and she must have shivered in her bedroom at the dreariness and terror of the prospect before her. Many, many times she must have resolved not to be beaten, and many, many times she must have admitted herself beaten as badly as any one can be.

Her life with the people downstairs was not intimate enough, nor were those people themselves perceptive enough for any realisation of what was occurring to penetrate.

"I hope you're happy with the children, Miss Jones," once or twice said Mrs. Cole.

"Very, thank you," said Miss Jones.

"They're good children, I think, although parents are always prejudiced, of course. Jeremy is a little difficult perhaps. It's so hard to tell what he's really thinking. You find him a quiet, reserved little boy?"

"Very," said Miss Jones.

"In a little while, when you know him better, he will come out. Only you have to let him take his time. He doesn't like to be forced——"

"No," said Miss Jones.

Meanwhile, that morning descent into the schoolroom was real hell for her. She had to summon up her courage, walking about her bedroom, pressing her hands together, evoking the memory of her magnificent iron-souled brother, who would, she knew, despise such tremors. If only she could have discovered some remedy! But sentiment, attempted tyranny, anger, contempt, at all these things they laughed. She could not touch them anywhere. And she saw Jeremy as a real child of Evil in the very baldest sense. She could not imagine how anyone so young could be so cruel, so heartless, so maliciously clever in his elaborate machinations. She regarded him with real horror, and on the occasions when she found him acting kindly towards his sisters or a servant, or when she watched him discoursing solemnly to Hamlet, she was helplessly puzzled, and decided that these better manifestations were simply masks to hide his devilish young heart. She perceived meanwhile the inevitable crisis slowly approaching, when she would be compelled to invite Mrs. Cole's support. That would mean her dismissal and a hopeless future. There was no one to whom she might turn. She had not a relation, not a friend—too late to make friends now.

She could see nothing in front of her at all.

The crisis did come, but not as she expected it.

There arrived a morning when the dark mist outside and badly made porridge inside tempted the children to their very worst. Miss Jones had had a wakeful night struggling with neuralgia and her own hesitating spirit. The children had lost even their customary half-humourous, half-contemptuous reserve. They let themselves appear for what they were—infant savages discontented with food, weather and education.

I will not detail the incidents of that morning. The
episodes that were on other mornings games were to-day
tortures. There was the Torture of Losing Things, the
Torture of Not Hearing, the Torture of Many Noises, the
Torture of Sudden Alarm, the Torture of Outright Defiance, the Torture of Expressed Contempt. When twelve
struck and the children were free, Miss Jones was
not far from a nervous panic that can be called, without
any exaggeration, incipient madness. The neuralgia tore
at her brain, her own self-contempt tore at her heart, her
baffled impotence bewildered and blinded her. She did
not leave the schoolroom with the children, but went to the
broad window-sill and sat there looking out into the dreary
prospect. Then, suddenly for no reason except general
weakness and physical and spiritual collapse she began to
cry.

Jeremy was considered to have a cold, and was, therefore, not permitted to accompany his mother and sisters
on an exciting shopping expedition, which would certainly
lead as far as old Poole's, the bookseller, and might even
extend to Martins', the pastrycook, who made lemon biscuits next door to the Cathedral. He was, therefore, in a
very bad temper indeed when he returned sulkily to the
schoolroom. He stood for a moment there unaware that
there was anybody in the room, hesitating as to whether
he should continue "A Flat Iron for a Farthing" or hunt
up Hamlet. Suddenly he heard the sound of sobbing. He
turned and saw Miss Jones.

He would have fled had flight been in any way possible,
but she had looked up and seen him, and her sudden ar-
rested sniff held them both there as though by some third
invisible power. He saw that she was crying; he saw her

red nose, mottled cheeks, untidy hair. It was the most awful moment of his young life. He had never seen a grown-up person cry before; he had no idea that they ever did cry. He had, indeed, never realised that grown-up persons had any active histories at all, any histories in the sense in which he and Mary had them. They were all a background, simply a background that blew backwards and forwards like tapestry according to one's need of them. His torture of Miss Jones had been founded on no sort of realisation of her as a human being; she had been a silly old woman, of course, but just as the battered weather-beaten Aunt Sally in the garden was a silly old woman.

Her crying horrified, terrified, and disgusted him. It was all so dreary, the horrible weather outside, the beginning of a cold in his head, the schoolroom fire almost out, everyone's bad temper, including his own, and this sudden horrible jumping-to-life of a grown-up human being. She, meanwhile, was too deeply involved now in the waters of her affliction to care very deeply who saw her or what anyone said to her. She did feel dimly that she ought not to be crying in front of a small boy of eight years old, and that it would be better to hide herself in her bedroom, but she did not mind—she *could* not mind—her neuralgia was too bad.

"It's the neuralgia in my head," she said in a muffled confused voice. That he could understand. He also had pains in his head. He drew closer to her, flinging a longing backward look at the door. She went on in convulsed tones:

"It's the pain—awake all night, and the lessons. I can't make them attend; they learn nothing. They're not afraid

of me—they hate me. I've never really known children
before——"

He did not know what to say. Had it been Mary or
Helen the formula would have been simple. He moved
his legs restlessly one against the other.

Miss Jones went on:

"And now, of course, I must go. It's quite impossible
for me to stay when I manage so badly——" She looked
up and suddenly realised that it was truly Jeremy.
"You're only a little boy, but you know very well that I
can't manage you. And then where am I to go to? No
one will take me after I've been such a failure."

The colour stole into his cheeks. He was immensely
proud. No grown-up person had ever before spoken to him
as though he was himself a grown-up person—always
laughing at him like Uncle Samuel, or talking down to him
like Aunt Amy, or despising him like Mr. Jellybrand. But
Miss Jones appealed to him simply as one grown-up to
another. Unfortunately he did not in the least know what
to say. The only thing he could think of at the moment
was: "You can have my handkerchief, if you like. It's
pretty clean——"

But she went on: "If my brother had been alive he
would have advised me. He was a splendid man. He
rowed in his college boat when he was at Cambridge, but
that, of course, was forty years ago. He could keep
children in order. I thought it would be so easy. Perhaps
if my health had been better it wouldn't have been so
hard."

"Do your pains come often?" asked Jeremy.

"Yes. They're very bad."

"I have them, too," said Jeremy. "It's generally, I

expect, because I eat too much—at least, the Jampot used to say so. They're in my head sometimes, too. And then I'm really sick. Do you feel sick?"

Miss Jones began to pull herself together. She wiped her eyes and patted her hair.

"It's my neuralgia," she said again. "It's from my eyes partly, I expect."

"It's better to be sick," continued Jeremy, "if you can be——"

She flung him then a desperate look, as though she were really an animal at bay.

"You see, I can't go away," she said. "I've nowhere to go to. I've no friends, nor relations, and no one will take me for their children, if Mrs. Cole says I can't keep order."

"Then I suppose you'd go to the workhouse," continued Jeremy, pursuing her case with excited interest. "That's what the Jampot always used to say, that one day she'd end in the workhouse; and that's a horrible place, *she* said, where there was nothing but porridge to eat, and sometimes they took all your clothes off and scrubbed your back with that hard yellow soap they wash Hamlet with."

His eyes grew wide with the horrible picture.

"Oh, Miss Jones, you mustn't go there!"

"Would you mind," she said, "just getting me some water from the jug over there? There's a glass there."

Still proud of the level to which he had been raised, but puzzled beyond any words as to this new realisation of Miss Jones, he fetched her the water, then, standing quite close to her, he said:

"You must stay with us, always."

She looked up at him, and they exchanged a glance.

With that glance Miss Jones learnt more about children than she had ever learnt before—more, indeed, than most people learn in all their mortal lives.

"I can't stay," she said, and she even smiled a little, "if you're always naughty."

"We won't be naughty any more." He sighed. "It was great fun, of course, but we won't do it any more. We never knew you minded."

"Never knew I minded?"

"At least, we never thought about you at all. Helen did sometimes. She said you had a headache when you were very yellow in the morning, but I said it was only because you were old. But we'll be good now. I'll tell them too——"

Then he added: "But you won't go away now even if we're not *always* good? We won't always be, I suppose; and I'm going to school in September, and it will be better then, I expect. I'm too old, *really,* to learn with girls now."

She wanted terribly to kiss him, and, had she done so, the whole good work of the last quarter of an hour would have been undone. He was aware of her temptation; he felt it in the air. She saw the warning in his eyes. The moment passed.

"You won't go away, will you?" he said again.

"Not if you're good," she said.

IV

Half an hour later, when Mary and Helen returned from their walk, they were addressed by Jeremy.

"She was crying because we'd been so naughty, and she

had pains in her head, and her brother was dead. Her
brother was very strong, and he used to row in a boat
forty years ago. She told me all about it, just as though
I'd been Aunt Amy or Mother. And she says that if we
go on being naughty she'll go away, and no one else will
have her, because they'll hear about our having been
naughty. And I told her about the workhouse and the porridge and the yellow soap that the Jampot told us of, and
it would be awful if she went there because of us, wouldn't
it ?"

"Awful," said Mary.

But Helen said: "She wouldn't go there. She'd take a
little house, like Miss Dobell, and have tea-parties on
Thursdays—somewhere near the Cathedral."

"No, she wouldn't !" said Jeremy excitedly. "How
could she take a little house if she hadn't any money ? She
told me she hadn't, and no friends, nor nobody, and she
cried like anything——" He paused for breath, then concluded: "So we've got to be good now, and learn sums, and
not make her jump. Really and truly, we must."

"I always thought you were very silly to make so much
noise," said Helen in a superior fashion. "You and Mary
—babies !"

"We're not babies," shouted Jeremy.

"Yes, you are."

"No, we're not."

Miss Jones was no longer the subject of the conversation.

That same day it happened that rumours were brought
to Mrs. Cole through Rose, the housemaid, or some other
medium for the first time, of Miss Jones's incapacity.

That evening Jeremy was spending his last half-hour

before bedtime in his mother's room happily in a corner with his toy village. He suddenly heard his mother say to Aunt Amy:

"I'm afraid Miss Jones won't do. I thought she was managing the children, but now I hear that she can't keep order at all. I'm sorry—it's so difficult to get anyone."

Jeremy sprang up from the floor, startling the ladies, who had forgotten that he was there.

"She's all right," he cried. "Really she is, Mother. We're going to be as good as anything, really we are. You won't send her away, will you?"

"My dear Jeremy," his mother said, "I'd forgotten you were there. Rose says you don't do anything Miss Jones tells you."

"Rose is silly," he answered. "She doesn't know anything about it. But you will keep her, won't you, Mother?"

"I don't know—if she can't manage you——"

"But she *can* manage us. We'll be good as anything. I promise. You will keep her, won't you, Mother?"

"Really, Jeremy," said Aunt Amy, "to bother your mother so! And it's nearly time you went to bed."

He brushed her aside. "You *will* keep her, Mother, won't you?"

"It depends, dear," said Mrs. Cole, laughing. "You see——"

"No—we'll be bad with everyone else," he cried. "We will, really—everyone else. And we'll be good with Miss Jones."

"Well, so long as you're good, dear," she said. "I'd no idea you liked her so much."

"Oh, she's all right," he said. "But it isn't that——"

Then he stopped; he couldn't explain—especially with that idiot Aunt Amy there, who'd only laugh at him, or kiss him, or something else horrible.

Afterwards, as he went slowly up to bed, he stopped for a moment in the dark passage thinking. The whole house was silent about him, only the clocks whispering.

What a tiresome bother Aunt Amy was! How he wished that she were dead! And what a bore it would be being good now with Miss Jones. At the same time, the renewed consciousness of her personal drama most strangely moved him—her brother who rowed, her neuralgia, her lack of relations. Perhaps Aunt Amy also had an exciting history! Perhaps she also cried!

The world seemed to be suddenly filled with pressing, thronging figures, all with businesses of their own.

It was very odd.

He pushed back the schoolroom door and blinked at the sudden light.

CHAPTER V

THE SEA-CAPTAIN

I

VERY few matter-of-fact citizens of the present-day world will understand the part that the sea used to play in our young lives thirty years ago in Polchester.

It is very easy to look at the map and say that the sea is a considerable distance from Polchester, and that even if you stood on the highest ridge of the highest corn-field above the town you would not be able to catch the faintest glimpse of it. That may be true, although I myself can never be completely assured, possessing so vividly as I do a memory of a day when I stood with my nurse at the edge of Merazion Woods and, gazing out to the horizon, saw a fleet of ships full-sail upon the bluest of seas, and would not be persuaded that it was merely wrack of clouds. That may be or no; the fact remains that Polchester sniffed the sea from afar, was caught with sea breezes and bathed in reflected sea-lights; again and again of an evening the Cathedral sailed on dust and shadow towards the horizon, a great white ghost of a galleon, and the young citizens of the town with wondering eyes, watched it go. But there were more positive influences than mere cloud and light. We had, in the lower part of our town, sailors, quite a number of them. There were the old white-bearded ones who would sit upon tubs and tell smuggling tales; these haunted the River Pol, fished in it, ferried people across it, and let out boats for hire. There were younger sailors who, tired of the still life of their little villages and dreading the real hard work of a life at sea, lurched and slouched by the Pol's river bed, fishing a little, sleeping, eating and drinking a great deal.

And there were the true sailors, passing through perhaps on their way to Drymouth to join their ships, staying in the town for a day or two to visit their relations, or simply stopping for an hour or so to gaze open-mouthed at the Cathedral and the market-place and the Canons and the old women. These men had sometimes gold rings in their ears, and their faces were often coloured a dark rich brown, and they carried bundles across their backs all in the traditional style.

Then there were influences more subtle than either clouds or men. There were the influences of the places that we had ourselves seen in our summer holidays—Rafiel and St. Lowe, Marion Bay or Borhaze—and, on the other coast, Newbock with its vast stretch of yellow sand, St. Borse with its wild seas and giant Borse Head, or St. Nails-in-Cove with its coloured rocks and sparkling shells. Every child had his own place; my place was, like Jeremy's, Rafiel, and a better, more beautiful place, in the whole world you will not find. And each place has its own legend: at Rafiel the Gold-laced Pirates, and the Turnip-Field; at Polwint the Giant Excise Man; at Borhaze the Smugglers of Trezent Rock; at St. Borse the wreck of "The Golden Galleon" in the year 1563, with its wonderful treasure; and at St. Maitsin Cove the famous Witch of St. Maitsin Church Town who turned men's bones into water and filled St. Maitsin Church with snakes. Back from

one summer holiday, treasuring these stories together with
our collections of shells and seaweed and dried flowers, we
came, and so the tales settled in Polchester streets and
crept into the heart of the Polchester cobbles and haunted
the Polchester corners by the fire, and even invaded with
their romantic, peering, mischievous faces the solemn aisles
of the Cathedral itself.

The sea was at the heart of all of them, and whenever
a sea-breeze blew down the street carrying with it wisps
of straw from the field, or dandelion seeds, or smell of sea-
pinks, we children lifted our noses and sniffed and sniffed
and saw the waves curl in across the shore, or breakers
burst upon the rock, and whispered to one another of the
Smugglers of Trezent or the Gold-laced Pirates of Rafiel.

But I think that none of us adored the sea as Jeremy
did. From that first moment when, as a small baby, he
had been held up in Rafiel Cove to see the tops of the waves
catch the morning light as they rolled over to shore, he had
adored it. He had never felt any fear of it; he had been
able to swim since he could remember, and he simply lived
for those days at the end of July when they would all, in a
frantic hurry and confusion, take the train for Rafiel and
arrive at Cow Farm in the evening, with the roar of the
sea coming across the quiet fields to mingle with the low-
ing of the cows and the bleating of the sheep. He had in
his bedroom a wonderful collection of dusty and sticky
sea-shells, and these he would turn over and over, letting
them run through his fingers as a miser counts his gold.

Let him catch the faintest glimpse of a shadow of a
sailor in the street and he was after it, and he had once,
when he was only four or five, been caught by the terrified Jampot, only just in time, walking away confidently

down the market-place, his hand in the huge grasp of a villainous looking mariner. He was exceedingly happy in his home, but he did often wonder whether he would not run away to sea; of course, he was going to be a sailor, but it seemed so long to wait until he was thirteen or fourteen, and there was the sea all the time rolling in and out and inviting him to come.

Mrs. Cole warned Miss Jones of this taste of Jeremy's: "Never let him speak to a sailor, Miss Jones. There are some horrible men in the town, and Jeremy simply is not to be trusted when sailors are concerned."

Miss Jones, however, could not be always on her guard, and Fate is stronger than any governess. . . .

II

Early in February there came one of those hints of spring that in Glebeshire more than in any other place in the world thrill and stir the heart. Generally they give very little in actual reward and are followed by weeks of hail and sleet and wind, but for that reason alone their burning promise is beyond all other promises beguiling. Jeremy got up one morning to feel that somewhere behind the thick wet mists of the early hours there was a blazing sun. After breakfast, opening the window and leaning out, he could see the leaves of the garden still shining with their early glitter and the earth channelled into fissures and breaks, dark and hard under the silver-threaded frost; beneath the rind of the soil he could feel the pushing, heaving life struggling to answer the call of the sun above it. Far down the road towards the Orchards a dim veil of gold was spreading behind the walls of mist; the sparrows

on the almond tree near his window chattered like the girls
of the High School, and blue shadows stole into the dim
grey sky, just as light breaks upon an early morning sea;
the air was warm behind the outer wall of the frosty morning, and the faint gold of the first crocus beneath the
garden wall near the pantry door, where always the first
crocuses came, caught his eye. Even as he watched the sun
burst the mist, the trees changed from dim grey to sharp
black, the blue flooded the sky, and the Cathedral beyond
the trees shone like a house of crystal.

All this meant spring, and spring meant hunting for
snowdrops in the Meads. Jeremy informed Miss Jones,
and Miss Jones was, of course, agreeable. They would
walk that way after luncheon.

The Meads fall in a broad green slope from the old
Cathedral battlement down to the River Pol. Their long
stretches of meadow are scattered with trees, some of the
oldest oaks in Glebeshire, and they are finally bounded by
the winding path of the Rope Walk that skirts the river
bank. Along the Rope Walk in March and April the daffo-
dils first, and the primroses afterwards, are so thick that,
from the Cathedral walls, the Rope Walk looks as though it
wandered between pools and lakes of gold. In the Orchards
on the hill also they run like rivers.

Upon this afternoon there were only the trees, faintly
pink, along the river and the wide unbroken carpet of
green. Miss Jones walked up and down the Rope Walk,
whilst Mary told her an endless and exceedingly confused
story that had begun more than a week ago and had reached
by now such a state of "To be continued in our next" that
Miss Jones had only the vaguest idea of what it was all
about. Her mind therefore wandered, as indeed, did al-

ways the minds of Mary's audiences, and Mary never noticed but stared with the rapt gaze of the creator through her enormous glasses, out into an enchanted world of golden princesses, white elephants and ropes and ropes of rubies. Miss Jones meanwhile thought of her young days, her illnesses and a certain hat that she had seen in Thornley's windows in the High Street. Jeremy, attended by Hamlet, hunted amongst the trees for snowdrops.

Hamlet had been worried ever since he could remember by a theory about rabbits. He had been told, of course, about rabbits by his parents, and it had even been suggested to him that he would be a mighty hunter of the same when he grew to a certain age. He had now reached that age, but never a rabbit as yet had he encountered. He might even have concluded that the whole Rabbit story was a myth and a legend were it not that certain scents and odours were for ever tantalising his nose that could, his instinct told him, mean Rabbit and only Rabbit. These scents met him at the most tantalising times, pulling him this way and that, exciting the wildest hopes in him, afterwards condemned to sterility; as ghosts haunt the convinced and trusting spiritualist, so did rabbits haunt Hamlet. He dreamt of Rabbits at night, he tasted Rabbits in his food, he saw them scale the air and swim the stream— now, he was close on their trail, now he had them round that tree, up that hill, down that hole . . . sitting tranquilly in front of the schoolroom fire he would scent them; always they eluded him, laughed at him, mocked him with their stumpy tails. They were rapidly becoming the obsession of his nights and days.

Upon this afternoon the air was full of Rabbit. The Meads seemed to breathe Rabbit. He left his master, rushed hither and thither, barked and whined, scratched the soil, ran round the trees, lay cautiously motionless waiting for his foes, and now and then sat and laughed at himself for a ludicrous rabbit-bemused idiot. He had a delightful afternoon. . . .

Jeremy then was left entirely to himself and wandered about, looking for snowdrops under the trees, talking to himself, lost in a chain of ideas that included food and the sea and catapults and a sore finger and what school would be like and whether he could knock down the Dean's youngest, Ernest, whom he hated without knowing why.

He was lost in these thoughts, and had indeed wandered almost into the little wood that lies at the foot of the Orchards, when he heard a deep rich voice say:

"I suppose you 'aven't such a thing as a match upon you anywhere, young gentleman?"

He liked to be asked for a match, a manly thing to be supposed to possess, but, of course, he hadn't one, owing to the stupidity of elderly relations, so he looked up and said politely: "No, I'm afraid I haven't." Then how his heart whacked beneath his waistcoat! There, standing in front of him, was the very figure of his dreams! Looking down upon Jeremy was a gentleman of middle-age whom experienced men of the world would have most certainly described as "seedy."

Jeremy did not see his "seediness." He saw first his face, which was of a deep brown copper colour, turning here and there to a handsome purple; ill-shaved, perhaps, but with a fine round nose and a large smiling mouth. He saw black curling hair and a yachting cap, faded this last and the white of it a dirty grey but set on jauntily at a magnificent angle. He saw a suit of dark navy blue, this again faded, spotted too with many stains, ragged at the trouser-ends and even torn in one place above the elbow, fitting also so closely to the figure that it must have been at bursting point. He saw round the neck a dark navy handkerchief, and down the front of the coat brass buttons that shook and trembled as their owner's chest heaved.

And what a chest! Jeremy had never conceived that any human being could be so thick and so broad. The back, spreading to the farthest limits of the shiny seams of the coat, was like a wall. The thighs were pillows, the arms bolsters and yet not fat, mind you, simply muscle, all of it. One could see in a minute that it was all muscle, the chest thrust forward, the legs spread wide, the bull-neck bursting the handkerchief, everything that Jeremy himself most wished to be. A sailor, a monument of strength, with the scent of his "shag" strong enough to smell a mile away, and—yes, most marvellous of all, gold rings in his ears! His chest would be tatooed probably, and perhaps his legs also!

There, on the back of his hand, was a blue anchor. . . . Jeremy looked up and trembled lest the vision should fade, then flung a hurried look around him to see whether Miss Jones were near. No one was about. He was alone with the desire of his life.

"I'm so so sorry I haven't a match," he said. "I'm not allowed to have them, you know."

"No, I suppose not," said the vision. "Just my blamed luck. There I am with 'undreds of pounds lying around my room at 'ome careless as you please, and then held up for a bloomin' match. What's gold to a man like me? But a match . . . there you are . . . that's life."

He looked at Jeremy with great interest; he took in, as

Jeremy realised, every detail of his personal appearance.

"I like boys," he said. " 'Ad two myself—'ealthy little nippers they was. Both dead—'ere to-day and gone to-morrer, as you might say. Got your nurse 'anging around anywhere?"

"Nurse?" said Jeremy indignantly. "I don't have a nurse. I'm much too old! There is a governess, but she's over there talking to Mary. She's my sister—but they won't bother yet—not till the Cathedral bell begins."

"No intention of 'urting your feelings, young fellow my lad. Didn't think you'd want a nurse of course—big chap like you. Thought you might 'ave a baby brother or such. No offence—I suppose you 'aven't begun to smoke yet. Can't offer you some tobacco."

Jeremy coloured. The man was laughing at him.

"I'm eight if you want to know," he said, "and I'm going to school in September."

"School!" said the mariner, sniffing contemptuously. "I don't think much of school if you ask me. Now I never went to school, and I can't see that I'm much the worse for not 'aving been there. Contrariwise—I've seen many a fine promising lad spoiled by too much schoolin'. Be a man of the world, I say; that's the direction you want to sail in."

"Did you really never go to school?" asked Jeremy.

"Not I!" replied the sailor. "Flung out at the age of six, I was, turned into a boat sailing to the West Indies and left to shift for myself—and 'ere I am to-day a Captain of as fine a craft as you're ever likely to see, with gold in 'er lockers and peacocks in the 'old—all in a manner of speaking, you know."

Jeremy's eyes glittered; his face was flushed a brilliant

red. Hamlet had returned from his rabbit hunting and sat with his tongue out and a wild adventurous eye glittering up at his master from behind his hair, yet he was not noticed.

"You were very lucky," he said devoutly, then he went on hurriedly: "Would you mind—you see, Miss Jones may come at any moment—would you mind——" he choked.

"Would I mind what?" asked the Captain.

"Would you mind telling me? Are you tatooed on your body, snakes and ships and things, like a gardener once we had? He had a sea-serpent all down his back. He showed me one day."

The Captain smiled proudly.

"Tatooed! Talk of tatooing! I'll show yer—and it isn't everybody I'd do it for neither. But I've taken a fancy to you, like my own young nipper what died."

With an air of vast ceremony, as though he were throwing open the door to all the universe, he slowly unwound from about his neck the dark blue handkerchief, unbuttoned his coat, then a grimy shirt and displayed a wall of deep brown chest. This fine expanse had no hair upon it, but was illuminated with a superb picture of a ship in full sail against a setting sun, all worked in the most handsome of blue tatoo. Jeremy gasped. He had never dreamed that such things could be. He ventured to touch the ship with his finger, and he could feel the Captain's manly heart thumping like a muffled hammer beneath the skin.

"There's Queen Victoria on my right thigh and Nelson on my left, and the battle of Trafalgar on the middle of my back. P'raps I'll show 'em you one day. It wouldn't be decent exactly 'ere—too public. But one day you come to my little place and I'll show 'em you."

"Will you really?" said Jeremy. "Didn't it hurt terribly?"

"Hurt!" said the Captain. "I should just think it did. I 'ad to put cotton wool behind my teeth to prevent myself from screaming. But that's nothing. What do you say to being tortured by the Caribbees natives every day after breakfast for three 'ole months. A tooth out a day——"

"But your teeth are all there," said Jeremy.

"False," said the Captain. "Every one of 'em. And the things they'll do to your toenails—it 'ud make your 'air creep on your 'ead to listen to the things I could tell you——"

"Oh, it's awful!" said Jeremy. "And where is your ship now?"

"Ah, my ship!" the Captain replied, winking in the most mysterious fashion; "it would be telling to say where that is. I can trust you, I know; I'm a great judge o' character, I am, but not even with my own mother, gone to glory now twenty years and as holy a soul as ever breathed, I wouldn't trust even 'er with the secret."

"Why is it a secret?" asked Jeremy breathlessly.

"Treasure," said the Captain, dropping his voice. "Treasure, nothing less nor more. Between you and me there's enough gold on that there ship to satisfy the Prime Minister 'imself, to say nothing of the jewels—rubies, pearls, diamonds. My word, if you could see them diamonds. I'm looking about me now for an extra man or two, and then I'm off again—silent come, silent go's my motto——"

"I suppose you don't happen to want a cabin-boy?" gasped Jeremy, his voice chocked in his throat.

"Well, now, that's a funny thing," said the Captain. "It's one of the very things. But I'm afraid you're a bit young. Yet I don't know. We might——"

He broke off, suddenly lifted his finger to his lip, whispered:

"Keep your eyes open. I'll be round again," and had vanished.

Directly after Jeremy heard Miss Jones's unwelcome voice: "Why, Jeremy, we couldn't find you anywhere. It's turning cold—tea-time——"

With a thump and a thud and a bang he fell back into the homely world.

III

Jeremy was a perfectly normal little boy, and I defy anyone to have discovered in him at this stage in his progress, those strange morbidities and irregular instincts that were to be found in such unhappy human beings as Dostoieffsky's young hero in "Podrostok," or the unpleasant son and heir of Jude and Sue. Nevertheless, eight years old is not too early for stranger impulses and wilder dreams than most parents ever conceive of, and the fortnight that followed Jeremy's meeting with the Sea-Captain was as peculiar and fantastic a fortnight as he was ever, in all his later life, to know.

For he was haunted—really haunted in the good old solid practical meaning of the term—haunted with the haunting that pursued Sintram and many another famous hero. And he was haunted not only by the Sea-Captain, but by a thousand things that attended in that hero's company. He was haunted by a picture—whence it had come to him he did not know—of a dead-white high road, dropping over the hill into shadow, the light fading around it, black, heavy hedges on every side of it. From below the hill came the pounding of the sea, exactly as he had heard it so many many times on the hill above Rafiel, and he knew, although his eyes could not catch it, that in the valley round the head of the road was the fishing village with the lights just coming in the windows, and beyond the village the sloping shingly Cove. But he could see only the dead-white road, and upon this his eyes were always fixed as though he were expecting someone. And he could smell the sea-pinks and the grass damp with evening dew, and the cold dust of the road, and the sea-smell in the wind. And he waited, knowing that the time would come when he would be told to descend the hill, pass through the village, and step out, under the heavy grey clouds, upon the little shingly beach. He was aware then that out at sea a dark, black ship was riding, slipping a little with the tide, one light gleaming and swinging against the pale glow of the dusky horizon. The church clock struck four below the hill; he was still on the high road waiting, his eyes straining for figures. . . . He was prepared for some journey, because he had at his feet a bundle. And he knew that he ought not to be there. He knew that something awful was about to happen and that, when it had occurred, he would be committed always to something or someone. . . . A little cold breeze then would rise in the hedges and against the silence that followed the chiming of the clock he could hear first the bleating of a sheep, then a sudden pounding of the sea as though the breakers responded to the sudden rising of the wind, then the hoofs of a horse, clear and hard, upon the road. . . . At that moment the picture clouded and was dim. Had this been a dream? Was it simply a confusion of summer visits to Rafiel, stories told him by Mary, pictures in books (a fine illustrated edition of "Redgauntlet" had been a treasure to him since he was a baby), the exciting figure of the Captain, and the beginning of spring? And yet the vision was so vividly detailed that it was precisely like a remembered event. He had always seen things in pictures; punishment meant standing in the corner counting the ships on the wallpaper; summer holidays meant the deep green meadows of Cow Farm, or a purple pool under an afternoon sun; religion meant walking up the great wide aisle of the Cathedral in creaking boots and clean underclothes, and so on. It was nothing new for him to make a picture, and to let that picture stand for a whole complex phase of life. But this? What had it to do with the Sea-Captain, and why was it, as he knew in his heart that it was, wicked and wrong and furtive? For this had begun as a high adventurous romance. There had been nothing wrong in that first talk in the Meads, when the Captain had shown him the tatooes. The wickedness of it had developed partly with his growing longing to see the Captain again, partly with the meeting that actually followed, and partly with the sense that grew and grew as the days passed that the Captain was always watching him.

The Captain, during these weeks, seemed to be everywhere. Never was there an afternoon that Jeremy walked out with Miss Jones and his sisters that he did not appear. It was not very difficult to snatch a conversation with him. Because the beauty of the spring weather continued, the children went every day for a walk in the Meads, and on at least three separate occasions Jeremy and the Captain enjoyed quite long conversations together. These were, none of them, so good as that first one had been. The Captain was not so genial, nor so light-hearted; it seemed that he had something on his mind. Sometimes he put his hand on Jeremy's shoulder, and the heavy pressure of his great fingers made Jeremy tremble, partly with terror, partly with pleasure. His face, also, was scarcely so agreeable as it had seemed at first sight. His tremendous nose seemed to burn down upon Jeremy like a malignant fire. His eyes were so small that sometimes they disappeared under his fat cheeks altogether, or only gleamed like little sharp points of light from under his heavy, shaggy eyebrows. Then, although he tried to make his voice pleasant, Jeremy felt that that complaisant friendliness was not his natural tone. Sometimes there would be a sharp, barking note that made Jeremy jump and his cheek pale. The Captain told him no more fascinating stories, and when Jeremy wanted to know about the ship with the diamonds and rubies and the little sea village where she lay hid and the Caribbees natives, and the chances of becoming a cabin-boy, and the further exploitation of the tatooes—all these things the Captain brushed aside as though they no longer interested him in the least. He, on the other hand, wanted now to know exactly where Jeremy lived, what the house was like, where the back doors were, how the windows opened, where Jeremy slept, and so on. Jeremy, pleased at this interest in his daily life, told him as many things as he could, hoping to pass on afterwards to more exciting topics; how, for instance, the kitchen windows were fastened always last thing at night, but you could undo them from the garden if you liked with your knife, and Jeremy

knew this because Uncle Samuel had done it once on a
Sunday afternoon when the maids were all out and he'd
forgotten his door key. He would have told the Captain
all about the schoolroom and the toy village and the Jampot and the fun they had had teasing Miss Jones had not
the Captain fiercely told him that these things did not interest him, and that he had better just answer the questions that were put to him. It was indeed strange to see
how, with every interview, the Captain grew fiercer and
fiercer and sharper and sharper. He made no allusions
now to "'is little nipper," said nothing about that holy
soul his mother, and never mentioned his liking for
Jeremy. There was evidently something on his mind, and
if he had seemed mysterious at their first meeting it was
nothing to the secrecy that he practised now.

And yet, in spite of all this, his hold over Jeremy grew
and grew. That dream of the bending white road was
always with Jeremy. He could think of nothing but the
Captain, and while he was certainly afraid and would
jump at the slightest sound, he was also certainly excited
beyond all earlier experience. He longed, as he lay awake
at night, to see the Captain. He seemed to have always in
front of his eyes the great wall of a chest with the blue
ship on it, and the bolster legs, and the gigantic hands.
Strangest of all was the sense of evil that came with the
attraction.

He longed to be in the man's company as he longed
to do something that he had been always told not to do,
and when he caught sight of him a sudden, hot, choking
hand was pressed upon his heart, and he was terrified, delighted, frightened, ashamed, all in one. The Captain
always alluded to the things that he would tell him, would

show him one day—"When you come to my little place I'll teach yer a thing or two"—and Jeremy would wonder for hours what this little place would be like and what the Captain would teach him. Meanwhile, he saw him everywhere, even when he was not there—behind lamp-posts, at street corners, behind the old woman's umbrella in the market-place, peering round the statues in the Cathedral, jerking up his head from behind chimney pots, looking through the nursery windows just when dusk was coming on, in the passages, under stairs, out in the dark garden— and always behind him that horrid dream of the dead-white road and the shingly Cove. . . . Yes, poor Jeremy was truly haunted.

IV

That Miss Jones suspected nothing of these meetings must be attributed partly to that lady's habit of wrapping herself in her own thoughts on her walks abroad, and partly to her natural short-sightedness. Once Mary said that she had noticed "a horrid man with a red face" staring at them; but Miss Jones, although she was not a vain woman, thought it nevertheless quite natural that men should stare, and fancied more frequently that they did so than was strictly the truth.

Jeremy, meanwhile, was occupied now with the thought as to what he would do did the Captain really want him to go away with him. He discussed it with himself, but he did not doubt what he would do; he would go. And he would go, he knew, with fear and dread, and with a longing to stay, and be warm in the schoolroom, and have jam for tea, and half an hour before bedtime downstairs, and York-shire pudding on Sundays. But the Captain could mak

him do anything. . . . Yes, the Captain could make him
do anything. . . .

His afternoon walks now were prolonged agonies. He
would turn his head at every moment, would stare into
dark corners, would start at the sound of steps. His sleep
now was broken with horrid dreams, and he would jump
up and cry out; and one night he actually dreamt of his
dead-white road and the sounds that came up from below
the hill, the bell and the sea, and the distant rattle of the
little carts.

Then the Captain drew near to the very house itself.
He haunted Orange Street, could be seen lounging against
a lamp-post opposite the High School, looked once into the
very garden of the Coles, Jeremy watching him with beating heart from the schoolroom window. It was incredible
to Jeremy that no one else of the house perceived him; but
no one ever mentioned him, and this made it appear all the
more a dream, as though the Captain were invisible to
everyone save himself. He began to hate him even more
than he feared him, and yet with that hatred the pleasure
and excitement remained. I remember how, years ago in
Polchester, when I could not have been more than six years
old, I myself was haunted with exactly that same mixture
of pleasure and horror by the figure of a hunch-backed
pedlar who used to come to our town. Many years after
I heard that he had been hung for the murder of some
wretched woman who had accompanied him on some of his
journeys. I was not surprised; but when I heard the story
I felt then again the old thrill of mingled pleasure and
fear.

One windy afternoon, near dusk, when they were returning from their walk, Jeremy suddenly heard the voice in his ear:

"I may be coming to visit yer one o' these nights. Keep yer eyes open and yer tongue quiet if I do."

Jeremy saw the figures of Miss Jones and his sisters pass round the corner of the road.

"What for?" he gasped.

The Captain's figure seemed to swell gigantic against the white light of the fading sky. The wind whistled about their ears.

"Just to visit yer, that's all. 'Cause I've taken a fancy to yer." The Captain chuckled and had vanished. . . .

Jeremy flung one glance at the grey desolate road behind him, then ran for his life to join the others.

What, after that, did he expect? He did not know. Only the Captain was drawing closer, and closer, and closer.

He could feel now always his hot breath upon his ear.

Two days after the whispered dialogue in the road, that first promise of spring broke down into a tempest of wind and rain. The Coles' house in Orange Street, although it looked, with its stout, white stone, strong enough, was old and shaky. Now, in the storm, it shook and wheezed and rattled in every one of its joints. Jeremy, at ordinary times, loved the sound of the wind about the house, when he himself was safe and warm and cosy; but this was now another affair. Lying in his bed he could hear the screams down the chimney, then the tug at his window-pane, the rattling clutch upon the wood, then the sweep under the bed and the rush up the wallpaper, until at last, from behind some badly defended spot where the paper was thin, there would come a wailing, whistling screech as though someone were being murdered in the next room. On other days Jeremy, when he heard this screech, shivered with a cosy, creeping thrill; but now he put his head under the bedclothes, shut his eyes very tight, and tried not to see the Captain with his ugly nose and tiny gimlet eyes.

He would be half asleep.

"Come," said the Captain from the window, "the boat is waiting! You promised, you know. Come just as you are—no time to dress," and poor Jeremy would feel the great, heavy hand upon his shoulder and wake shivering and shaking from head to foot.

On the third day following his last interview with the Captain he went to bed a little reassured and comforted. Perhaps the Captain had gone away. For three days he had seen and heard nothing of him at all.

That was a night of rain—rain that slashed and whipped the house as though it would batter it to the ground. The rain would come with a wild fury upon the panes, trembling with its excited anger, would crash against the glass, then fall back and hang waiting for a further attack; next the results of the first attack would slip and slide like the crawling of a thousand snakes, then fall and drop slowly and heavily as though every drop were foretelling some awful peril. Jeremy lay and listened; but he resolved that to-night he would not be frightened, would not think of the Captain.

He said the Lord's Prayer five times, then counted sheep jumping over the gate, a safe solution for sleepless hours. He saw the sheep—first one a very fat one, then one a very thin one; but the gate stood at the bottom of a little hill, so that it was very difficult for the poor creatures, who jumped and slipped back on the incline. Then a lot of sheep insisted on jumping together, and he could hardly count them—forty-five, forty-six, forty-seven, forty-eight. . . . He was asleep.

After a long, long time of soundlessness, of lying upon a sea that was like a bed of down, and looking up, happily into clear blue light, he was once more conscious of the rain. Yes, there it was with its sweeping rush, its smash upon the pane, its withdrawal, its trickling patter and heavy drops as though it were striking time. Yes, that was the rain and that—What was that?

He was wide awake, lying back against his pillow, but his eyes staring in front of them till they burnt. The house was absolutely dark, absolutely silent, but between the attacks of the rain there was a sound, something that had not to do with the house nor with the weather. He strained with his ears, sitting up in bed, his hands clutching the bed clothes. He heard it quite clearly now. Some-one was moving in the nursery.

With that the whole of his brain was awake and he knew quite clearly, beyond a shadow of any doubt, what had happened; the Captain had come to fetch him. With that knowledge an icy despair gripped him. He did not want to go. Oh, he did not want to go! He was trembling from head to foot so that the bed shook beneath him, his breath came in little hot gasping pants, and his eyes were wide with terror. He was helpless. The Captain would only say "Come," and go he must, leave his warm house and his parents whom he loved and Mary and Helen and Hamlet, yes, and even Miss Jones. He would be dragged down the long white road, through the lighted village, out on to the shiny beach, in a boat out to the dark ship—and then he would be alone with the Captain, alone in the dark ship, with the Captain's heavy hand upon his shoulder, his mouth smiling, his great legs drawing him in as a spider draws a fly into its web, and everyone asleep, only the stars and the dark water. He tried to say the Lord's Prayer again, but the words would not come. The sweat began to trickle down his nose. . . .

Then he heard in the next room some movement against a piece of furniture and a voice muttering. That decided him: better to go and face it than to wait there, so as though he were moving in his sleep, he got out of bed, crossed the floor and entered the schoolroom.

The first sound that he heard was the ticking of the old nursery clock, a strange familiar voice in this awful world, then suddenly, although the room was in black darkness, he himself was staring into blazing light.

He started back and uttered a little cry, but even as he did so that well-remembered hand was upon his shoulder and the well-known voice in his ear:

"Move an inch, utter a sound, and I blow yer brains out, yer——" the voice, very low, faded into the dark. He was staring into a lantern, and above the lantern was the dark body of the Captain. Then as he looked up he was indeed near his last moment, for had he not been a brave boy, old for his years, and determined, he would have cried out with a scream that would have raised the house.

The Captain had no face. . . . The Captain had no face. . . . Only out of a deep darkness those little eyes glittered like candle-points. Jeremy uttered no sound.

Then catching the Captain's coat because he trembled so, he said: "I'm coming at once—but don't wake Mary and Helen. They'd be frightened. May I get a coat, because it raining ?"

"Coming!" whispered the Captain, his voice coming
from that space in the air where were his eyes. "You
move one inch from 'ere or utter one sound and I do yer
in, yer—— I'm watchin' yer, mind!"

The lantern light suddenly vanished. The room was
black. There was no sound but the ticking of the clock,
and now the rain, which had seemed to stop during this
terrible dialogue, beat with friendly comfort once more
upon the pane. Jeremy stood there, his body held together
as though in an iron case, scarcely breathing. There was
no more sound at all. Quite clearly now Mary's snores
could be heard coming from her room.

Jeremy had only one thought—only one thought in all
the world. The Captain did not want him. The Captain
had gone and not taken him with him. He was safe; he
was freed; the terror was over and he was at liberty.

At last he moved back to his room. He got into bed
again. He was terribly cold, and little spasms of shivers
seized him, but he did not care. The Captain was gone,
and he had not taken him with him. . . .

V

He was not aware whether he slept or no, but suddenly
sunlight was in the room, the bath-water was running, the
canary was singing and Hamlet was scratching upon his
door. He jumped out of bed and let the dog in. Then he
heard Rose's voice from the next room:

". . . and 'e's taken everything, 'e 'as. All the silver
candlesticks and the plate what was give to master by
the Temp'rance Society, and Master Jeremy's mug what
he 'ad at 'is christening and all the knives and forks—

'e 'as—and the gold clock out o' the drorin'-room, and the mess! Why, I says to Cook 'e couldn't 'ave made more mess, I say, not if 'e'd come to do nothin' else. Grease everywhere, you never see nothin' like it, and all the drawers open and the papers scattered about. Thank 'Eaven 'e never found Cook's earrings. Real gold they was, ever so many carat and give to Cook ever so many years ago by 'er John. Poor woman! She'd 'ave been in a terrible takin' if she'd lost 'em. . . . And so quiet too—not a sound and everyone sleepin' all round 'im. Wonderful 'ow they does it! I thank the Lord I didn't 'ear 'im; I'd 'ave died of fright—shouldn't like! Why, Cook says she knew a 'ouse once . . ."

But Jeremy did not listen, he did not care. As Hamlet sprang about him and licked his hand he thought of one thing alone.

The Captain was gone! The Captain was gone! He was free! The Captain had not taken him, and he was free at last!

CHAPTER VI

FAMILY PRIDE

I

I AM afraid that too great a part of this book is about old maids, but it is hard for anyone who knows only the thriving bustling world of to-day to realise how largely we children were hemmed in and surrounded by a proper phalanx of elderly single ladies and clergymen. I don't believe that we were any the worse for that, and to such heroines as Miss Jane Maple, Miss Mary Trefusis and old Miss Jessamin Trenchard, I here publicly acknowledge deep and lasting debt—but it did make our life a little monotonous, a little unadventurous, a little circumscribed —and because I am determined to give the whole truth and nothing but the truth about the year of Jeremy's life that I am describing, this book will also, I am afraid, be a little circumscribed, a little unadventurous.

The elderly lady who most thoroughly circumscribed Jeremy was, of course—putting Miss Jones, who was a governess and therefore did not count, aside—Aunt Amy.

Now Aunt Amy was probably the most conceited woman in Polchester. There is of course ordinary human conceit, of which every living being has his or her share. I am not speaking of that; Miss Amy Trefusis might be said to be fanatically conceited.

Although she was now a really plain elderly woman it is possible that when she was a little girl she was pretty. In any case, it is certain that she was spoiled when she was a little girl, and because she was delicate and selfish she received a good deal more attention and obedience from weak and vacillating elders than she deserved.

After her growing up she had a year or two of moderate looks and she received, during this period, several proposals; these she refused because they were not good enough and something better must be coming very shortly, but what really came very shortly was middle-age, and it came of course entirely unperceived by the lady. She dressed and behaved as though she were still twenty, although her brother Samuel tried to laugh her out of such absurdities. But no sister ever pays attention to a brother on such matters, and Aunt Amy wore coloured ribbons and went to balls and made eyes behind her fan for season after season. Then as time passed she was compelled by her mirror to realise that she was not quite so young as she had once been, so she hurriedly invented a thrilling past history for herself, alluding to affair after affair that had come to nothing only because she herself had ruthlessly slain them, and dressing herself more reasonably, but with little signs and hints, in the shape of chains and coloured bows and rings, that she could still be young if she so pleased, and that she was open to offers, although she could not promise them much encouragement. She liked the society of Canons, and was to be seen a great deal with old Canon Borlase, who was as great a flirt as he was an egotist, so that it did not matter to him in the least with whom he flirted, and sat at the feet of old Canon Morpheu, who was so crazy about the discoveries that he had made in the life of Ezekiel that it was quite immaterial to him to whom he explained them.

She descended from these clerical flights into the bosom of family life with some natural discontent. Her brother Samuel she had always disliked because he laughed at her; her sister she did not care for because she was very innocently, poor lady, flaunting her superior married state; and her brother-in-law she did not like because he always behaved as though she were one of a vast public of elderly ladies who were useful for helping in clerical displays, but were otherwise non-existent. Then she hated children, so that she really often wondered why she continued to live with her brother-in-law, but it was cheap, comfortable and safe, and although she assured herself and everyone else that there were countless homes wildly eager to receive her, it was perhaps just as well not to put their eagerness too abruptly to the test.

There had been war between her and Jeremy since Jeremy's birth, but it had been war of a rather mild and inoffensive character, consisting largely in Jeremy on his side putting out his tongue at her when she could not see him, and she on her side sending him to wash his ears when they really did not require to be washed. She had felt always in Jeremy an obstinate dislike of her, and as he had seemed to her neither a very clever nor intelligent child she had consoled herself very easily with the thought that he did not like her simply because he was stupid. So it had been until this year, and then suddenly they had been flung into sharper opposition. It was hard to say what had brought this about, but it was perhaps that Jeremy had sprung suddenly from the unconscious indifference of a young child into the active participation of a growing boy. Whatever the truth might have been, the coming of Hamlet had drawn their attitudes into positive conflict.

Aunt Amy had felt from the first that Hamlet laughed at her. Had you asked her to state, as a part of her general experience, that she really believed that dogs could laugh at human beings she would indignantly have repudiated any idea so fantastic, nevertheless, unanalysed and unconfronted, that was her conviction. The dog laughed at her, he insulted her by walking into her bedroom with his muddy feet and then pretending that he hadn't known that it was her bedroom, regarding her through his hair with an ironical and malicious glance, barking suddenly when she made some statement as though he enjoyed immensely an excellent joke, but, above all, despising her, she felt, so that the wall of illusion that she had built around herself had been pulled down by at least one creature, more human, she knew, in spite of herself, than many human beings. Therefore, she hated Hamlet, and scarcely a day passed that she did not try to have him flung from the house, or at least kept in the kitchen offices.

Hamlet had, however, won the hearts of the family; it was, indeed, Aunt Amy alone to whom he had not thought it worth while to pay court. To her alone he would not come when she called, by her alone he would not be cajoled, even though she offered him sugary tea, his deadliest temptation. No, he sat and looked at her through his hair, his fiery eye glinting, his peaked beard ironically humorous, his leg stuck out from his body, a pointing signal of derision.

She resolved to wait for an opportunity when she might conquer Hamlet and Jeremy together, but her power in the house was slight, so long as Mr. and Mrs. Cole were there. "If I only had the children to myself," she would say, "I would improve their manners in many ways. Poor Alice——!" Then suddenly she did have them. At the beginning of May Mr. Cole was summoned to take a mission to the seamen of Drymouth, and Mrs. Cole, who had relations in Drymouth, accompanied him. They would be absent from Polchester a whole week.

"Oh, won't Aunt Amy be a nuisance," said Jeremy, realising the situation. Then turning to Mary he added: "We'll pretend to do what she tells us and not do it really. That's much the easiest."

A week is a short time, especially at the beginning of a shining and burning May, but Aunt Amy did her best not only with the children but with the servants, and even old Jordan, the gardener, who had been with the Cole family for twenty years. During that short week the cook, the parlourmaid, Rose, the housemaid, and the boot-boy all gave notice, and Mrs. Cole was only able to keep them (on her return) by raising the wages of all of them. Jordan, who was an old man with a long white beard, said to her when she advised him to plant pinks where he had planted tulips and tulips where he had planted pinks, and further inquired why the cauliflower that he sent in was so poor and the cabbages so small: "Leave things alone, Miss, Nature's wiser than we be, not but what you mayn't mean well, but fussin's never done any good where Nature's concerned, nor never will"; and when she said that he was very rude to her, he shook his head and answered:

"Maybe yes, and maybe no. What's rude to one ain't rude to another"—out of which answer she could make nothing at all.

In the schoolroom she sustained complete defeat. At the very outset she was baffled by Miss Jones. She had always despised Miss Jones as a poor unfortunate female who was forced to teach children in her old age because she must earn her living—a stupid, sentimental, cowed, old woman at whom the children laughed. She found now that the children instead of laughing at her laughed with her, formed a phalanx of protection around her and refused to be disobedient. Miss Jones herself was discovered to have a dry, rather caustic, sense of humour that Aunt Amy felt to be impertinence, but could not penetrate.

"And is that really how you teach them history, Miss Jones? Not quite the simplest way, surely. . . . I remember an excellent governess whom we once had——"

"Perhaps," said Miss Jones, gently, "you would give them a history lesson yourself, Miss Trefusis. I would be so glad to pick up any little hints——"

"I have, of course, no time," said Aunt Amy hurriedly, "but, speaking generally, I am afraid I can't approve altogether of your system."

"It isn't very good, I'm afraid," said Miss Jones weakly. "The children would be glad, I know, to have a few hints from you if you could spare a moment——"

Jeremy, who was listening, giggled, tried to turn the giggle into a sneeze and choked.

"Jeremy!" said Aunt Amy severely.

"Oh, do look, Aunt Amy!" cried Mary, always Jeremy's faithful ally, "all your hairpins are dropping out!"

She devoted herself then to Jeremy and worried him in every possible way, and after two days of this he hated her with a deep and bitter hatred, very different from that earlier teasing of Miss Jones. That had sprung from a sudden delicious discovery of power, and had been directed against no one. This was a real personal hatred that children of a less solid and tenacious temperament than Jeremy would have been incapable of feeling.

He did not laugh at her, he did not tease her, he no longer put out his tongue at her. He was older than that now—he was simply reserved and silent, watching her with his large eyes, his square body set, and resolved as though he knew that his moment would come.

Her experience with him was baffling. She punished him, petted him, she ignored him, she stormed at him; it seemed that she would do anything could she only win from him an acknowledgment of her power, her capability. But she could not. He only said: "Yes, Aunt Amy." "No, Aunt Amy."

She burst out: "You're a sullen, wicked little boy, Jeremy. Do you know what happens to little boys who sulk?"

"No, Aunt Amy."

"They grow into cross, bad-tempered men whom nobody likes and nobody trusts. Do you want to be like that when you're a man?"

"I don't care."

"You know what happened to 'Don't Care.' I shall have to punish you if you're rude to me."

"What have I done that's rude?"

"You mustn't speak to me like that. Is that the way you speak to your mother?"

"No, Aunt Amy."

"Well, then, if you don't speak to your mother like that, you mustn't speak to me like that, either."

"No, Aunt Amy."

"Well, then . . ."

This hatred was quite new to him. He had once, years ago, hated a black-faced doll that had been given to him. He had not known why he hated it, but there it had been. He had thrown it out of the window, and the gardener had found it and brought it into the house again, battered and bruised, but still alive, with its horrid red smile, and this had terrified him. . . . He had begun to burn it, and the nurse had caught him and slapped him. He had begun to cut it with scissors, and when the sawdust flowed he was more terrified than ever. But that doll was quite different from Aunt Amy. He was not terrified of her at all. He hated her. Hated the fringe of her black hair, the heavy eyelashes, the thin down on her upper lip, the way that the gold cross fell up and down on her breast, her thin, blue-veined hands, her black shoes. She was his first enemy, and he waited, as an ambush hides and watches, for his opportunity. . . .

II

One of our nicest old maids, Miss Maddison, gave every year what she called her "early summer party." This was different from all our other parties, because it occurred neither in the summer nor in the winter, but always during those wonderful days when the spring first began to fade into the high bright colours, the dry warmth, the deep green shadows of the heat of the year. It was early in May that Miss Maddison had her party, and we played games on her little sloping green lawn, and peered over her pink-brick wall down on to the brown roofs of the houses below the Close, and had a tremendous tea of every kind of cake and every kind of jam in her wainscoted dining-room that looked out through its tall open windows on to the garden.

Those old houses that run in a half-moon round the Close, and face the green sward and the great western door of the Cathedral, are the very heart of Polchester. Walking down the cobbled street, one may still to-day look through the open door, down the dusky line of the little hall, out into the swimming colour of the garden beyond. In these little gardens, what did not grow? Hollyhocks, pinks, tulips, nasturtiums, pansies, lilies of the valley, roses, honeysuckle, sweet-williams, stocks—I remember them all at their different seasons in that muddled, absurd profusion. I can smell them now, can see them in their fluttering colours, the great grey wall of the Cathedral, with its high carved door and watching saints behind me, the sun beating on to the cobbles, the muffled beat of the summer day, the sleepy noises of the town, the pigeons cutting the thin, papery blue into arcs and curves and circles, the little lattice-windowed houses, with crooked chimneys and shining doors, smiling down upon me. I can smell, too, that especial smell that belonged to those summer hours, a smell of dried blotting-paper, of corn and poppies from the fields, of cobble-stones and new-baked bread and lemonade; and behind the warmth and colour the cool note of the Cathedral bell echoed through the town, down the High Street, over the meads, across the river, out into the heart of the dark woods and the long spaces of the summer fields. I can see myself, too, toiling up the High Street, my cap on the back of my head, little beads of perspiration on my forehead, and my eyes always gazing into the air, so that I stumbled over the cobbles and knocked against doorsteps. All these things had to do with Miss Maddison's party, and it was always her party

that marked the beginning of them for us; she waited for
the fine weather, and so soon as it came the invitations
were sent out, the flower-beds were trimmed, the little green
wooden seats under the mulberry tree were cleaned, and
Poupée, the black poodle, was clipped.

It happened this year that Miss Maddison gave her
party during the very week that Mr. and Mrs. Cole went
to Drymouth. She sent out her invitations only three days
before the great event, because the summer had come with
so fine a rush. "Master Jeremy and the Misses Cole. . . .
Would they give Miss Maddison the pleasure . . . ?" Yes,
of course they would. Aunt Amy would take them.

On the morning of the great day Jeremy poured the
contents of his watering-can upon Aunt Amy's head. It
was a most unfortunate accident, arranged obviously by
a malignant fate. Jeremy had been presented with a pot
of pinks, and these, every morning, he most faithfully
watered. He had a bright-red watering-can, bought with
his own money, and, because it held more water than the
pinks needed, he was in the daily habit of emptying the
remnant in a glittering shower out of the pantry window
on to the bed nearest the garden wall. Upon this morning
someone called him; he turned his head; the water still
flowed, and Aunt Amy, hatless and defenceless, received
it as it tumbled with that sudden rush which always seizes
a watering-can at its last gasp. Jeremy was banished into
his bedroom, where he employed the sunny morning in
drawing pictures of Aunt Amy as a witch upon the wallpaper. For doing this he was caned by Aunt Amy herself
with a ruler, and at the end of the operation he laughed
and said she hadn't hurt him at all. In return for this
impertinence he was robbed, at luncheon, of his pudding—

which was, of course, on that very day, marmalade pudding —and then, Mary being discovered putting some of hers into a piece of paper, to be delivered to him in due course, they were both stood in different corners of the room "until you say you're sorry."

When the jingle arrived at three o'clock they had still not made this acknowledgment, and Jeremy said he never would, "not if he lived till he was ninety-nine."

At quarter past three Jeremy might have been seen sitting up very straight in the jingle, his face crimson from washing and temper. He was wearing his new sailor suit, which tickled him and was hot and sticky; he sat there devoting the whole of his energies to the business of hating Aunt Amy.

As I have said, he had never hated anyone before, and he was surprised at the glow of virtuous triumph that this new emotion spread over his body. He positively loved to hate Aunt Amy, and as Parkes, the pony, slowly toiled up the hill to the Cathedral, he sat stiff and proud with an almost humorous anger. Then, as they turned over the hot shining cobbles into the Close and saw the green trees swimming in the sun, he turned his mind to the party. What games would they play? Who would be there? What would there be for tea? He felt creeping over him the stiff shyness that always comes when one is approaching a party, and he wished that the first handshaking and the first plunge into the stares of the critical guests might be over. But he did not really care. His hatred of Aunt Amy braced him up; when one was capable of so fine and manly an emotion as this hatred, one need not bother about fellow-guests. Then the jingle stopped outside a house immediately opposite the great west-end door of the

Cathedral; in the little hall Miss Maddison was standing, and from the glittering garden behind her the sun struck through the house into the shadowed street.

Jeremy's public manners were, when he pleased, quite beautiful—"the true, old-fashioned courtesy," gushing friends of the Cole family used to say. He was preparing to be very polite now, when suddenly the voice of the Dean's Ernest ordering people about in the garden struck upon his ear. He had not seen the Dean's Ernest for nearly three months, for the very good reason that that gentleman had been experiencing his first term at his private school. Last year young Ernest and Jeremy had been, on the whole, friendly, although Ernest, who was nine, and strong for his age, had always patronised. And now? Jeremy longed to inform his friend that he also shortly would proceed to school, that in another six months' time there would be practically no difference between them. Nevertheless, at the present moment there was a difference. . . . Ernest had a whole term to his credit.

New arrivals gently insinuated the Cole family into the garden. Helen, proud and cold, Mary, blinking and nervous, stood pressed close together whilst other little girls stared and giggled, moved forward and then backward again, until suddenly Canon Lasker's Emily, who was fifteen and had such long legs that she was known as "the Giraffe," came up and said: "Isn't it hot! Do you play croquet? Please—do! I'll have—the—blue ball. . . ." And the Coles were initiated.

Meanwhile, Aunt Amy had said: "Now, Jeremy, dear, run about and make friends." Which so deeply infuriated him that he choked. Oh! supposing the Dean's Ernest had heard her! . . .

And he had! A mocking voice behind him said: "Now, Jeremy, dear——"

Jeremy turned round and beheld the Dean's Ernest mockingly waiting his retort. And he could not retort. No words would come, and he could only stand there, his cheeks flushed, aware that Ernest had grown and grown during those three months, that he wore a straw hat with a black-and-red ribbon upon it, that round his long ugly neck was a stiff white collar, and across his waistcoat a thick silver watch-chain.

"Hallo!" said Jeremy.

"Hallo!" said the new Ernest scornfully.

A long pause.

Then Ernest, turning on his heel, said to someone behind him: "Let's get away from all these girls!"

The tears burnt in Jeremy's eyes, hot and salt. He clenched his fists and gazed upon a garden that swam in a mist of tears and sunlight. He felt a sudden strange impulse of family affection. He would like to have gathered behind him his father and mother, Mary, Helen, Hamlet, Uncle Samuel—yes, and even Aunt Amy, and to have advanced not only upon Ernest, but upon the whole Dean's family. It would have given him great pleasure to have set his teeth into the fat legs of the Dean himself; he would gladly have torn the hat from the head of Mrs. Dean. . . . Upon Ernest there was no torture he would not employ.

He would get even; he resolved that before he left that house he would have his revenge.

Kind Miss Maddison, tripping along and seeing him as a pathetic little boy in a sailor suit without guile or malice, swept him into an "I spy" party composed for the most part of small girls who fell down and cried and said they would go home.

Jeremy, hiding behind a tree, watched the thin back of Ernest as it lifted itself autocratically above two small boys who looked up to him with saucer-eyes. Ernest was obviously talking about his school. Jeremy, lost in the contemplation of his vengeance, forgot his game, and was taken prisoner with the greatest of ease. He did not care. The afternoon was spoilt for him. He was not even hungry. Why could he not go to school to-morrow, and then challenge Ernest to combat? But he might challenge Ernest without going to school. . . . He had never fought a real fight, but the sight of his enemy's thin, peaky body was encouraging.

"Now, Jeremy, dear," said Miss Maddison, "it's your turn to hide. . . ."

Soon they all went in to tea. Everyone was thoroughly at home by this time, and screamed and shouted quite in the most natural manner in the world. The long table stretched down the whole room, almost from wall to wall; the sunlight played in pools and splashes upon the carpet and the flowers and the pictures. There was every sort of thing to eat—thin bread-and-butter rolled up into little curly sandwiches, little cakes and big cakes, seed cakes and sugar cakes, and, of course, saffron buns, jam in little shining dishes, and hot buttered toast so buttery that it dripped on to your fingers.

Jeremy sat next to Mary, and behind him hovered Aunt Amy. Only half an hour ago how this would have angered him! To have her interfering with him, saying: "Not two at a time, Jeremy," or "Pass the little girl the sugar, Jeremy—remember your manners," or "Not so big a piece,

Jeremy." But now—he did not know. . . . She was one
of the family, and he felt as though the Dean's Ernest had
scorned her as well as himself. Also Mary. He felt kind
to Mary, and when she whispered "Are you enjoying it,
Jeremy?" he answered "Yes; are you?" Not because he
was really enjoying it, but because he knew that she wanted
him to say that.

He could see Ernest from where he sat, and he knew
that Ernest was laughing at him. He remembered that
he had given Ernest three splendid marbles, just before
his departure to school, as a keepsake. How he wished
that he had kept them! He would never give Ernest
anything again except blows. Mary might be tiresome
sometimes, but she *was* his sister, and he greatly preferred
her as a girl to Ernest's sisters. He could see them now,
greedy, ugly things. . . .

"Now, Jeremy, wipe your mouth," said Aunt Amy.
He obeyed at once.

III

Tea over, they all trooped out into the garden again.
The evening light now painted upon the little green lawn
strange trembling shadows of purple and grey; the old
red garden wall seemed to have crept forwards, as though
it would protect the house and the garden from the night;
and a sky of the faintest blue seemed, with gentle approval,
to bless the quiet town fading into dusk beneath it. Over
the centre of the lawn the sun was still shining, and there
it was warm and light. But from every side the shadows
stealthily crept forward. A group of children played
against the golden colour, their white dresses patterns that
formed figures and broke and formed again. The Cathedral

bell was ringing for evensong, and its notes stole about the garden, and in and out amongst the children, as though some guardian spirit watching over their safety counted their numbers.

Jeremy, feeling rather neglected and miserable, stood in the shadow near the oak on the farther side of the lawn. He did not want to play with those little girls, and yet he was hurt because he had not been asked. The party had been a most miserable failure, and a year ago it would have been such a success. He did not know that he was standing now, in the middle of his eighth year, at the parting of the ways; that only yesterday he had been a baby, and that he would never be a baby again. He did not feel his independence—he felt only inclined to tears and a longing, that he would never, never confess, even to himself, that someone should come and comfort him! Nevertheless, even at this very moment, although he did not know it, he, a free, independent man, was facing the world for the first time on his own legs. His mother might have realised it had she been there—but she was not. Mary, however, was there, and in the very middle of her game, searching for him, as she was always doing, she found him desolate under the shadow of the oak. She slipped away, and, coming up to him with the shyness and fear that she always had when she approached him, because she loved him so much and he could so easily hurt her, said:

"Aren't you coming to play, Jeremy?"

"I don't care," he answered gruffly.

"It isn't any fun without you." She paused, and added: "Would you mind if I stayed here too?"

"I'd rather you played," he said; and yet he was comforted by her, determined, as he was, that she should never know it!

"I'd rather stay," she said, and then gazed, with that melancholy stare through her large spectacles that always irritated Jeremy, out across the garden.

"I'm all right," he said again; "only my stocking tickles, and I can't get at it—it's the back of my leg. I say, Mary, don't you hate the Dean's Ernest?"

"Yes, I do," she answered fervently, although she had not thought about him at all—enough for her that Jeremy should hate him! Then she gasped: "Here he comes——"

He was walking towards them with a swagger of his long yellow neck and his thin leggy body that Jeremy found especially offensive. Jeremy "bristled," and Mary was conscious of that bristling.

"Hallo!" said Ernest.

"Hallo!" said Jeremy.

"What rot these silly games are!" said Ernest. "Why can't they have something decent, like cricket?"

Jeremy had never played cricket, so he said nothing. "At our school," said Ernest, "we're very good at cricket. We win all our matches always——"

"I don't care about your school," said Jeremy, breathing through his nose.

The Dean's Ernest was obviously surprised by this; he had not expected it. His pale neck began to flush.

"Look here, young Cole," he said, "none of your cheek."

This was a new dialect to Jeremy, who had no friends who went to school. All he said, however, breathing more fiercely than before, was: "I don't care——"

"Oh, don't you?" said Ernest. "Now, look here——" Then he paused, apparently uncertain, for a moment, of his courage. The sight of Mary's timorous anxiety, however, reassured him, and he continued: "It's all right for you, this sort of thing. You ought to be in the nursery with your old podge-faced nurse. Kids like you oughtn't to be allowed out of their prams."

"I don't care," said Jeremy again, seeing in front of him the whole family of the Reverend Dean. "Your school isn't much anyway, I expect, and I'm going to school in September, and I'll wear just the same things as you do and——"

He wanted to comment upon the plain features of Ernest's sisters, but his gentlemanly courtesy restrained him. He paused for breath, and Ernest seized his advantage.

"You have to have an old aunt to look after you anyway—an ugly old aunt. I wouldn't have an old aunt always hanging over me—'Now, Jeremy dear—' 'Blow your nose, Jeremy dear—' 'Wipe your feet, Jeremy dear.' Look at the things she wears and the way she walks. If I did have to have an aunt always I'd have a decent one, not an old clothes bag."

What happened to Jeremy at the moment? Did he recollect that only a few hours before he had been hating Aunt Amy with a fine frenzy of hatred? For nearly a week he had been chafing under her restraint, combating her commands, defying her orders. He had been seeing her as everything that the Dean's Ernest had but now been calling her. Now he only saw her as someone to be defended, someone who was his, someone even who depended on him for support. He would have challenged a whole world of Deans in her defence.

He said something, but no one could hear his words; then he sprang upon the startled Ernest.

It was not a very distinguished combat; it was Jeremy's first battle, and he knew at that time nothing of the science of fighting. The Dean's Ernest, in spite of his term at school, also knew nothing—and the Dean's Ernest was a coward. . . .

It lasted but a short while, for Mary, after the first pause of horrified amazement (aware only that Ernest was twice as big as her Jeremy), ran to appeal to authority. Jeremy himself was aware neither of time nor prudence. He realised immediately that Ernest was a coward, and this realisation filled him with joy and happiness. He had seized Ernest by his long yellow neck, and, with his other hand, he struck at eyes and cheeks and nose. He did not secure much purchase for his blows because their bodies were very close against one another, but he felt the soft flesh yield and suddenly something wet against his hand which must, he knew, be blood. And all the time he was thinking to himself: "I'll teach him to say things about Aunt Amy! Aunt Amy's mine! I'll teach him! He shan't touch Aunt Amy! He shan't touch Aunt Amy! . . ."

Ernest meanwhile kicked and kicked hard; he also tried to bite Jeremy's hand and also to pull his hair. But his own terror handicapped him; every inch of his body was alarmed, and that alarm prevented the freedom of his limbs. Then when he felt the blood from his nose trickle on to his cheek his resistance was at an end; panic flooded over him like water. He broke away and flung himself howling on to the ground, kicking his legs and screaming:

"It isn't fair! He's bitten me! Take him away! Take him away!"

Jeremy himself was no beautiful sight. His hair was wild, his white navy collar crumpled and soiled, the buttons of his tunic torn, his stocking down, and his legs already displaying purple bruises. But he did not care; he was well now; he was no longer unhappy.

He had beaten Ernest and he was a man; he had risen victorious from his first fight, and Authority might storm as it pleased. Authority soon arrived, and there were, of course, many cries and exclamations. Ernest was led away still howling; Jeremy, stubborn, obstinate, and silent, was also led away. . . . A disgraceful incident.

Aunt Amy, of course, was disgusted. Couldn't leave the boy alone one minute but he must misbehave himself, upset the party, be the little ruffian that he always was. She had always said that his mother spoiled him, and here were the fruits of that foolishness. How could she ever say enough to Miss Maddison? Her delightful party completely ruined! . . . Shocking! . . . Shocking! . . . Too terrible! . . . And Ernest, such a quiet, well-behaved little boy as a rule. It must have been Jeremy who . . .

While they were waiting in the decent dusk of Miss Maddison's sitting-room for a cleaned and chastened Jeremy, Mary touched her aunt's arm and whispered in her nervous voice:

"Aunt Amy—Jeremy hit Ernest because he said rude things about you."

"About me! Nonsense, child."

"No, but it was, really. Ernest said horrid things about you, and then Jeremy hit him."

"About me? What things?"

"That you were ugly," eagerly continued Mary—never a tactful child, and intent now only upon Jeremy's reputation—"and wore ugly clothes and horrid things. He did really. I heard it all."

Aunt Amy was deeply moved. Her conceit, her abnormal all-embracing conceit was wounded—yes, even by so insignificant a creature as the Dean's Ernest, but she was also unexpectedly touched. She would have greatly preferred not to be touched, but there it was, she could not help herself. She did not know that, in all her life before, anyone had ever fought for her, and that now of all champions in the world fate should have chosen Jeremy, who was, she had supposed, her enemy—never her defender!

And that horrid child of the Dean—she had always disliked him, with his long yellow neck and watery eyes! How dared he say such things about her! He had always been rude to her. She remembered once——

Jeremy arrived, washed, brushed, and obstinate. He would, of course, be scolded to within an inch of his life, and he did not care. He had seen the Dean's Ernest howling and kicking on the ground; he had soiled his straw hat for him, dirtied his stiff white collar for him, and made his nose bleed. He glared at his aunt (one eye was rapidly disappearing beneath a blue bruise), and he was proud, triumphant, and very tired.

Farewells were made—again many apologies—"Nothing, I assure you, nothing. Boys will be boys, I know," from Miss Maddison.

Then they were seated in the jingle, Jeremy next to Aunt Amy, awaiting his scolding. It did not come. Aunt Amy tried; she knew what she should say. She should be very angry, disgusted, ashamed. She could not be any of these things. That horrid boy had insulted her. She was touched and proud as she had never been touched and proud in her life before.

Jeremy waited, and then as nothing came his weariness grew upon him. As the old fat pony jogged along, as the evening colours of street and sky danced before him, sleep came nearer and nearer.

He nodded, recovered, nodded and nodded again. His body pressed closer to Aunt Amy's, leaned against her. His head rested upon her shoulder.

After a moment's pause she put her arm round him— so, holding him, she stared, defiantly and crossly, upon the world.

CHAPTER VII

RELIGION

I

ALWAYS in after years Jeremy remembered that party of Miss Maddison's, not because it had been there that he had won his first fight, but for the deeper reason that from that day his life received a new colour, woven into the texture of it; even now when he thinks of those hours that followed Miss Maddison's party he catches his breath and glances around him to see whether everything is safe. The children, on arriving home that evening, found that their father and mother had already returned from Drymouth. Jeremy, sleepy though he was, rushed to his mother, held her hand, explained his black eye, and then suddenly, in a way that he had, fell asleep, there as he was, and had to be carried up to bed.

When he awoke next morning his first thought was of his mother. He did not know why; she was so definitely part of the background of his daily life that he felt too sure of her continual and abiding presence to need deliberate thought of her. But this morning he wanted to get up quickly and find her. Perhaps her absence had made him feel more insecure, but there had also been something that night, something in her face, something in the touch of her hand.

And the other thing that he realised was that summer

had truly come. He knew at once that hot smell that pressed even through the closed window-panes of his room; the bars and squares of light on the floor when he jumped out of bed and stood upon them seemed to burn the soles of his feet, and the rays of light on the ceiling quivered as only summer sunlight can quiver. The two windows of his bedroom looked back behind Polchester over fields and hedges to a dim purple line of wood. A tiny stream ran through the first two fields, and this little river was shining now with a white hot light that had yet the breeze of the morning ruffling it. He ran to his window and opened it. Beyond the wall that bordered their house was a little brown path, and down this path, even as he watched, a company of cows were slowly wandering along. Already they were flapping their ears lazily in anticipation of the flies, and the boy who was driving them was whistling as one only whistles on a summer morning. He could see the buttercups, too, in the nearest field; they seemed to have sprung to life in the space of a night. Someone was pulling the rope of a well somewhere and someone else was pouring water out upon some stone court. Even as he watched, a bee came blundering up to his window, hesitated for a moment, and then went whirring off again, and through all the sun and glitter and the sparkle of the little river there was a scent of pinks, and mignonette, and even, although it could not really be so, of the gorse. The sky was a pale white blue, so pale that it was scarcely any colour at all and a few puffs of clouds, dead white like the purest smoke, hovered in dancing procession, above the purple wood. The sun burnt upon his bare feet and his head and his hands.

This coming of summer meant so much more to him

than merely the immediate joy of it—it meant Rafiel and
Cow Farm and the Cove and green pools with crabs in
them, and shrimping and paddling and riding home in the
evening on haycarts, and drinking milk out of tin cans,
and cows and small pigs, and peeling sticks and apples,
and collecting shells, and fishermen's nets, and sandwiches,
and saffron buns mixed with sand, and hot ginger beer,
and one's ears peeling with the sun, and church on Sunday
with the Rafiel sheep cropping the grass just outside the
church door, and Dick Marriott, the fisherman, and slipping along over the green water, trailing one's fingers in
the water, in his boat, and fishy smells by the sea-wall,
and red masses of dog-fish on the pier, and the still cool
feel of the farmhouse sheets just after getting into bed—
all these things and a thousand more the coming of summer meant to Jeremy.

But this morning he did not feel his customary joy.
Closing his window and dressing slowly, he wondered
what was the matter. What could it be? It was not his
eye—certainly it was a funny colour this morning and it
hurt when you touched it, but he was proud of that. No,
it was not his eye. And it was not the dog, who came
into his room, after scratching on the door, and made his
usual morning pretence of having come for any other
purpose than to see his friend and master, first looking
under the bed, then going up to the window pretending
to gaze out of it (which he could not do), barking, then
rolling on a square of sunlit carpet, and, after that, lying
on his back, his legs out stiff, his ridiculous "Imperial"
pointed and ironical, then suddenly turning, with a twist
on his legs, rushing at last up to Jeremy, barking at him,
laughing at him, licking him, and even biting his stockings

—last of all seizing a bedroom slipper and rushing wildly into the schoolroom with it.

No, there was nothing the matter with Hamlet. Nor was there anything the matter with Miss Jones, free, happily, from her customary neuralgia, and delighted with the new number of the *Church Times*. Nor was it the breakfast, which to-day included bacon and strawberry jam. Nor, finally, was it Mary or Helen, who, pleased with the summer weather (and Mary additionally pleased with the virtues of Lance as minutely recorded in the second volume of "The Pillars of the House"), were both in the most amiable of tempers. No, it must be something inside Jeremy himself.

He waited until the end of breakfast to ask his question:

"Can I go and see Mother, Miss Jones?"

Mary and Helen looked across at him inquisitively.

"What do you want to see your mother for now, Jeremy? You always see her at twelve o'clock." Miss Jones pushed her spectacles lower upon her nose and continued her reading.

"I want to."

"Well, you can't now."

"Why not?"

"Because I say not—that's enough."

But Jeremy was gentle to-day. He got off his chair, went round to Miss Jones's chair, and, looking up at her out of his bruised eye, said in the most touching voice:

"But, please, Miss Jones, I want to. I really do."

Then she said what he had known all the time was coming:

"I'm afraid you won't see your mother to-day, dear. She's not well. She's in bed."

"Why? Is she ill?"

"She's tired after her journey yesterday, I expect."

He said no more.

He tried during the whole of that day not to think of his mother, and he found that, for the first time in his life, he could do nothing else but think of her. During the morning he sat very silently over his lessons, did all that he was told, did not once kick Mary under the table, nor ask Miss Jones to sharpen his pencil, nor make faces at Hamlet. Once or twice, in a way that he had, he leaned his head on his hand as though he were an ancient professor with a whole library of great works behind him, and when Miss Jones asked him whether he had a headache he said: "No, thank you," instead of seizing on the wonderful opportunity of release that such a question offered him. When they all went for a walk in the afternoon, he sprang for a moment into something of his natural vivacity. They came upon a thin, ill-shaven tramp dressed as a sailor, with a patch over one eye, producing terrible discordance from a fiddle. This individual held in one hand a black tin cup, and at his side crouched a mongrel terrier, whose beaten and dishevelled appearance created at once hopes in the breast of the flamboyant Hamlet. This couple were posted just outside Mr. Poole's second-hand bookshop, close to the "2d." box, and for a moment Jeremy was enthralled. He wanted to give the hero his week's penny, and upon finding that his week's penny was not, owing to sweet purchases on the previous day, he began elaborate bargainings with Miss Jones as to the forestalling of future pennies. Meanwhile, Hamlet leapt, with every sign of joyful expectation, upon the pauper dog; the blind sailor began to hit wildly about with his stick, Mr. Poole's

"2d." box was upset, and the sailor's black patch fell off, revealing him as the possessor of two beautiful eyes, just like any other gentleman, and a fine, vigorous stock of the best Glebeshire profanities. Mr. Poole, an irascible old man, himself came out, a policeman approached, two old ladies from the Close, well known to Jeremy, were shocked by the tramp, and the Cathedral bell, as though it had just awoken up to its real responsibilities, suddenly began to ring.

All this was, of course, delightful to Jeremy, and offered so many possible veins of interest that he could have stayed there for hours. He wanted very badly to ask the sailor why he covered up a perfectly wholesome eye with a black patch, and he would have liked to see what Hamlet could do in the direction of eating up the scattered remnants of Mr. Poole's "2d." box; but he was dragged away by the agitated hand of Miss Jones, having to console himself finally with a wink from the august policeman, who, known throughout Polchester as Tom Noddy, was a kindly soul and liked gentlemanly little boys, but persecuted the street sort.

For a moment this exciting adventure carried him away, and he even listened for a minute or two to Mary, who, seizing her opportunity, began hurriedly: "Once upon a time there lived a sailor, very thin, and he never washed, and he had a dog and a violin——" But soon he remembered, and sighed and said: "Oh, bother, Mary!" and then walked on by himself. And still, all through that hot afternoon, when even the Rope Walk did not offer any shade, and when the Pol was of so clear a colour that you could see trout and emerald stones and golden sand as under glass, and when Hamlet was compelled to run ahead and find a piece of shade and lie there stretched, panting, with his tongue out, until they came up to him—even all these signs of a true and marvellous summer did not relieve Jeremy of his burden. Something horrible was going to happen. He knew it with such certainty that he wondered how Mary and Helen could be so gaily light-hearted, and despised them for their carelessness. This was connected in some way with the hot weather; he felt as though, were a cold breeze suddenly to come, and rain to fall, he would be happy again. There had been once a boy, older than he, called Jimmy Bain, a fat, plump boy, who had lived next door to the Coles. Whenever he had the opportunity he bullied Jeremy, pinching his arms, putting pins into his legs, and shouting suddenly into his ears. Jeremy, who had feared Johnny Bain, had always "felt" the stout youth's arrival before he appeared. The sky had seemed to darken, the air to thicken, the birds to gather in the "rooky" wood.

He had trembled and shaken, his teeth had chattered and his throat grown dry for no reason at all. As he had once felt about Johnny Bain so now he felt about life in general. Something horrible was going to happen. . . . Something to do with Mother. . . . As he came up the road to their house his heart beat so that he could not hear his own steps.

II

They entered the house, and at once even Mary, pre-occupied as she was with her story about the sailor, noticed that something was wrong.

"Rose! Rose!" she called out loudly.

"Hush!" said Miss Jones. "You must be quiet, dear."

"Why?" said Mary. "I want Rose to——"

"Your mother isn't at all well, dear. I——"

And she was interrupted by Rose, who, coming suddenly downstairs, with a face very different from her usual cheerful one, said something to Miss Jones in a low voice.

Miss Jones gave a little cry: "So soon? . . . A girl. . . ." And then added: "How is she?"

Then Rose said something more, which the children could not catch, and vanished.

"Very quietly, children," said Miss Jones, in a voice that trembled; "and you mustn't leave the schoolroom till I tell you. Your mother——" She broke off as though she were afraid of showing emotion.

"What is it?" said Jeremy in a voice that seemed new to them all—older, more resolute, strangely challenging for so small a boy.

"Your mother's very ill, Jeremy, dear. You must be a very good boy, and help your sisters."

"Mightn't I go for just a minute?"

"No, certainly not."

They all went upstairs. Then, in the schoolroom, Miss Jones said an amazing thing. She said:

"I must tell you all, children, that you've got a new little sister."

"A new sister!" screamed Mary.

Helen said: "Oh, Miss Jones!"

Jeremy said: "What did she come for just now, when Mother is ill?"

"God wanted her to come, dear," said Miss Jones. "You must all be very kind to her, and do all you can——"

She was interrupted by a torrent of questions from the two girls. What was she like? What was her name?

Could she walk? Where did she come from? Did Father and Mother find her in Drymouth? And so on. Jeremy was silent. At last he said: "We don't want any more girls here."

"Better than having another boy," said Helen.

But he would not take up the challenge. He sat on his favourite seat on the window-ledge, dragged up a reluctant Hamlet to sit with him, and gazed out down into the garden that was misty now in the evening golden light, the trees and the soil black beneath the gold, the rooks slowly swinging across the sky above the farther side of the road. Hamlet wriggled. He always detested that he should be cuddled, and he would press first with one leg, then with another, against Jeremy's coat; then he would lie dead for a moment, suddenly springing, with his head up, in the hope that the surprise would free him; then he would turn into a snake, twisting his body under Jeremy's arm, and dropping with a flop on to the floor. All these manœuvres to-day availed him nothing; Jeremy held his neck in a vice, and dug his fingers well into the skin. Hamlet whined, then lay still, and, in the midst of indignant reflections against the imbecile tyrannies of man, fell, to his own surprise, asleep.

Jeremy sat there whilst the dusk fell and all the beautiful lights were drawn from the sky and the rooks went to bed. Rose came to draw the curtains, and then he left his window-seat, dragged out his toy village and pretended to play with it. He looked at his sisters. They seemed quite tranquil. Helen was sewing, and Mary deep in "The Pillars of the House." The clock ticked. Hamlet, lost in sleep, snored and sputtered; the whole world pursued its ordinary way. Only in himself something was changed; he was unhappy, and he could not account for his unhappiness. It should have been because his mother was ill, and yet she had been ill before, and he had been only disturbed for a moment. After all, grown-up people always got well. There had been Aunt Amy, who had had measles, and the wife of the Dean, who had had something, and even the Bishop once. . . . But now he was frightened. There was some perception, coming to him now for the first time in his life, that this world was not absolutely stable—that people left it, people came into it, that there was change and danger and something stronger. . . . Gradually this perception was approaching him as though it had been some dark figure who had entered the house, and now, with muffled step and veiled face, was slowly climbing the stairs towards him. He only knew that his mother could not go; she could not go. She was part of his life, and she would always be so. Why, now, when he thought of it, he could do nothing without his mother; every day he must tell her what he had done and what he was going to do, must show her what he had acquired and must explain to her what he had lost, must go to her when he was hurt and when he was frightened and when he was glad. . . . And of all these things he had never even thought until now.

As he sat there the house seemed to grow ever quieter and quieter about him. He felt as though he would have liked to have gone to the schoolroom door and listened. It was terrible imagining the house behind the door— quite silent—so that the clocks had stopped, and no one walked upon the stairs and no one laughed down in the pantry. He wished that they would make more noise in the schoolroom. He upset the church and the orchard and Mrs. Noah.

But the silence after the noise was worse than ever.

Soon Miss Jones took the two girls away to her room to fit on some clothes, an operation which Helen adored and Mary hated. Jeremy was left alone, and he was, at once, terribly frightened. He knew that it was of no use to be frightened, and he tried to go on with his game, putting the church with the apple trees around it and the Noah family all sleeping under the trees, but at every moment something compelled him to raise his head and see that no one was there, and he felt so small and so lonely that he would like to have hidden under something.

Then when he thought of his mother all alone and the house so quiet around her and no one able to go to her he felt so miserable that he turned round from his village and stared desolately into the fireplace. The thought of his new sister came to him, but was dismissed impatiently. He did not want a new sister—Mary and Helen were trouble enough as it was—and he felt, with an old weary air, that it was time, indeed, that he was off to school. Nothing was the same. Always new people. Never any peace.

He was startled by the sound of the opening door, and, turning, saw his father. His father and he were never very easy together. Mr. Cole had very little time for the individual, being engaged in saving souls in the mass, and his cheery, good-tempered Christianity had a strange, startling fashion of proving unavailing before some single human case.

He did not understand children except when they were placed in masses before him. His own children, having been named, on their arrival, "Gifts from God," had kept much of that incorporeal atmosphere throughout their growing years.

But to-night he was a different man. As he looked at his small son across the schoolroom floor there was terror in his eyes. Nothing could have been easier or more simple than his lifelong assumption that, because God was in His heaven all was right with the world. He had given thanks every evening for the blessings that he had received and every morning for the blessings that he was going to receive, and he had had no reason to complain. He had the wife, the children, the work that he deserved, and his life had been so hemmed in with security that he had had no difficulty in assuring his congregation on every possible occasion that God was good and far-seeing, and that "not one sparrow . . ."

And now he was threatened—threatened most desperately. Mrs. Cole was so ill that it was doubtful whether she would live through the night. He was completely helpless. He had turned from one side to another, simply demanding an assurance from someone or something that she could not be taken from him. No one could give him that assurance. Life without her would be impossible; he would not know what to do about the simplest matter. Life without her . . . oh! but it was incredible!

Like a blind man he had groped his way up to the schoolroom. He did not want to see the children, nor Miss Jones, but he must be moving, must be doing something that would break in upon that terrible ominous pause that the whole world seemed to him, at this moment, to be making.

Then he saw Jeremy. He said:

"Oh! Where's Miss Jones?"

"She's in the next room," said Jeremy, looking at his father.

"Oh!" He began to walk up and down the schoolroom. Jeremy left his toy village and stood up.

"Is Mother better, Father?"

He stopped in his walk and looked at the boy as though he were trying to recollect who he was.

"No. . . . No—that is—No, my boy, I'm afraid not."

"Is she very bad, Father—like the Dean's wife when she had fever?"

His father didn't answer. He walked to the end of the room, then turned suddenly as though he had seen something there that terrified him, and hurried from the room.

Jeremy, suddenly left alone, had a desperate impulse to scream that someone must come, that he was frightened, that something horrible was in the house. He stood up, staring at the closed door, his face white, his eyes large and full of fear. Then he flung himself down by Hamlet and, taking him by the neck, whispered:

"I'm frightened! I'm frightened! Bark or something! . . . There's someone here!"

III

Next morning Mrs. Cole was still alive. There had been no change during the night; to-day, the doctor said, would be the critical day. To-day was Sunday, and Mr. Cole took his morning service at his church as usual. He had been up all night; he looked haggard and pale, still wearing that expression as of a man lost in a world that he had always trusted. But he would not fail in his duty. "When

two or three are gathered together in my name. . . ."
Perhaps God would hear him.

It was a day of wonderful heat for May. No one had
ever remembered so hot a day at so early a time of year.
The windows of the church were open, but no breeze blew
through the aisles. The relentless blazing blue of the sky
penetrated into the cool shadows of the church, and it
was as though the congregation sat there under shimmering glass. The waves of light shifted, rose and fell above
the bonnets and hats and bare heads, and all the little
choir boys fell asleep during the sermon.

The Cole family did not fall asleep. They sat with
pale faces and stiff backs staring at their father and thinking about their mother. Mary and Helen were frightened;
the house was so strange, everyone spoke in whispers, and,
on the way into church, many ladies had asked them how
their mother was.

They felt important as well as sad. But Jeremy did
not feel important. He had not heard the ladies and their
questions—he would not have cared if he had. People
had always called him "a queer little boy," simply because
he was independent and thought more than he spoke.
Nevertheless, he had always in reality been normal enough
until now. To-day he was really "queer," was conscious
for the first time of the existence of a world whose adja-
cence to the real world was, in after days, to trouble him
so often and to complicate life for him so grievously.
The terror that had come down upon him when his father
had left him seemed to-day utterly to soak through into the
very heart of him. His mother was going to die unless
something or somebody saved her. What was dying? Going away, he had always been told, with a golden harp, to

sing hymns in a foreign country. But to-day the picture would not form so easily. There was silence and darkness and confusion about this Death. His mother was going, against her will, and no one could tell him whither she was going. If he could only stop her dying, force God to leave her alone, to leave her with them all as she had been before. . . .

He fixed his eyes upon his father, who climbed slowly into his pulpit and gave out the text of his sermon. To-day he would talk about the sacrifice of Isaac. "Abraham, as his hearers would remember . . ." and so on.

Jeremy listened, and gradually there grew before his eyes the figure of a strange and terrible God. This was no new figure. He had never thought directly about God, but for a very long time now he had had Him in the background of his life as Polchester Town Hall was in the background. But now he definitely and actively figured to himself this God, this God Who was taking his mother away and was intending apparently to put her into some dark place where she would know nobody. It must be some horrible place, because his father looked so frightened, which he would not look if his mother was simply going, with a golden harp, to sing hymns. Jeremy had always heard that this God was loving and kind and tender, but the figure whom his father was now drawing for the benefit of the congregation was none of these things.

Mr. Cole spoke of a God just and terrible, but a God Who apparently for the merest fancy put His faithful servant to terrible anguish and distress, and then for another fancy, as light as the first, spared him his sorrow. Mr. Cole emphasised the necessity for obedience, the need for a willing surrender of anything that may be dear to us, "because the love of God must be greater than anything that holds us here on earth." But Jeremy did not listen to these remarks; his mind was filled with this picture of a vast shadowy figure, seated in the sky, his white beard flowing beneath eyes that frowned from dark rocky eyebrows out upon people like Jeremy who, although doing their best, were nevertheless at the mercy of any whim that He might have. This terrible figure was the author of the hot day, author of the silent house and the shimmering darkened church, author of the decision to take his mother away from all that she loved and put her somewhere where she would be alone and cold and silent— "simply because He wishes. . . ."

"From this beautiful passage," concluded Mr. Cole, "we learn that God is just and merciful, but that He demands our obedience. We must be ready at any instant to give up what we love most and best. . . ."

Afterwards they all trooped out into the splendid sunshine.

IV

There was a horrible Sunday dinner when—the silence and the roast beef and Yorkshire pudding, and the dining-room quivering with heat, emphasised every minute of the solemn ticking clock—Mary suddenly burst into tears, choked over a glass of water, and was led from the room. Jeremy ate his beef and rice pudding in silence, except that once or twice in a low, hoarse voice whispered: "Pass the mustard, please," or "Pass the salt, please." Miss Jones, watching his white face and the tremble of his upper lip, longed to say something to comfort him, but wisely held her peace.

After dinner Jeremy collected Hamlet and went to the conservatory. This, like so many other English conservatories, was a desolate and desperate little place, where boxes of sand, dry corded-looking bulbs, and an unhappy plant or two languished, forgotten and forlorn. It had been inherited with the house many years ago, and, at first, the Coles had had the ambition to make it blaze with colour, to grow there the most marvellous grapes, the richest tomatoes, and even—although it was a little out of place in the house of a clergyman of the Church of England—the most sinister of orchids. Very quickly the little conservatory had been abandoned; the heating apparatus had failed, the plants had refused to grow, the tomatoes never appeared, the bulbs would not burst into colour.

For Jeremy the place had had always an indescribable fascination. When he was very young there had been absolute trust that things would grow; that every kind of wonder might spring before one's eyes at any moment of the day. Then, when no wonder came, there had been the thrill of the empty boxes of earth; the probing with one's fingers to see what the funny-looking bulbs would be, and watching the fronds of the pale vine. Afterwards, there was another fascination—the fascination of some strange and sinister atmosphere that he was much too young to define. The place, he knew, was different from the rest of the house. It projected, conventionally enough, from the drawing-room; but the heavy door with thick windows of red glass shut it off from the whole world. Its rather dirty and obscure windows looked over the same country that Jeremy's bedroom window commanded. It also caught all the sun, so that in the summer it was terribly hot. But Jeremy loved the heat. He was discovered

once by the scandalised Jampot quite naked dancing on
the wooden boards, his face and hands black with grime.
No one could ever understand "what he saw in the dirty
place," and at one time he had been forbidden to go there.
Then he had cried and stamped and shouted, so that he
had been allowed to return. Amongst the things that he
saw there were the reflections that the outside world made
upon the glass; it would be stained, sometimes, with a
strange, green reflection of the fields beyond the wall;
sometimes it would catch the blue of the sky, or the red
and gold of the setting sun; sometimes it would be grey
with waving shadows across its surface, as though one
were under water. Through the dirty windows the country, on fine days, shone like distant tapestry, and in the
glass that covered the farther side of the place strange
reflections were caught: of cows, horses, walls, and trees
—as though in a kind of magic mirror.

Another thing that Jeremy felt there, was that he was
in a glass cage swinging over the whole world. If one
shut one's eyes one could easily fancy that one was swinging out—swinging—swinging, and that, suddenly perhaps,
the cage would be detached from the house and go sailing,
like a magic carpet, to Arabia and Persia, and anywhere
you pleased to command.

To-day the glass burnt like fire, and the green fields
came floating up to be transfigured there like running
water. The house was utterly still; the red glass door
shut off the world. Jeremy sat, his arms tightly round
Hamlet's neck, on the dirty floor, a strange mixture of
misery, weariness, fright, and anger. There was already
in him a strain of impatience, so that he could not bear
simply to sit down and bewail something as, for instance,

both his sisters were doing at this moment. He must act. They could not be happy without their mother; he himself wanted her so badly that even now, there in the flaming conservatory, if he had allowed himself to do such a thing, he would have sat and cried and cried and cried. But he was not going to cry. Mary and Helen could cry —they were girls; he was going to do something.

As he sat there, getting hotter and hotter, there grew, larger and larger before his eyes, the figure of Terrible God. That image of Someone of a vast size sitting in the red-hot sky, his white beard flowing, his eyes frowning, grew ever more and more awful. Jeremy stared up into the glass, his eyes blinking, the sweat beginning to pour down his nose, and yet his body shivering with terror. But he had strung himself up to meet Him. Somehow he was going to save his mother and hinder her departure. At an instant, inside him, he was crying: "I want my mother! I want my mother!" like a little boy who had been left in the street, and at the other, "You shan't have her! You shan't have her!" as though someone were trying to steal his Toy-Village or Hamlet away from him. His sleepy, bemused, heated brain wandered, in dazed fashion, back to his father's sermon of that morning. Abraham and Isaac! Abraham and Isaac!

Abraham and Isaac! Suddenly, as though through the flaming glass something had been flung to him, an idea came. Perhaps God, that huge, ugly God was teasing the Coles just as once He had teased Abraham. Perhaps He wished to see whether they were truly obedient as the Jampot had sometimes wished in the old days. He was only, it might be, pretending. Perhaps He was demanding that one of them should give up something—

something of great value. Even Jeremy, himself! . . .

If he had to sacrifice something to save his mother, what would be the hardest sacrifice? Would it be his Toy-Village, or Mary or Helen, or his soldiers, or his paint-box, or his gold fish that he had in a bowl, or—— No, of course, he had known from the first what would be hardest—it would, of course, be Hamlet.

At this stage in his thinking he removed his arm from Hamlet's neck and looked at the animal. At the same moment the light that had filled the glass-house with a fiery radiance that burnt to the very heart of the place was clouded. Above, in the sky, black, smoky clouds, rolling in fold after fold, as though some demon were flinging them out across the sky as one flings a carpet, piled up and up, each one darker than the last. The light vanished; the conservatory was filled with a thick, murky glow, and far across the fields, from the heart of the black wood, came the low rumble of thunder. But Jeremy did not hear that; he was busy with his thoughts. He stared at the dog, who was lying stretched out on the dirty floor, his nose between his toes. It cannot truthfully be said that the resolve that was forming in Jeremy's head had its birth in any fine, noble idealisms. It was as though some bully, seizing his best marbles, had said: "I'll give you these back if you hand over this week's pocket-money!" His attitude to the bully could not truthfully be described as one of homage or reverence; rather was it one of anger and impotent rebellion.

He loved Hamlet, and he loved his mother more than Hamlet; but he was not moved by sentiment. Grimly, his legs apart, his eyes shut tight, as they were when he said his prayers, he made his challenge.

"I'll give you Hamlet if you don't take Mother——"
A pause. "Only I can't cut Hamlet's throat. But I could
lose him, if that would do. . . . Only you must take him
now—I couldn't do it to-morrow." His voice began to
tremble. He was frightened. He could feel behind his
closed eyes that the darkness had gathered. The place
seemed to be filled with rolling smoke, and the house was
so terribly still!

He said again: "You can take Hamlet. He's my best
thing. You can—You can——"

There followed then, with the promptitude of a most
admirably managed theatrical climax, a peal of thunder
that seemed to strike the house with the iron hand of a
giant. Two more came, and then, for a second, a silence,
more deadly than all the earlier havoc.

Jeremy felt that God had leapt upon him. He opened
his eyes, turned as though to run, and then saw, with a
freezing check upon the very beat of his heart, that Hamlet
was gone.

v

There was no Hamlet!

In that second of frantic unreasoning terror he received
a conviction of God that no rationalistic training in later
years was able to remove.

There was no Hamlet!—only the dusky dirty p ace with
a black torrent-driven world beyond it. With a rush as
of a thousand whips slashing the air, the rain came down
upon the glass. Jeremy turned, crying "Mother! Mother!
I want Mother!" and flung himself at the red glass doors;
fumbling in his terror for the handle, he felt as though
the end of the world had come; such a panic had seized

him as only belongs to the most desperate of nightmares. God had answered him. Hamlet was gone and in a moment Jeremy himself might be seized. . . .

He felt frantically for the door; he beat upon the glass. He cried "Mother! Mother! Mother!"

He had found the door, but just as he turned the handle he was aware of a new sound, heard distantly, through the rain. Looking back he saw, from behind a rampart of dusty flower-pots, first a head, then a rough tousled body, then a tail that might be recognised amongst all the tails of Christendom.

Hamlet (who had trained himself to meet with a fine natural show of bravery every possible violence save only thunder) crept ashamed, dirty and smiling towards his master. God had only played His trick—Abraham and Isaac after all.

Then with a fine sense of victory and defiance Jeremy turned back, looked up at the slashing rain, gazed out upon the black country, at last seized Hamlet and dragging him out by his hind-legs, knelt there in the dust and suffered himself to be licked until his face was as though a snail had crossed over it.

The thunder passed. Blue pushed up into the grey. A cool air blew through the world.

Nevertheless, deep in his heart, the terror remained. In that moment he had met God face to face; he had delivered his first challenge.

P. S.—To the incredulous and cynical of heart authoritative evidence can be shown to prove that it was on the evening of that Sunday that Mrs. Cole turned the corner towards recovery.

CHAPTER VIII

TO COW FARM!

I

THIS next episode in Jeremy's year has, be it thoroughly understood, no plot nor climax to it—it is simply the chronicle of an Odyssey. Nor can it be said to have been anything but a very ordinary Odyssey to the outside observer who, if he be a parent, will tell you that going to the seaside with the family is the most bothering thing in the world, and if he is a bachelor or old maid will tell you that being in the same carriage with other people's children who are going to the sea is an abominable business and the Law ought to have something to say to it.

All through May, June and July Mrs. Cole slowly pulled back to something like her natural health. The new infant, Barbara by name, was as strong as a pony, and kicked and screamed and roared so that the house was quite a new place. Her arrival had done a great deal for Helen, whose gaze had hitherto been concentrated entirely upon herself; now she suddenly discovered a new element in life, and it was found that she was "ideal with a baby" and "a great help to nurse." This made her more human, and Barbara, realising as babies always do who understands and who does not, would behave with Helen when she would behave with no one else. Mary could not be expected to transfer her allegiance from Jeremy, and then Barbara

182

was frightened at her spectacles; Jeremy, having Hamlet, did not need a baby!

There came a fine hot morning towards the end of July when Miss Jones said, suddenly, in the middle of the history lesson: "Saturday week we go to Rafiel." Jeremy choked, kicked Mary under the table, and was generally impossible during the rest of the morning. It was Miss Jones's fault; she should have chosen her occasion more carefully. Before the evening Jeremy was standing in the corner for drawing on his bedroom wallpaper enormous figures in the blackest of black lead. These were to mark the days that remained before Saturday week, and it was, Jeremy maintained, a perfectly natural thing to do and didn't hurt the old wall-paper which was dirty enough anyway, and Mother had said, long ago, he should have a new one.

Meanwhile, impossible to describe what Jeremy felt about it. Each year Cow Farm and Rafiel had grown more wonderful; this was now the fifth that would welcome them there. At first the horizon had been limited by physical incapacity, then the third year had been rainy, and the fourth—ah, the fourth! There had been very little the matter with that! But this would be better yet. For one thing, there had never been such a summer as this year was providing—a little rain at night, a little breeze at the hottest hour of the day—everything arranged on purpose for Jeremy's comfort. And then, although he did not know it, this was to be truly the wonderful summer for him, because after this he would be a schoolboy and, as is well known, schoolboys believe in nothing save what they can see with their own eyes and are told by other boys physically stronger than themselves.

Five or six days before the great departure he began
to worry himself about his box. Two years ago he had
been given a little imitation green canvas luggage box
exactly like his father's, except that this one was light
enough to carry in one's hand. Jeremy adored this box
and would have taken it out with him, had he been permitted, on all his walks, but he had a way of filling it
with heavy stones and then asking Miss Jones to carry it
for him; it had therefore been forbidden.

But he would, of course, take it with him to Cow Farm,
and it should contain all the things that he loved best. At
first "all the things that he loved best" had not seemed
so very numerous. There would, first of all, of course, be
the Hottentot, a black and battered clown for whom he
had long ceased to feel any affection, but he was compelled
by an irritating sense of loyalty to include it in the party
just as his mother might include some tiresome old maid
"because she had nowhere to go to, poor thing." After
the Hottentot there would be his paint-box, after the paint-
box a blue writing-case, after the writing-case the family
photographs (Father, Mother, Mary and Helen), after
the photographs a toy pistol, after the pistol Hamlet's ball
(a worsted affair rendered by now shapeless and incoherent), after the ball "Alice in Wonderland" (Mary's
copy, but she didn't know), after "Alice," "Herr Baby,"
after "Herr Baby" the Prayer Book that Aunt Amy gave
him last birthday, after the Prayer Book some dried flowers which were to be presented to Mrs. Monk, the lady of
Cow Farm (this might be called carrying coals to New-
castle), after the flowers a Bible, after the Bible four
walnuts (very dry and hard ones), after the walnuts some
transfer papers, after the transfer papers six marbles—

the box was full and more than full, and he had not included the hammer and nails that Uncle Samuel had once given him, nor the cigarette-case (innocent now of cigarettes, and transformed first into a home for walking snails, second a grave for dead butterflies, third a mouse-trap), nor the butterfly net, nor "Struuwelpeter," nor the picture of Queen Victoria cut from the chocolate-box, nor—most impossible omission of all—the toy-village. The toy-village! What must he do about that? Obviously impossible to take it all—and yet some of it he must have. Mr. and Mrs. Noah and the church, perhaps—or no, Mrs. Monk would want to see the garden—it would never do not to show her the orchard with the apple-trees, and then the youngest Miss Noah! She had always seemed to Jeremy so attractive with her straight blue gown and hard red cheeks. He must show *her* to Mrs. Monk. And the butcher's shop, and then the sheep, and the dogs and the cows!

He was truly in despair. He sat on the schoolroom floor with his possessions all around him. Only Helen was in the room, and he knew that it would be no use to appeal to her—she had become so much more conceited since Barbara's arrival—and yet he must appeal to somebody, so he said to her very politely:

"Please, Helen, I've got my box and so many things to put into it and it's nearly Saturday already—and I want to show the Noahs to Mrs. Monk."

This would have been a difficult sentence for the most clear-headed person to unravel, and Helen was, at that moment, trying to write a letter to an aunt whom she had never seen and for whom she had no sort of affection, so she answered him rather roughly:

"Oh, don't bother with your box, Jeremy. Can't you see I'm busy?"

"You may be busy," said Jeremy, rising indignantly to his feet, "but I'm busy too, and my business is just as good as yours with your silly old letter."

"Oh, *don't bother!*" said Helen, whereupon Jeremy crept behind her and pinched her stocking. A battle followed, too commonplace in its details to demand description here. It need only be said that Hamlet joined in it and ran away with Helen's letter which had blown to the ground during the struggle, and that he ate it, in his corner, with great satisfaction. Then, when they were at their angriest, Helen suddenly began to laugh which she did sometimes, to her own intense annoyance, when she terribly wanted to be enraged, then Jeremy laughed too, and Hamlet yielded up fragments of the letter—so that all was well.

But the problem of the box was not solved—and, in the end, the only part of the toy village that Mrs. Monk ever saw was the youngest Miss Noah and one apple-tree for her to sit under.

II

The ritual of the journey to Cow Farm was, by this time, of course, firmly established, and the first part of the ritual was that one should wake up at three in the morning. This year, however, for some strange mysterious reason Jeremy overslept himself and did not wake up until eight o'clock, to find then that everyone was already busy packing and brushing and rushing about, and that all his own most sacred preparations must be squeezed into no time at all if he were to be ready. Old Tom Collins's bus came along at twelve o'clock to catch the one o'clock train, so that Jeremy might be considered to have the whole morning for his labours, but that was not going to be enough for him unless he was very careful. Grown-up people had such a way of suddenly catching on to you and washing your ears, or making you brush your teeth, or sitting you down in a corner with a book, that circumnavigating them and outplotting them needed as much nerve and enterprise as tracking Red Indians. When things were fined down to the most naked accuracy he had apparently only two "jobs": one to accustom Hamlet to walking with a "lead," the other to close the green box; but of course Mary would want advice, and there would, in all probability, be a dispute or two about property that would take up the time.

It was indeed an eventful morning. Trouble began with Mary suddenly discovering that she had lost her copy of "Alice in Wonderland" and rushing to Jeremy's box and upsetting all Jeremy's things to see whether it were there. Jeremy objected to this with an indignation that was scarcely in the sequel justified, because Mary found the book jammed against the paint-box and a dry walnut nestling in its centre. She cried and protested and then suddenly, with the disgusting sentimentality that was so characteristic of her, abandoned her position altogether and said that Jeremy could have it, and then cried again because he said he didn't want it.

Then Jeremy had to put everything back into the box again, and in the middle of this Hamlet ran off with the red-cheeked Miss Noah between his teeth and began to lick the blue off her dress, looking up at the assembled company between every lick with a smile of the loveliest satisfaction. Then, when the box was almost closed, it was discovered by a shocked and virtuous Helen that Jeremy had left out his Bible.

"There'll be one there," said Jeremy in an angry agitated whisper, hoping to escape the attention of Miss Jones.

"What's that, Jeremy dear?" said Miss Jones.

"Oh, fancy, Miss Jones!" said Helen. "He's taking all his dirty old toys and even his old clown, and he's leaving out his Bible."

"I'm not!" cried Jeremy, taking it and trying to squeeze it down between three walnuts and the toy pistol.

"Oh, Jeremy dear, that's not the way to treat your Bible. I'll give you some paper to wrap it up in, and you'd better take the things out again and put it in at the bottom of the box." Yes, obviously he would not be ready in time.

The matter of Hamlet and the "lead" was also very exhausting. Hamlet had never, in all his days, been tied to anyone or anything. Of course no one could tell what had been his history before he came strolling on to the Cole horizon, and it may be that once as a very small puppy he *had* been tied on to something. On the whole, that is probable, his protests on this occasion being of a kind so vehement as to argue some reminiscences behind them. Mrs. Cole had bought a beautiful "lead" of black leather; of course he had already a collar studded with little silver nails, and the point was very simply to fasten the "lead" on to the collar. Jeremy had been promised that he should conduct Hamlet, and it had seemed, when the promise had been made, as though it would be a very simple thing to carry out. Hamlet no sooner saw the cord than he began his ingenious protests, sitting up and smil ing at it, suddenly darting at the recumbent Miss Noah and rushing round the room with her, finally catching the "lead" itself in his teeth and hiding with it under Miss Jones's skirt.

The result was that Tom Collins's bus arrived when no one in the schoolroom was in the least prepared for it. Then what confusion there was! Mrs. Cole, looking strange in her hat and veil, as though she were dressed up for a play, came urging them to hurry, "because Father was waiting." Then Hamlet tied himself and his "lead" round the leg of the table; then Mary said in her most tiresome manner, apropos of nothing at all, "You *do* love me, Jeremy, don't you?" just at the moment when he was trying to unlace Hamlet, and her lip began to tremble when he said, "Oh, don't bother," so that he was compelled to add "Of course I do"; then Father came running up the stairs with "Really, this is too disgraceful. We shall miss that train!"

Then Uncle Samuel appeared, looking so queer that Jeremy was compelled to stare at him. Jeremy had seen very little of Uncle Samuel during these last months. He had hoped, after that wonderful adventure of the Christmas Pantomime, that they were going to be friends, but it had not been so. He had been away somewhere, in some strange place, painting, and then, on his return, he had hid himself and his odd affairs away in some corner of the house where no one saw him. He had had *his* life and Jeremy had had *his*.

Nevertheless Jeremy was delighted to see him. It would be fun to have him at Cow Farm with his squashy brown hat, his fat cheeks, his blue painting smock, and his short legs with huge boots. He was different, in some way, from all the rest of the world, and Jeremy, even at that early stage of his education, already perceived that he could learn more from Uncle Samuel than from any other member of the family.

Now he put his head in through the door and said: "Well, you kids, aren't you ready? It's time!" Then, seeing Miss Jones, he said: "Good morning," and bolted like a rabbit. Even then Jeremy noticed that he had paint on his fingers, and that two of his waistcoat buttons were unfastened.

Then down in the hall what confusion there was! Boxes here, there and everywhere. Mother, Father, Aunt Amy, Uncle Samuel, and, most interesting of all, Barbara and the new nurse. The new nurse was called Mrs. Patcham, and she was stout, red-cheeked, and smiling. The bundle in white called Barbara was, most happily, sleeping; but Hamlet barked at Mrs. Patcham, and that woke Barbara, who began to cry. Then Collins came in with his coat off, and the muscles swelling on his shoulders, and handled the boxes as though they were paper, and the cook, and Rose, and William, the handy-boy, and old Jordan, the gardener, and Mrs. Preston, a lady from two doors down, who sometimes came in to help, all began to bob and smile, and Father said: "Now, my dear. Now, my dear," and Hamlet wound himself and his lead round everything that he could see, and Helen fussed and said: "Now, Jeremy," and Miss Jones said: "Now, children," and last of all Collins said: "Now, mum; now, sir," and then they all were bundled into the bus, with the cart and the luggage coming along behind.

The drive through the streets was, of course, as lovely as it could be; not in the least because anyone could see anything—that was hindered by the fact that the windows of the bus were so old that they were crusted with a kind of glassy mildew, and no amount of rubbing on the window-panes provided one with a view—but because the inside of the bus was inevitably connected with adventure—partly through its motion, partly through its noise, and partly through its lovely smell. These were, of course, Jeremy's views, and it can't definitely be asserted that all grown-up people shared them. But whenever Jeremy had ridden in that bus he had always been on his way to something delightful. The motion, therefore, rejoiced his heart, although the violence of it was such that everyone was thrown against everyone else, so that Uncle Samuel was suddenly hurled against the bonnet of Miss Jones, and Helen struck Aunt Amy in the chest, and Jeremy himself dived into his sister Barbara. As to the smell, it was that lovely well-known one that has in it mice and straw, wet umbrellas and whisky, goloshes and candle-grease, dust and green paint! Jeremy loved it, and sniffed on this occasion so often that Miss Jones told him to blow his nose. As to the noise, who is there who does not remember that rattle and clatter, that sudden, deafening report as of the firing of a hundred firearms, the sudden pause when every bolt and bar and hinge sighs and moans like the wind or a stormy sea, and then that sudden scream of the clattering windows, when it is as though a frenzied cook, having received notice to leave, was breaking every scrap of china in the kitchen? Who does not know that last maddened roar as the vehicle stumbles across the last piece of cobbled road—a roar that drowns, with a savage and determined triumph, all those last directions not to forget this, that, and the other; all those inquiries as to whether this, that, and the other had been remembered? Cobbles are gone now, and old buses sleep in deserted courts, and Collins, alas, is not. His youngest son has a motor-garage, and Polchester has asphalt—*sic transit gloria mundi*.

Jeremy, clutching his green box with one hand and Hamlet's lead with the other, was in an ecstasy of happiness. The louder the noise, the rocking motion, the stronger the smell, the better. "Isn't it lovely?" he murmured to Miss Jones during one of the pauses.

It may be that it was at this moment that Uncle Samuel finally made up his mind about Jeremy. In spite of his dislike, even hatred of children, he had been coming slowly, during the last two years, to an affection for, and interest in, his nephew that was something quite new to his cynical, egoistic nature. It had leapt into activity at Christmas time, then had died again. Now as, flung first into his sister's bony arms, then on to the terrified spectacles of his niece Mary, he tried to recover himself, he was caught and held by that picture of his small nephew, seated, solid and square, in his blue sailor suit, his bare knees swinging, his hand clutching his precious box with an energy that defied Fate itself to take it from him, his mouth set, his eyes staring, radiant with joy, in front of him.

On arrival at the station it was found that the one o'clock to Liskane was "just about due," so that there was no time to be lost. They had to rush along under the great iron dome, passing by the main line, disregarding the tempestuous express from Truxe that drew up, as it were disdainfully, just as they passed, and finding the modest side line to Liskane and St. Lowe. Here there was every kind of excitement for Jeremy. Anyone who has any kind of passion for observation must have discovered long ago that a side line has ever so much more charm and appeal about it than a main line. A main line is scornful of the station in whose heart it consents for a moment to linger, its eyes are staring forward towards the vast cities who are impatiently awaiting it; but a side line has its very home here. So much gossip passes from day to day above its rails (and gossip that has for its circumference five green fields, a country road, and a babbling brook), that it knows all its passengers by heart.

To the people who travel on a side line, the train itself is still something of a wonder. How much more was that true thirty years ago. On this especial line there were only two stations—Liskane and St. Lowe, and, of a certainty, these stations would not even now be in existence were it not that St. Lowe was a fishing centre of very great importance. The little district that comprehended St. Lowe, Garth in Roselands, Stoep in Roselands, Lucent-Polwint, Rafiel, and all the smaller hamlets around them, was fed by this line; but, even so, the little train was never crowded. Tourists did not, and even now do not, go to Polwint and St. Lowe because "they smell so fishy," nor to Rafiel "because it's too far from the railway," nor to the Roseland valleys "because there's nothing to see there.", May these reasons hold good for many years to come!

To-day there were three farmers in brown leggings, with pipes, and thick knotted walking-sticks, two or three women with baskets, and a child or so, and an amiable, absent-minded clergyman in a black cloth so faded that it was now green, reading *The Times,* and shaking his head over it as he stumbled up and down the platform. One of the farmers had a large, woolly sheep-dog, who, of course, excited Hamlet to a frenzy. Jeremy, therefore, had his

time fully occupied in checking this; but he had, nevertheless, the opportunity to observe how one of the farmers
puffed the smoke out of his cheeks as though he were an
engine; how one of the women, with a back as broad as a
wall, had red stockings; and how the clergyman nearly
fell on to the railway-line every time he turned round, and
only saved himself from disaster by a miracle. The train
arriving at last, they all climbed into it, and then had to
wait for a hot, grilling half-hour whilst the engine made up
its mind that it was worth its while to take all the trouble
to start off again.

"An hour late, upon my word," said Mr. Cole angrily,
when at last, with a snore and a heave, and a grunt and a
scream, they started. "It's really too bad. I shall have to
complain," which, as everyone present knew, he had not
the slightest intention of doing. In Jeremy's carriage
there were his father, his mother, Uncle Samuel, himself,
Mary, and, of course, Hamlet. Hamlet had never been in
a train before, and his terror at the way that the ground
quivered under him was pitiful to see. He lay first under
the seat, trying to hold himself tightly together, then, when
that failed, he made startled frenzied leaps on to laps (the
lead had been removed for the time), finally he cowered
up into the corner behind Uncle Samuel, who seemed to
understand his case and sympathised with it. Whenever
the train stopped (which, being a Glebeshire train, it did
continually), he recovered at once his *savoir-faire,* asserted
his dignity, gazed through the windows at the fields and
cows as though he owned them all, and barked with the
friendly greeting of comrade to comrade whenever he saw
another dog.

The next thing that occupied Jeremy's attention was

lunch. Many people despise sandwiches and milk out of beer-bottles and bananas and seed-cake. Jeremy, of course, did not. He loved anything eaten out of paper, from the ice-cream sold by the Barney man in Polchester Square (only once did he secure some) down to the frills that there are round the tail of any self-respecting ham. But the paper on this journey to Rafiel! There was nothing in the world to touch it. In the first place you spread newspaper on your knees, then there was paper under the sandwiches (chicken), and more paper under the sandwiches (beef), and still more under the sandwiches (egg); there was paper round the seed-cake, and, most wonderful of all, paper round the jam-puffs. Jam-puffs with strawberry jam eaten in the odour of ginger-beer and eggshells! Is it possible for life at its very best to hold more? He kept his jam-puff so long as he could, until at last Mr. Cole said: "Now, my boy! Finish it up—finish it up. Paper out of the window—all neat and tidy; that's right!" speaking in that voice which Jeremy hated, because it was used, so especially, when cod-liver oil had to be taken. He swallowed his puff in a gulp, and then gazed out of the window lamenting its disappearance.

"Did you like it?" whispered Mary hoarsely.

"You've got some jam on the side of your nose," said Jeremy.

He was sitting next to his father, who had the corner seat, and he now devoted all his energies to prevent himself from falling asleep against his father's leg. But the ginger-beer, the glazed and shining fields beyond the window, the little blobs of sunlight that danced upon the floor of the carriage, the scents of food and flowers, and the hot breeze, the hum of the train, and the dancing of the telegraph

wires—all these things were against him. His head began
to nod and then to jump back with a sudden terrible spring
as though an evil demon pulled it with a rope from behind,
the carriage swelled like a balloon, then dwindled into a
thin, straight line. The strangest things happened to his
friends and relations. His mother, who was reading *The
Church Family Newspaper,* developed two faces and a nose
like a post, and Uncle Samuel, who had, in harsh reality,
two chins, seemed to be all folds and creases like a balloon
when it is shivering down into collapse. Jeremy fought
with these fantasies; the lines on the newspaper doubled
and redoubled, vanished and sprang to life again. He
said: "I will not," and, instantly, his head on the soft
part of his father's thigh, was asleep.

III

In his dreams he was riding on a cloud all pink and
gold, and behind came a row of shining, white clouds
fluffy like bales of wool wrapped round lighted lanterns.

His cloud rose and fell, rose and fell, and a voice said in
his ear: "All is well! All is well! You can go on like
this for ever. There will be jam-puffs soon, and ice-cream,
and fish-cakes, and you can go to China this way whenever
you like."

And he said: "Can't I take Hamlet with me?"

And the voice answered: "Hamlet is with you already,"
and there, behold, was Hamlet sitting on the pink cloud
with a stiff gold collar round his neck, wagging his tail.
And then the voice shouted so loudly that Jeremy jumped
off the pink cloud in his astonishment: "Liskane! Liskane! Liskane!" and Jeremy jumped and fell and fell—

right into his father's lap, with someone crying in his ear:
"Wake up, Jeremy! We're there! We're there!"

His first thought was for his green box, which was, he
found, safely and securely in his hand. Then for Hamlet,
who was, he saw with horror, already upon the platform,
the lead trailing behind him like a neglected conscience, his
burning eyes piercing his hair in search of another dog,
whom he smelt but could not see.

Jeremy, rushing out of the train, seized the lead, scolded
his recovered property, who wore an expression of injured
and abandoned innocence, and looked about him. Yes,
this was Liskane—wonderful, marvellous, magical Liskane! To the bored and cynical adult Liskane may easily
appear to be one of the ugliest, most deserted stations in
the whole of Europe, having nothing on either side of it
save barren grey fields that never grow grass but only
stones and bottles, with its single decoration—a heavy iron
bridge that crosses the rails and leads up to the higher
road and the town of Liskane. Ugly enough, but to
Jeremy, on this summer afternoon, the gate to a sure and
certain Paradise.

Although his family were fussing around him, Barbara
crying, Mr. Cole saying: "Four, Five, Six. . . . But
where's the black box? Your black box, Amy. . . . Six,
Seven. . . . But there should be Eight. . . . Seven
. . . " and Mrs. Cole saying: "And there's my brown
bag. The little one with the black handle," and Helen saying. "OO, was it adidums, then? Nandy-Pandy, Nandy-
Pandy. . . ." and Miss Jones: "Now, Mary! Now,
Jeremy! Now, Helen!"; although this was going on just
as it always had gone on, his eyes were searching for the
wagonette. Ah, there it was! He could just see the top of

it beyond the iron bridge, and Jim, the man from the Farm, would be coming down to help with the boxes; yes, there he was crossing the bridge now, with his red face and broad shoulders, and the cap on the side of his head, just as he always wore it. Jeremy recognised him with a strange, little choking sensation. It was "coming home" to him, all this was—the great event of his life, and as he looked at the others he realised, young as he was, that none of them felt it as he did, and the realisation gave him a strange feeling, half of gratification, half of loneliness. He stood there, a little apart from the rest of them, clutching his box, and holding on to Hamlet's lead, feeling so deeply excited that his heart was like a hard, cold stone jumping up and down, bump, bump, behind his waistcoat.

"That's Jim! That's Jim!" he whispered in a hoarse gasp to Miss Jones.

"Now mind, dear," she answered in her kindly, groping voice. "You'll be falling on to the rail if you aren't careful."

It strangely annoyed him that his father should greet Jim just as though he were some quite ordinary man in Polchester. He himself waited in a strange agitation until Jim should notice him. The man turned at last, bending down to pick up a box, saw him, touched his cap, smiling a long, crooked smile, and Jeremy blushed with happiness. It was the first recognition that he had had from the farm, and it pleased him.

They all moved up to the higher road. Uncle Samuel, coming on at the last, in a dreamy, moody way, stopping on the bridge to look down at the railway-line, and then suddenly saying aloud:

"Their minds are full of the number of boxes, and whether they'll get tea, and who's to pay what, and 'How badly I want a wash!' and already to-morrow they'll be wondering whether they oughn't to be getting home to Polchester. All sham! All sham!"

He wasn't speaking to Jeremy, but to himself. However, Jeremy said: "Did you see Jim, Uncle?"

"No, I did not."

"He's fatter and redder than last year."

"I shouldn't wonder."

"Are you going to paint, Uncle?"

"I am."

"What?"

"Oh, just lines and circles."

Jeremy paused, standing for a moment, and looked puzzled. Then he said:

"Do you like babies, Uncle Samuel?"

"No, I do not."

"Not even Barbara?"

"No—certainly not."

"I don't, too. . . . Why don't you paint cows and houses like other people, Uncle Samuel? I heard Father say once that he never knew what your pictures meant."

"That's why I paint them."

"Why?"

"So that your father shan't know what they mean."

Although he did not understand this any more than he understood his uncle, Jeremy was pleased with this conversation. It had been, somehow, in tone with the place and the hour; it had conveyed to him in some strange fashion that his uncle cared for all of this rather as he himself cared. Oh! he liked Uncle Samuel!

He had hoped that he might have sat on the box next to Jim, but that place was now piled up with luggage, so he was squeezed in between his mother and Mrs. Patcham, with Hamlet, very uncomfortable, between his knees. They drove off down the high road, the hot smell of the grass came to his nostrils, the sun blazed down upon them, turning the path before them into gleaming steel, and the high Glebeshire hedges, covered with thin powder, rose on both sides above them, breaking once and again to show the folding valleys, and the faint blue hills, and the heavy, dark trees with their thick, black shadows staining the grass.

The cows were clustered sleeping wherever they could find shadow; faintly sheep-bells tinkled in the distance, and now and then a stream, like broken glass, floated, cried, and was gone. They drove into a dark wood, and the sun scattered through the trees in pieces of gold and shadowy streams of arrowed light. The birds were singing, and whenever the hoofs of the horses and the wheels turned onto soft moss or lines of grass, in the sudden silence the air was filled with birds' voices. That proved that it must now be turning to the evening of the day; the sun was not very high above the wood, and the sea of blue was invaded by a high galleon of cloud that hovered with spreading sail, catching gold into its heart as it moved.

They left the wood, crossed the River Garth, and came out on to moorland. Here, for the first time, Jeremy smelt the sea; the lanes had been hot, but here the wind blew across the moor, with the smell of sea-pinks and sea-gulls in it. The grass was short and rough; the soil was sand. On the horizon was the grey, melancholy tower of a deserted mine. Some bird flew with swiftly driving wings,

crying as it went. The smell of the moor was as fresh as
though the foot of man had never crossed it—deserted, but
not alone; bare, but not empty; uninhabited, but peopled;
silent, but full of voices.

Jeremy's excitement grew. He knew now how every
line of the road would be. They left the moor and were
on the road leading to Rafiel. These were the days before
they built the road from Liskane wide enough for motor-
cars and other horrible inventions. Thirty years ago the
way was so narrow that the briars and ferns brushed your
face as you passed, and you could reach out your hand and
pluck snap-dragons and dandelions and fox-gloves. Many
roads twisted in and out upon one another; the corners
were so sharp that sometimes the wagonette seemed to hang
upon one wheel as it turned. Still no sight of the sea, but
the smell of it now was everywhere, and sometimes at a
sudden bend there would come a faint beat, beat upon the
ear with something rhyming and measured in it, like the
murmur of a sleeping giant.

They came to the bend where the hill suddenly dips at
a fearful angle down into Rafiel. Here they turned to
the right, deep between edges again, then through a little
copse, and then, as though with a whisk of the finger, right
on to Cow Farm itself.

It was an old square house, deep red brick, with crooked
chimneys, and a stone court in front of it. To either side
of the court there were barns. Behind the house thick
trees, clouded with green, showed. In the middle of the
court was a pump, and all about the flagged stones pigeons
were delicately walking. As they drove up, the pigeons
rose in a wheeling flight against the sky now staining
faintly with amber; dogs rushed barking from the barns; a

haycart turned the corner, its wheels creaking, and four little children perched high on the top of the hay. Then the hall-door opened, and behold Mrs. Monk, Mr. Monk, and, clustering shyly behind, the little Monks.

In the scene that followed Jeremy was forgotten. He did not know what it was that made him hang behind the others, but he stood beside the wagonette, bent down and released Hamlet, and then waited, hiding under the shadow of the cart. His happiness was almost intolerable; he could not speak, he could not move, and in the heart of his happiness there was a strange unhappiness that he had never known before. The loneliness that he had felt at Liskane Station was intensified, so that he felt like a stranger who was seeing his father, or his mother, or aunt, or sisters for the first time. Everything about him emphasised the loneliness: the slow evening light that was stealing into the sky, the sound of some machine in the farm-house turning with a melancholy rhythmic whine, a voice calling in the fields, the rumble of the sea, the twittering of birds in the garden trees, the bark of a dog far, far away, and, through them all, the sense that the world was sinking down into silence, and that all the sounds were slipping away, like visitors hurrying from the park before the gates are shut; he stood there, listening, caught into a life that was utterly his own and had no share with any other. He looked around and saw that they were all going into the house, that Jim and Mr. Monk were busy with the boxes, and that no one was aware of him. He knew what he wanted.

He slipped across the court and dropped into the black cavernous hole of the farther barn. At first the darkness stopped him; but he knew his way, found the steps that led up to the loft, and was soon perched high behind a little square window that was now blue and gold against the velvety blackness behind him. This was his favourite spot in all the farm. Here, all the year, they stored the apples, and the smell of the fruit was thick in the air, sweet and strong, clinging about every fibre of the place, so that you could not disturb a strand nor a stone without sending some new drift of the scent up against your nostrils. All the year after his first visit, Jeremy had been longing to smell that smell again, and now he knelt up against the window, drinking it in. With his eyes he searched the horizon. From here you could see the garden with the sundial, the fields beyond, the sudden dip with the trees at the edge of it bent crossways by the wind, and there, in such a cup as one's hands might form, just beyond, was the sea. . . .

He stared as though his eyes would start from his head. Behind him was the cloudy smoke of the apple-scent; in front of him the sun was sinking towards the dark elms. Soon the trees would catch the sun and hide it; the galleon cloud that had been over them as they drove was now banked in red and gold across the horizon; birds slowly, lazily fled to their homes.

He heard someone call, "Jeremy! Jeremy!" With a last gaze he saw the blue cup turn to gold, the sun reached the tops of the elms; the fields were lit with the glitter of shining glass, then, even as he watched, they were purple, then grey, then dim like smoke.

Again the voice called "Jeremy!" He slipped from the window, found the little stair, ran across the dusky court and entered the house.

CHAPTER IX

THE AWAKENING OF CHARLOTTE

I

TOWARDS the end of the first fortnight's stay at Cow Farm it was announced that very shortly there would be a picnic at Rafiel Cove.

Jeremy had been waiting for this proclamation; once or twice he had asked whether they were going to the Cove and had been told "not to bother," "all in good time," and other ridiculous elderly finalities, but he knew that the day must come, as it had always come every year. The picnic at Rafield was always the central event of the summer.

And he had this year another reason for excited anticipation—the wonderful Charlotte Le Page was to be present. Until now Jeremy had never taken the slightest interest in girls. Mary and Helen, being his sisters, were necessities and inevitabilities, but that did not mean that he could not get along very easily without them, and indeed Mary with her jealousies, her strange sulky temper and sudden sentimental repentances was certainly a burden and restraint. As to the little girls in Polchester, he had frankly found them tiresome and stupid, thinking of themselves, terrified of the most natural phenomena and untruthful in their statements. He had been always independent and reserved with everyone, and had never, in all his life, had a close friend, but there had been, especially of late, boys with whom it had been amusing to spend an hour or two, and since his fight with the Dean's Ernest he had thought that it would be rather interesting to make a further trial of strength with whomsoever . . .

Girls were stupid, uninteresting, conceited and slow. He never, in all his life, wanted to have anything to do with girls. But Charlotte Le Page was another matter. She had, in the first place, become quite a tradition in the Cole family. She was the daughter of a wealthy landowner, who always spent his holidays in Rafiel. She and her very beautiful, very superior mother had been seen on many occasions by the Coles driving about the Glebeshire roads in a fine and languid manner, a manner to which the Coles knew, very well, they themselves could never attain. Then Mrs. Cole had called, and Mrs. Le Page and Charlotte had come to tea at Cow Farm. This had been a year ago, when Jeremy had been only seven; nevertheless, he had been present during the first part of the ceremony, and Charlotte had struck him as entirely amazing.

He had simply gazed at her with his mouth open, forgetting all his good manners. She was at this time nine or ten years of age but very small and, as they say of the most modern kind of doll, "perfect in every particular." She had wonderful hair of a bright rippling gold; her cheeks were pink and her eyes were blue, and she was so beautifully dressed that you could not take in details but must simply surrender yourself to a cloudy film of white or blue, with everything so perfectly in its place that it seemed to the rough and ready Jeremy quite unearthly. Of course she had to be very careful how she walked, when she sat down, in what way she moved her hands and feet, and how she blew her nose. It was wonderful to see

her do these things, she did them so naturally and yet
always with a sense of an effort overcome for the
good of humanity. Her mother never ceased to empty
praises at her feet, appealing to visitors with: "Isn't
Charlotte too lovely to-day?" or "Really, Mrs. Cole, did
you ever see anything like Charlotte's hair?" or "Just a
moment, Mrs. Cole, I'm sure you've never seen such hands
and feet on any human being before!"—and it was impossible to tell whether or no Charlotte was moved by these
praises, because she never said anything at all. She was
almost completely silent, and once, at the tea-gathering in
Cow Farm, when she suddenly said: "I'm tired, Mama,"
Jeremy nearly jumped from his chair, so astonished he
was.

Jeremy had, during the year that intervened between
that visit and this, sometimes thought of Charlotte, and he
had looked back upon her, not as a little girl but as something strange, fantastic, wonderfully coloured, whom it
would be interesting to see again. He wondered why Mary
and Helen could not be like that, instead of running about
and screaming and becoming red in the face. He said
once to Mary that she should imitate Charlotte, and the
scene that followed was terrible. Mary, from that moment, hated Charlotte with an overpowering hatred.

Here this year they were again, Mrs. Le Page with her
long neck, her beautiful pearl ear-rings, her pale watery
eyes and her tapering fingers; Charlotte just as before,
silent, beautiful and precious. There was again a tea-
party at Cow Farm, and on this occasion Jeremy was asked
to show Hamlet. But Hamlet behaved badly, trying to
jump upon Charlotte's white frock and soil her blue ribbons. Charlotte screamed exactly as a doll screams when

you press it in the stomach, and Hamlet was so deeply
astonished at the unexpected noise that he stopped his bad
behaviour, sat on his hind legs, and gazed up at her with
an anxious wondering expression. In spite of this unfortunate incident, the visit went off well, and Mrs. Cole
said that she had never seen anything so lovely as Charlotte, and Mrs. Le Page said, "No, had anyone ever ?" and
Charlotte never turned a hair. The final arrangement was
that there should be a picnic and soon, because "Mr. Le
Page has to return to Warwickshire to look after the Estate
—so tiresome, but I've no doubt it's all going to wrack
and ruin without him."

After the picnic had been arranged the Coles were,
frankly, a little uneasy. The family of Le Page was not
the easiest in the world to entertain, and the thought of a
whole day with Mr. Le Page, who was a very black, very
silent gentleman and looked as though he were always
counting sums over in his head, was truly alarming. Moreover, in the ordinary way, a picnic, which depended so
entirely for its success on the weather, was no great risk,
because the Coles were indifferent to rain, as all true
Glebeshire people must be. But that the Le Pages should
be wet was quite another affair; the thought of a dripping
Mrs. Le Page was intolerable, but of a dripping Charlotte
quite impossible; moreover, the plain but excellent food—
pasties, saffron cake, apples and ginger beer—enjoyed by
the Coles seemed quite too terrestrial for the Le Pages.
Mrs. Le Page and ginger beer ! Charlotte and pasties !
. . . nevertheless, the invitation had been given and accepted. The Coles could but anxiously inspect the
sky. . . .

II

There was another reason why Jeremy looked forward to the picnic with impatience. A funny old lady, named Miss Henhouse, who lived near Cow Farm in a little cottage all by herself, called sometimes upon the Coles and told them stories about the people and the place, which made them "sit up in their chairs." She was an old lady with sharp eyes, a black moustache and a double chin, wore an old shabby bonnet, grey mittens and large shoes which banged after her as she walked. She leant on a cane with a silver knob to it, and she wore a huge cameo brooch on her breast with a miniature of herself inside it. She was what is called in novels "a character." There was no one who knew so much about Rafiel and its neighbourhood; she had lived here for ever, her father had been a friend of Wellington's and had known members of the local Press Gang intimately. It was from her that Jeremy heard, in detail, the famous story of the Scarlet Admiral. It was, of course, in any case, a well-known story, and Jeremy had often heard it before, but Miss Henhouse made it a new, a most vivid and realistic thing. She sat forward in her chair, leaning on her silver-headed cane, her eyes staring in front of her, her two chins bobbing, gazing, gazing as though it all had happened before her very nose.

How one night outside Rafiel Cove there was a terrible storm, and on the morning afterwards a wonderful, smiling calm, and how the village idiot, out for his early morning stroll, saw a splendid ship riding beyond the Cove, a ship of gold with sails of silk and jewelled masts. As he watched, from the ship a boat pushed out, and then landed on the sand of the Cove a wonderful company in cocked hats of gold lace, plush breeches of red, and shoes with diamond buckles. The leader of them was a little man with a vast cocked hat and a splendid sword all studded with jewels. The fool, peering over the hedge, saw him give orders to his men, and then walk, alone, up the little winding path, to the cliff-top. Straight up the path he came, then right past the fool himself, standing at last upon the turnip field of Farmer Ede, one of the greatest of the farmers of those parts. And here he waited, staring out to sea, his arms crossed, his eyes very fierce and very, very sad. Then a second time from the golden ship a boat pushed out, cutting its way through the glassy sea—and there landed on the beach a young man, very beautiful, in a suit of blue and gold, and he, without a glance at the waiting sailors, also slowly climbed the sea-path, and at last he too reached Farmer Ede's turnip field. Then he and the Scarlet Admiral bowed to one another, very beautifully, very sadly, and very, very fiercely. As the sun rose high in the sky, as the cows passed clumsily down the lane behind the field so the fool, with eyes staring and heart thumping, saw these two fight a duel to the death. There could be no question, from the first, how it would end. The beautiful young man in his fine blue suit and his white cambric shirt had despair upon his face. He knew that his hour had come. And the eyes of the Scarlet Admiral were ever sadder and ever fiercer. Then, with a sudden move, a little turn of his agile body, the Scarlet Admiral had the young man through the breast. The young man threw up his arms and cried; and as the Scarlet Admiral withdrew his sword, dripping with blood from his body, the young man fell backwards over the cliff into the sea. Then the Scarlet Admiral wiped his sword on the grass and, slowly and sadly, walked down the cliff-path even as he had walked up. He joined his men, they found their boat, pushed out to their ship, and even as they landed upon her she had disappeared. A moment later the fool saw the parson of Rafiel Church coming round the corner for his morning bathe, and two minutes afterwards nothing human was to be seen save the naked limbs of the parson and his little bundle of black clothes lying neatly upon a stone. Then the fool ran all the way home to his mother who was a widow, and sat and cried and cried for the beautiful young man who had been slain, nor would he eat, nor taste the excellent Rafiel beer, and he pined away, and at last he died, first telling this history to his mother, who, like all widows, was a garulous woman and loved a good story. . . .

Impossible to imagine with what life and fire old Miss Henhouse gave this history. You could see with your own eyes the golden ship, the diamond buckles of the Scarlet Admiral, the young man's sad eyes, the parson's black clothes. When she had finished it seemed to Jeremy that it must have been just so. She told him that now on a summer morning or evening the Scarlet Admiral might still be seen, climbing the cliff-path, wiping his sword upon the grass, gazing out with sad eyes to sea. Jeremy swore to himself that on the next occasion of visiting the Cove he would watch . . . he would watch—but to no single human being would he speak anything of this.

This was the second reason why he had looked forward so eagerly to the sea-picnic.

III

The day arrived, and it was marvellously fine—one of those days in August when heat possesses the world and holds it tranced and still, but has in the very strength of its possession some scent of the decay and chill of autumn that is to follow so close upon its heels. There was no breeze, no wind from the sea, only a sky utterly without cloud and a world without sound.

Punctually at eleven of the morning the splendid Le Page equipage arrived at Cow Farm. Splendid it was! A large wagonette, with a stout supercilious fellow on the box who sniffed at the healthy odours of the farm and stared haughtily at Mrs. Monk as though she should be ashamed to be alive. The Coles had provided a small plump "jingle" with a small plump pony, their regular conveyance; the pony was Bob, and he would not go up hills unless persuaded with sugar, but Jeremy loved him and would not have ridden behind any other steed in the whole world. How contemptuously the big black horses of the wagonette gazed down their nostrils at Bob, and how superbly Mrs. Le Page, sitting very upright under her white sunshade, greeted Mrs. Cole!

"Dear Mrs. Cole. Such a hot morning, isn't it? Lovely, of course, but so hot."

"I'm afraid," Jeremy heard his mother say, "that your carriage will never get down the Rafiel Lane, Mrs. Le Page. We hoped you'd come in the dog-cart. Plenty of room. . . ."

Superb to witness the fashion in which Mrs. Le Page gazed at the dog-cart.

"For all of us? . . . Dear Mrs. Cole, I scarcely think—— And Charlotte's frock . . ."

Then Jeremy turned his eyes to Charlotte. She sat under a miniature sunshade of white silk and lace, a vision of loveliness. She was a shimmer of white, a little white cloud that had settled for a moment upon the seat of the carriage to allow the sun to dance upon it, to caress it with fingers of fire, so to separate it from the rest of the world for ever as something too precious to be touched. Jeremy had never seen anything so lovely.

He blushed and scraped his boots the one against the other.

"And this is Jeremy?" said Mrs. Le Page as though she said: "And this is where you keep your little pigs, Mr. Monk?"

"Yes," said Jeremy, blushing.

"Charlotte, you know Jeremy. You must be friends."

"Yes," said Charlotte, without moving. Then Jeremy tumbled into the stern gaze of Mr. Le Page who, arrayed as he was in a very smart suit of the whitest flannels, looked with his black beard and fierce black eyebrows like a pirate king disguised.

"How are you?" said Mr. Le Page in a deep bass voice.

"Very well, thank you," said Jeremy.

To tell the truth, Mrs. Cole's heart sadly misgave her when she saw the Le Page family all sitting up so new and so bright in their new and bright carriage. She thought of the simple preparations that had been made—the pasties, the saffron buns and the ginger beer; she looked around her at the very plain but useful garments worn by her family, her husband in faded grey flannel trousers and a cricketing shirt, Helen and Mary in the simplest blue cotton, and

Jeremy in his two-year-old sailor suit. She had intended to bring their bathing things in a bundle, but now she put them aside. It was obvious that the Le Pages had no intention of bathing. She sighed and foresaw a difficult day ahead of her.

It was evident that the Le Pages did not intend to come one step farther into Cow Farm than was necessary.

"Dear Mrs. Cole, on a hot day—how can you endure the smells of a farm . . . such a charming farm, too, with all its cows and pigs, but in this weather. . . . Charlotte darling, you don't feel the heat? No? Hold your sunshade a little more to the right, love. That's right. She was not quite the thing last night, Mrs. Cole. I had some doubts about bringing her, but I knew you'd all be so disappointed. She's looking rather lovely to-day, don't you think? You must forgive a mother's partiality. . . . Oh, you're not bringing that little dog, are you? Surely——"

Jeremy, who had from the first hated Mrs. Le Page, forgot his shyness and brought out fiercely:

"Of course he's coming. Hamlet always goes everywhere with us."

"Hamlet!" said Mr. Le Page in his deep bass voice.

"What a strange name for a dog!" said Mrs. Le Page in tones of vague distrust.

At last it was settled that one member of the Cole party should ride with the Le Pages, and Mary was selected. Poor Mary! inevitably chosen when something unpleasant must be done. To-day it was especially hard for her, because she entertained so implacable a hatred for the lovely Charlotte and looked, it must be confessed, so plain and shabby by the side of her. Indeed, to any observer with a heart it must have been touching to see Mary driven away in that magnificent black carriage, staring with agonised hostility in front of her through her large spectacles, compelled to balance herself exactly between the magnificent sunshade of Mrs. Le Page and the smaller but also magnificent sunshade of the lovely Charlotte. Mrs. Cole, glancing in that direction, may have felt with a pang that she would never be able to make her children handsome and gay as she would like to do—but it was certainly a pang of only a moment's duration.

She would not have exchanged her Mary for a wagonload of Charlottes.

And Jeremy, bumping along in the jingle, also felt the contrast. Why could not Mary wear her straw hat straight, and why must she have elastic under her chin? Why did she look so cross and so stupid? Why did she bother him so with her worries? Charlotte would never worry him. She would just sit there, looking beautiful, with her golden hair, and blue eyes and pink cheeks. Next week was to be Miss Jones's birthday, and in preparation for this he had bought for her in Polchester a silver thimble. He wondered whether he would not give Charlotte this thimble instead of Miss Jones. He could give Miss Jones some old thing he would find somewhere, or he would go out and pick for her some flowers. She would be pleased with anything. He wondered what Charlotte would say when he gave her the thimble. She would like it, of course. She would smile. She would open her eyes and look at him. Fortunately he had the thimble even now in his pocket. He had bought it when he was wearing this same suit. Yes, he would give it to her. As he decided this he looked at Miss Jones guiltily, but she was making such odd faces as she squinted to escape from the sun that he did not feel ashamed.

They came to that steep hill just beyond Garth woods, and Bob, of course, refused to move. The superb Le Page affair dashed past them, shouted something at them, and disappeared over the brow of the hill. The last thing to be seen of them were the fierce despairing eyes of the imprisoned Mary. A strange sensation of relief instantly settled upon the Coles. For a moment they were alone; they began slowly to walk up the hill, dragging with them the reluctant Bob. About them was peace, absolute and unstained. The hard glitter of the day shone upon the white road, but behind them the wood was dark and cool, a green cloud against the sky. Behind the steep hedges the harvesters were moving. In the air a lark was singing, and along the ditch at the road side a tiny stream tumbled. And beyond these sounds there was a vast tranquil silence.

The Coles moved up the hill very slowly, only Hamlet racing ahead to find spots of shadow where he might lie down and pant. They would not confess to themselves that this promised to be the happiest moment of their day. They went bravely forward.

On the bend of the hill the Le Pages were waiting for them. What Mrs. Cole had foreseen had in truth occurred. The Le Page carriage would not go down the Rafiel Lane. No, it would not. . . . Nothing would induce it to.

"James," said Mrs. Le Page to her stout and disdainful attendant.

"Nothing, ma'am," said James.

"Dear me, dear me," said Mrs. Le Page. "Well then, we must walk," said the deep despairing voice of the Pirate King.

And walk they did.

That walk was, as Mrs. Cole afterwards said, "a pity," because it destroyed the Le Page tempers when the day was scarcely begun. Mr. Le Page was, it was quickly descried, not intended for walking. Strong and fierce though he seemed, heat instantly crumpled him up. The perfect crease of his white trousers vanished, his collar was no longer spotless, little beads of perspiration appeared almost at once on his forehead, and his black beard dripped moisture. Mrs. Le Page, with her skirts raised, walked as though she were passing through the Valley of Destruction; every step was a risk and a danger, and the difficulty of holding her skirts and her sunshade at the same time, and of seeing that her shoes were not soiled and her hat not caught by an offending bough gave her face an expression of desperate despair.

There was, unfortunately, one spot very deep down in the lane where the ground was never dry even in the height of the hottest summer.

A little stream ran here across the path, and the ground on either side was soft and sodden. Mrs. Le Page, struggling to avoid an overhanging branch, stepped into the mud; one foot stuck there, and it needed Mr. Cole's strong arm to pull her out of it.

"Charlotte! Charlotte!" she cried. "Don't let Charlotte step into that! Mr. Cole! Mr. Cole! I charge you —my child!" Charlotte was conveyed across, but the damage was done. One of Mrs. Le Page's beautiful shoes was thick with mud.

When, therefore, the party, climbing out of the Lane, came suddenly upon the path leading down to the Cove, with the sea, like a blue cloud in front of them, no one

exclaimed at the view. It was a very beautiful view—
one of the finest of its kind in the United Kingdom, the
high rocks closing in the Cove and the green hills closing
in the rocks. On the hill to the right was the Rafiel Old
Church, with its graveyard that ran to the very edge of
the cliff, and behind the Cove was a stream and a green
orchard and a little wood. The sand of the Cove was
bright gold, and the low rocks to either side of it were a
dark red—the handsomest place in the world, with the
water so clear that you could see down, far down, into
green caverns laced with silver sand. Unfortunately, at
the moment when the Coles and their friends beheld it,
it was blazing in the sun; soon the sun would pass and,
during the whole afternoon, half of it at least would lie
in shadow, but the Le Pages could not be expected to think
of that.

The basket was unloaded from the jingle and carried
down to the beach by Mr. Cole and Jim. Jeremy, finding
himself at the side of the lovely Charlotte, was convulsed
with shyness, the more that he knew that the unhappy
Mary was listening with jealous ears. Charlotte, walking
like Agag, "delicately," had a piteous expression in her
eyes as though she were being led to the torture.

Jeremy coughed and began: "We always come here
every year. Don't you like it?"

"Yes," she said miserably.

"And we paddle and bathe. Do you like bathing?"

"Going into the sea?"

"Yes."

"Oh, no! Mother says I mustn't, because it'll hurt my
hair. Do you like my hair?"

"Yes," said Jeremy, blushing at so direct an invitation to compliment.

"Mother says I've got to be very careful of my hair because it's my chief beauty."

"Yes," said Jeremy.

"I have a maid, Alice, and she brushes a whole hour every morning and a whole hour every evening."

"Don't you get very tired?" asked Jeremy. "I know I should."

"Mother says if you have such beautiful hair you must take trouble with it," Charlotte gravely replied.

Her voice was so like the voice of a parrot that Jeremy's grandmother had once possessed that it didn't seem as though a human being was speaking at all. They were near the beach now and could see the blue slipping in, turning into white bubbles, then slipping out again.

"Do you like my frock?" said Charlotte.

"Yes," said Jeremy.

"It was bought in London. All my clothes are bought in London."

"Mary's and Helen's aren't," said Jeremy with some faint idea of protecting his sisters. "They're bought in Polchester."

"Mother says," said Charlotte, "that if you're not pretty it doesn't matter where you buy your clothes."

They arrived on the beach and stared about them. It became at once a great question as to where Mrs. Le Page would sit. She could not sit on the sand which looked damp, nor equally, of course, on a rock that was spiky and hard. What to do with her? She stood in the middle of the beach, still holding up her skirts, gazing desperately about her, looking first at one spot and then at another.

"Oh, dear, the heat!" she exclaimed. "Is there no shade anywhere? Perhaps in that farm-house over there. . . ." It was probable enough that no member of the Cole family would have minded banishing Mrs. Le Page into the farmhouse, but it would have meant that the whole party must accompany her. That was impossible. They had come for a picnic and a picnic they would have.

Mrs. Cole watched, with growing agitation, the whole situation. She saw from her husband's face that he was rapidly losing his temper, and she had learnt, after many experiences, that when he lost his temper he was capable of anything. That does not mean, of course, that he ever was angry to the extent of swearing or striking out with his fists—no, he simply grew sadder, and sadder, and sadder, and this melancholy had a way of reducing to despair all the people with whom he happened to be at the time.

"What does everyone say to our having lunch now?" cried Mrs. Cole cheerfully. "It's after one, and I'm sure everyone's hungry."

No one said anything, so preparations were begun. A minute piece of shade was found for Mrs. Le Page, and here she sat on a flat piece of rock with her skirts drawn close about her as though she were afraid of rats or crabs. A tablecloth was laid on the sand and the provisions spread out—pasties for everybody, egg-sandwiches, seed-cake, and jam-puffs—and ginger beer. It looked a fine feast when it was all there, and Mrs. Cole, as she gave the final touch to it by placing a drinking glass containing two red rose-buds in the middle, felt proud of her efforts and hoped that after all the affair might pass off bravely. But alas, how easily the proudest plans fall to the ground.

"I hope, Alice, you haven't forgotten the salt!"

Instantly Mrs. Cole knew that she had forgotten it. She could see herself standing there in Mrs. Monk's kitchen forgetting it. How could she? And Mrs. Monk, how could *she?* It had never been forgotten before.

"Oh, no," she said wildly. "Oh, no! I'm sure I can't have forgotten it."

She plunged about, her red face all creased with anxiety, her hat on one side, her hands searching everywhere, under the tablecloth, in the basket, amongst the knives and forks.

"Jim, you haven't dropped anything?"

"No, mum. Beggin' your pardon, mum, the basket was closed, so to speak—closed it was."

No, she knew that she had forgotten it.

"I'm so sorry, Mrs. Le Page, I'm afraid——"

"My dear Mrs. Cole! What does it matter? Not in the least, I assure you. In this heat it's impossible to feel hungry, isn't it? I assure you I don't feel as though I could touch a thing. A little fruit, perhaps—an apple or a . peach——"

Fruit? Why hadn't Mrs. Cole brought fruit? She might so easily have done so, and she had never thought about it. They themselves were rather tired of fruit, and so——

"I'm afraid we've no fruit, but an egg-sandwich——"

"Eggs need salt, don't you think? Not that it matters in the very least, but so that you shouldn't think me fussy. Really, dear Mrs. Cole, I never felt less hungry in my life. Just a drop of milk and I'm perfectly satisfied."

"Jeremy shall run up to the farm for the milk. You don't mind, Jeremy dear, do you? It's only a step. Just take this sixpence, dear, and say we'll send the jug back this afternoon if they'll spare one."

Jeremy did mind. He was enjoying his luncheon, and he was gazing at Charlotte, and he was teasing Hamlet with scraps—he was very happy. Nevertheless, he started off.

So soon as he left the sands the noise of the sea was shut off from him, and he was climbing the little green path up which the Scarlet Admiral had once stalked.

Suddenly he remembered—in his excitement about Charlotte he had forgotten the Admiral. He stood for a moment, listening. The green hedge shut off the noise of the sea—only above his head some birds were twittering. He fancied that he heard footsteps, then that beyond the hedge something was moving. It seemed to him that the birds were also listening for something. "Well, it's the middle of the afternoon, anyway." He thought to himself, "He never comes there—only in the morning or evening," but he hurried forward after that, wishing that he had called to Hamlet to accompany him. It was a pleasant climb to the farm through the green orchard, and he found at the farm door an agreeable woman who smiled at him when she gave him the milk. He had to come down the hill carefully, lest the milk should be spilt. He walked along very happily, humming to himself and thinking in a confused summer afternoon kind of manner of Charlotte, Hamlet, Mrs. Le Page and himself. "Shall I give her the thimble or shan't I? I could take her to the pools where the little crabs are. She'd like them. I wonder whether we're going to bathe. Mrs. Le Page will look funny bathing. . . ." Then he was in the green lane again, and at once his discomfort returned to him, and he looked around his shoulder and into the hedges, and stopped once and again to listen. There was no sound. The birds, it seemed, had all fallen to sleep. The hedges, he thought, were closer about him. It was very hot here, with no breeze and no comforting sound of the sea. "I wonder whether he really does come," he thought. "It must be horrid to see him—coming quite close." And the thought of the Fool also frightened him. The Fool with his tongue out and his shaking legs, like the idiot who lived near the Cathedral at home. At the thought of this Jeremy suddenly took to his legs and ran, covering the top of his jug with his hand; then, when he came out on to the strip of grass that crossed the top of the beach, he stopped, suddenly ashamed of himself. Scarlet Admirals! Scarlet Admirals! How could there be Scarlet Admirals in a world that also contained so blazing a sun, so blue a sea, and the gorgeous realities of the Le Page family. He arrived at the luncheon party hot and proud and smiling, so cheerful and stolid and agreeable that even Mrs. Le Page was compelled to say, "Really, Mrs. Cole, that's a very nice little boy of yours. Come here, little Jeremy, and talk to me!" How deeply he hated being called "little Jeremy" only Mary and Helen knew. Their eyes flew to his face to see how he would take it. He took it very well. He sat down beside Mrs. Le Page, who very gracefully and languidly sipped at her glass of milk.

"How old are you, Jeremy dear?" she asked him.

"Eight," he answered, wriggling.

"What a nice age! And one day you'll go to school?"

"In September."

"And what will you be when you're a man?"

"Oh, I don't know. I'll be a soldier, perhaps."

"Oh, I'm sure you wouldn't like to be a soldier and kill people."

"Yes, I would. There's lots of people I'd like to kill."

Mrs. Le Page drew her skirts back a little.

"How horrible! I'm sure your mother wouldn't like to hear that."

But Mr. Cole had caught the last words of the dialogue and interrupted with:

"But what could be finer, Mrs. Le Page, than the defence of one's country? Would you have our young lads grow up faint-hearted and fail their Motherland when she calls? What can be finer, I say, than to die for Queen and country? Would not every mother have her son shed his blood for liberty and freedom? . . . No, Jeremy, not another. You've had quite enough. It would indeed be a disheartening sight if we elders were to watch our sons and grandchildren turning their swords into plough-shares——"

He was interrupted by a shrill cry from Mrs. Le Page:

"Charlotte, darling, do hold your sunshade up. All the left side of your face is exposed. That's better, dear. I beg your pardon, Mr. Cole."

But Mr. Cole was offended.

"I hope no son of mine will ever show himself a faint heart," he concluded severely.

The luncheon, in fact, had been a most dismal failure. The Coles could fling their minds back to luncheons on this same beach that had been simply riotous successes. What fun they had had! What games! What bathes? Now the very sight of Mr. Le Page's black beard was enough. Even Jeremy felt that things were wrong. Then he looked at Charlotte and was satisfied. There she sat, straight and stiff, her hands on her lap, her hair falling in lovely golden ripples down her back, her gaze fixed on distance. Oh! she was beautiful! He would do whatever she told him; he would give her Miss Noah and the apple tree; he would—— A sound disturbed his devotions. He turned. Both Mr. and Mrs. Le Page were fast asleep.

IV

"Children," whispered Mrs. Cole, "very quietly now, so that you don't disturb anyone, run off to the farther beach and play. Helen, you'll see that everything is all right, won't you ?"

It was only just in time that Jeremy succeeded in strangling Hamlet's bark into a snort, and even then they all looked round for a moment at the sleepers in the greatest anxiety. But no, they had not been disturbed. If only Mr. Le Page could have known what he resembled lying there with his mouth open! But he did not know. He was doubtless dreaming of his property.

The children crept away. Charlotte and Jeremy together. Jeremy's heart beat thickly. At last he had the lovely creature in his charge. It was true that he did not quite know what he was going to do with her, and that even now, in the height of his admiration, he did wish that she would not walk as though she were treading on red-hot ploughshares, and that she could talk a little instead of giving little shivers of apprehension at every step.

"I must say," he thought to himself, "she's rather silly in some ways. Perhaps it wouldn't be fun to see her always."

They turned the corner round a projecting finger of

rock, and a new little beach, white and gleaming, lay in front of them.

"Well," said Jeremy, "here we are. What shall we play?"

There was dead silence.

"We might play pirates," he continued. "I'll be the pirate, and Mary can sit on that rock until the water comes round her, and Charlotte shall hide in that cave——"

There was still silence. Looking about him, he discovered from his sisters' countenances that they were resolved to lend no kind of assistance, and he then from that deduced the simple fact that his sisters hated Charlotte and were not going to make it pleasant for her in any way if they could help it. Oh! it was a miserable picnic! The worst that he'd ever had.

"It's too hot to play," said Helen loftily. "I'm going to sit down over there."

"So am I," said Mary.

They moved away, their heads in the air and their legs ridiculously stiff.

Jeremy gazed at Charlotte in distress. It was very wicked of his sisters to go off like that, but it was also very silly of Charlotte to stand there so helplessly. He was beginning to think that perhaps he would give the thimble to Miss Jones after all.

"Would you like to go and see the pool where the little crabs are?" he asked.

"I don't know," she answered, her upper lip trembling as though she were going to cry. "I want to go home with Mother."

"You can't go home," he said firmly, "and you can't see your mother, because she's asleep."

"I've made my shoes dirty," she said, looking down at her feet, "and I'm so tired of holding my sunshade."

"I should shut it up," Jeremy said without any hesitation. "I think it's a silly thing. I'm glad I'm not a girl. Do you have to take it with you everywhere?"

"Not if it's raining. Then I have an umbrella."

"I think you'd better come and see the crabs," he settled. "They're only just over there."

She moved along with him reluctantly, looking back continually to where her mother ought to be.

"Are you enjoying yourself?" Jeremy asked politely.

"No," she said, without any hesitation, "I want to go home."

"She's as selfish as anything," he thought to himself. "We're giving the party, and she ought to have said 'Yes' even if she wasn't."

"Do you like my dog?" he asked, with another effort at light conversation.

"No," she answered, with a little shiver. "He's ugly."

"He isn't ugly," Jeremy returned indignantly. "He isn't perhaps the very best breed, but Uncle Samuel says that that doesn't matter if he's clever. He's better than any other dog. I love him more than anybody. He isn't ugly!"

"He is," cried Charlotte with a kind of wail. "Oh! I want to go home."

"Well, you can't go home," he answered her fiercely. "So you needn't think about it."

They came to the little pools, three of them, now clear as crystal, blue on their surface, with green depths and red shelving rock.

"Now you sit there," he said cheerfully. "No one will touch you. The crabs won't get at you."

He looked about him and noticed with surprise where he was. He was sitting on the farther corner of the very beach where the Scarlet Admiral had landed with his men. It was out there beyond that bend of rock that the wonderful ship had rode, with its gold and silk, its jewelled masts and its glittering board. Directly opposite to him was the little green path that led up the hill, and above it the very field—Farmer Ede's field!

For a long, long time they sat there in silence. He forgot Charlotte in his interest over his discovery, staring about him and watching how quickly the August afternoon was losing its heat and colour, so that already a little cold autumnal wind was playing about the sand, the colours were being drawn from the sky, and a grey web was slowly pulled across the sea.

"Now," he said cheerfully at last to Charlotte, "I'll look for the crabs."

"I hate crabs," she said. "I want to go home."

"You can't go home," he answered furiously. "What's the good of saying that over and over again? You aren't going yet, so it's no use saying you are."

"You're a horrid little boy," she brought out with a kind of inanimate sob.

He did not reply to that; he was still trying to behave like a gentleman. How could he ever have liked her? Why, her hair was not so much after all. What was hair when you come to think of it? Mary got on quite well with hers, ugly though it was. She was stupid, stupid, stupid! She was like someone dead. As he searched for the crabs that weren't there he felt his temper growing.

Soon he would lead her back to her mother and leave her there and never see her again.

But this was not the climax of the afternoon.

When he looked up from gazing into the pool the whole world seemed to have changed. He was still dazzled perhaps by the reflection of the water in his eyes, and yet it was not altogether that. It was not altogether because the day was slipping from afternoon into evening.

The lazy ripple of the water as it slutched up the sand and then broke, the shadows that were creeping farther and farther from rock to rock, the green light that pushed up from the horizon into the faint blue, the grey web of the sea, the thick gathering of the hills as they crept more closely about the little darkening beach . . . it was none of these things.

He began hurriedly to tell Charlotte about the Scarlet Admiral. Even as he told her he was himself caught into the excitement of the narration. He forgot her; he did not see her white cheeks, her mouth open with terror, an expression new to her, that her face had never known before, stealing into her eyes. He told her how the Fool had seen the ship, how the Admiral had landed, then left his men on the beach, how he had climbed the little green path, how the young man had followed him, how they had fought, how the young man had fallen. What was that? Jeremy jumped from his rock. "I say, did you hear anything?"

And that was enough for Charlotte. With one scream, a scream such as she had never uttered in her life before, she turned, and then, running as indeed she had never run before, she stumbled, half fell, stumbled, finally ran as though the whole world of her ghosts was behind her. Her screams were so piercing that they may well have startled the villagers of Rafiel.

Jeremy followed her, but his mind was not with her. Was he going to see something? What was it? Who was it?

Then the awful catastrophe that finished the afternoon occurred. Turning the corner of the rock, Charlotte missed her footing and fell straight into a pool. Jeremy, Mary and Helen were upon her almost as she fell. They dragged her out, but alas! what a sight was there! Instead of the beautiful and magnificent Charlotte there was a bedraggled and dirty little girl.

But also, instead of an inanimate and lifeless doll, there was at last a human being, a terrified soul.

The scene that followed passes all power of description. Mrs. Le Page wailed like a lost spirit; Mr. Le Page was so rude to Mr. Cole that it might confidently be said that those two gentlemen would never speak to one another again. Mrs. Cole, dismayed though she was, had some fatalistic consolation that she had known from the first that the picnic would be a most dreadful failure and that the worst had occurred; there was no more to come.

Everyone was too deeply occupied to scold Jeremy. They all moved up to the farm, Charlotte behaving most strangely, even striking her mother and crying: "Let me go! Let me go! I don't want to be clean! I'm frightened! I'm frightened!"

Jeremy hung behind the others. At the bottom of the little lane he stood and waited. Was there a figure coming up through the dusk? Did someone pass him? Why did he suddenly feel no longer afraid, but only reassured and with the strangest certainty that the lane, the beach, the field belonged to him now? He would come there and live when he grew up. He would come often. Had the Scarlet Admiral passed him? If not the Scarlet Admiral, then the other.

The sea picnic had, after all, been not quite a misfortune.

Jeremy had been made free of the land.

And Charlotte? Charlotte had been woken up, and never would go to sleep again.

CHAPTER X

MARY

I

MARY COLE had been, all her life, that thing beloved of the sentimental novelist, a misunderstood child. She was the only misunderstood member of the Cole family, and she was misunderstood, as is very often the case, in a large measure because she was so plain. Had she been good-looking as Helen, or independent as Jeremy, she would have either attracted the world in general, or have been indifferent as to whether she attracted it or not. As it was, she longed to attract everyone, and, in truth, attracted nobody. She might have found consolation in books or her own highly-coloured imaginations had it not been for the burning passions which she formed, at a very early age, for living people. For some years now her life had centred round her brother Jeremy. Had the Coles been an observant family they might, perhaps, have found some pathos in the way in which Mary, with her pale sallow complexion, her pear-shaped face with its dull, grey eyes, her enormous glasses, her lanky colourless hair, and her thin, bony figure, gazed at her masculine and independent brother.

Uncle Samuel might have noticed, but he was occupied with his painting. For the rest they were not observant. Mary was only seven years of age, but she had the capacity

231

for being hurt of a person of thirty. She was hurt by
everything and everybody. When somebody said: "Now,
Mary, hurry up. You're always so slow," she was hurt.
If Helen told her that she was selfish, she was hurt, and
would sit wondering whether she was selfish or no. If
Mrs. Cole said that she must brush her hair more carefully
she was hurt, and when Jeremy said anything sharp to
her she was in agony. She discovered very quickly that
no one cared for her agonies. The Coles were a plain,
matter-of-fact race, and had the day's work to finish. They
had no intention of thinking too much of their children's
feelings. Thirty years ago that was not so popular as it
is now. Meanwhile, her devotion to her brother grew with
every month of her life. She thought him, in all honesty,
the most miraculous of all human beings. There was
more in her worship than mere dog-like fidelity. She
adored him for reasons that were real and true; for his
independence, his obstinacy, his sense of fun, his sudden,
unexpected kindnesses, his sudden helplessness, and above
all, for his bravery. He seemed to her the bravest hero in
all history, and she felt it the more because she was herself
compact of every fear and terror known to man. It was
not enough for her, the ordinary panic that belongs to all
human life at every stage of its progress. She feared
everything and everybody, and only hid her fear by a
persistent cover of almost obstinate stupidity, which de-
ceived, to some extent, her relations, but never in any
degree herself. She knew that she was plain, awkward
and hesitating, but she knew also that she was clever. She
knew that she could do everything twice as fast as Jeremy
and Helen, that she was often so impatient of their slow
progress at lessons that she would beat her foot on the

ground in a kind of agonised impatience. She knew that she was clever, and she wondered sometimes why her cleverness did not give her more advantage. Why, for instance, should Helen's good looks be noticed at once by every visitor and her own cleverness be unnoticed? Certainly, on occasions, her mother would say: "And Mary? I don't think you've met Mary. Come and say, how do you do, Mary. Mary is the clever one of the family!" but it was always said in a deprecating, apologetic tone, which made Mary hang her head and hate both herself and her mother.

She told herself stories of the times when Jeremy would have to depend entirely upon the splendour of her brains for his delivery from some horror—death, torture or disgrace. At present those times were, she was bound to confess to herself, very distant. He depended upon no one for anything; he could not be said to need Mary's assistance in any particular. And with this burning desire of hers came, of course, jealousy. There are some happy, easy natures to whom jealousy is, through life, unknown. They are to be envied. Jealousy in a grown-up human being is bad; in a child it is terrible. Had you told Mrs. Cole —good mother though she was—that her daughter Mary, aged seven, suffered tortures through jealousy, she would have assured you that it was not, in reality, jealousy, but rather indigestion, and that a little medicine would put it right.

Mary was quite helpless. What is a child to do if she is jealous? Other children do not understand her, her elders laugh at her. Mary, with a wisdom greatly beyond her years, realised very quickly that this was some sort of horrible disease, with which she must wrestle alone. Above all, she must never allow Jeremy to know anything about it. He was, of course, sublimely unaware of the matter; he knew that Mary was silly sometimes, but he attributed that to her sex; he went on his way, happily indifferent whether anyone cared for him or no. . . .

Mary suffered agonies when, as sometimes happened, Jeremy sat with his arm round Helen's neck and his cheek up against hers. She suffered when, in a mood of tempestuous affection to the whole world, he kissed Miss Jones. She even suffered when he sat at his mother's feet whilst she read "The Dove in the Eagle's Nest," or "Engel the Fearless."

Most of all, however, she suffered over Hamlet. She knew that at this present time Hamlet was the one creature for whom Jeremy passionately cared. He loved his mother, but with the love that custom and habit has tamed and modified, although since Mrs. Cole's illness in the early summer he had cared for her in a manner more demonstrative and openly affectionate. Nevertheless, it was Hamlet who commanded Jeremy's heart, and Mary knew it. Matters were made worse by the undoubted truth that Hamlet did not care very much for Mary—that is, he never gave any signs of caring, and very often walked out of the room when she came into it. Mary could have cared for the dog as enthusiastically as Jeremy—she was always sentimental about animals—but now she was shut out from their alliance, and she knew that when she came up to them and began to pat or stroke Hamlet, Jeremy was annoyed and Hamlet's skin wriggled in a kind of retreating fashion under her fingers. Wise people will say that it is impossible for this to be a serious trouble to a child. It was increasingly serious to Mary.

Jeremy was not, perhaps, so tactful as he might have been. "Oh bother, Mary!" he would say. "You've gone and waked Hamlet up!" or "Don't stroke Hamlet that way, Mary; he hates it!" or "No, I'm going for a walk with Hamlet; we don't want anyone!" Or Hamlet himself would suddenly bark at her as though he hated her, or would bare his teeth and grin at her in a mocking, sarcastic way that he had. At first, as an answer to this, she had the ridiculous idea of herself adopting an animal, and she selected, for this purpose, the kitchen cat, a dull, somnolent beast, whose sleek black hair was furtive, and green, crooked eyes malignant. The cat showed no signs of affection for Mary, nor could she herself honestly care for it. When she brought it with her into the schoolroom, Hamlet treated it in a scornful, sarcastic fashion that was worse than outrageous attack. The cat was uncleanly, and was speedily banished back into the kitchen. Mary's jealousy of Hamlet then grew apace, and with that jealousy, unfortunately, her secret appreciation of his splendours. She could not help admitting to herself that he was the most attractive dog in the world. She would look at him from under her spectacles when she was supposed to be reading and watch him as he rolled, kicking his legs in the air, or lay stretched out, his black wet nose against his paws, his eyes gleaming, his gaze fixed like the point of a dagger raised to strike, upon some trophy, or enemy, or spoil, or sat, solemn and pompous, like the Lord Mayor holding a meeting, as Jeremy said, up against his master's leg, square and solid as though he were cut out of wood, his peaked beard supercilious, his very ears at a patronising angle; or, as Mary loved best of all to see him, when he was simply childish, playing, as though he was still a new-found puppy, with pieces of paper or balls of string, rolling and choking, growling, purring, staggering and tumbling. At such times, again and again, her impulse would be to go forward and applaud him, and then the instinct that she would be checked by Jeremy stayed her.

She knew very well that Jeremy realised nothing of this. Jeremy was not given to the consideration of other people's motives—his own independence saved him from anxiety about others. He had the English characteristic of fancying that others must like and dislike as he himself liked and disliked. Of sentiment he had no knowledge whatever.

As this year grew towards summer Mary had the feeling that Jeremy was slipping away from her. She did not know what had happened to him. In the old days he had asked her opinion about many things; he had seemed to enjoy the long stories that she had told him—at any rate, he had listened to them very politely—and he had asked her to suggest games or to play with his toys. Now as the summer drew near, he did none of these things. He was frankly impatient with her stories, never asked her advice about anything, and never played with her. Was he growing very conceited? Was it because he was going to school, and thought himself too old for his sisters? No, he did not seem to be conceited—he had always been proud, but never conceited. It was rather as though he had lately had thoughts of his own, almost against his will, and that these had shut him off from the people round him.

Then, when their mother was so ill and Barbara made her startling appearance Jeremy kept more to himself. He never talked about his mother's illness, as did the others, and yet Mary knew that he had been more deeply concerned than any of them. She had been miserable, of course, but to Jeremy it had been as though he had been led into a new world altogether; Helen and she were still in their old places, and Jeremy had left them.

At last just before they all moved to Cow Farm Mary made a silly scene. She had not intended to make a scene. Scenes seemed to come upon her, like evil birds, straight out of the air, to seize her before she knew where she was, to envelop and carry her up with them; at last, when all the mischief was done, to set her on her feet again, battered, torn and bitterly ashamed. One evening she was sitting deep in "Charlotte Mary," and Hamlet, bunched up against his master's leg, stared at her. She had long ago told herself that it was ridiculous to mind what Hamlet did, that he was not looking at her, and, in any case, he was only a dog—and so on.

But to-night she was tired, and had read so long that her head ached—Hamlet was laughing at her, his eyes stared through his hair at her, cynically, superciliously, contemptuously. His lip curled and his beard bristled. Moved by a sudden wild impulse she picked up "The Chaplet of Pearls" and threw it at him. It hit him (not very severely), and he gave the sharp, melodramatic howl that he always used when it was his dignity rather than his body that was hurt. Jeremy looked up, saw what had happened, and a fine scene followed. Mary had hysterics, stamped and screamed and howled. Jeremy, his face white, stood and said nothing, but looked as though he hated her, which at that moment he undoubtedly did. It was that look which more than anything else in the world she dreaded.

She made herself sick with crying; then apologised with an abjection that only irritated him the more; finally remembered the smallest details of the affair long after he had forgotten all about it.

II

During the first weeks at Cow Farm Mary was happy. She had then many especial private joys, such as climbing into one of the old apple trees behind the house and reading there, safe from the world, or inventing for herself wonderful adventures out of the dark glooms and sunlit spaces of the orchard, or creeping about the lofts and barns as though they were full of the most desperate dangers and hazards that she alone had the pluck and intelligence to overcome. Then Mrs. Monk was kind to her, and listened to her imaginative chatter with a most marvellous patience. Mary did not know that, after these narrations, she would shake her head and say to her husband: "Not long for this world, I'm thinking, poor worm . . . not long for this world."

Then, at first Jeremy was kind and considerate. He was so happy that he did not mind what anyone did, and he would listen to Mary's stories quite in the old way, whistling to himself, not thinking about her at all perhaps, really, but very patient. After the first fortnight he slipped away from her again—and now more than ever before. He went off for long walks with Hamlet, refusing to take her with them; he answered her questions so vaguely that she could see that he paid her no attention at all; he turned upon her and rent her if she complained. And it was all, she was sure, that horrible dog. Jeremy was always with Hamlet now. The free life that the farm gave them, no lessons, no set hours, no care for appearances, left them to choose their own ways, and so developed their individualities. Helen was now more and more with her elders, was becoming that invaluable thing, "a great help to her mother," and even, to her own inexhaustible pride, paid two calls with Mrs. Cole on the wives of neighbouring farmers. Then, Barbara absorbed more than ever of Helen's attention, and Mary was not allowed to share in these rites and services because "she always made Barbara cry."

She was, therefore, very much alone, and felt all her injuries twice as deeply as she had felt them before. Hamlet began to be an obsession with her. She had always had a habit of talking to herself, and now she could be heard telling herself that if it were not for the dog, Jeremy would always be with her, would play with her, walk with her, laugh with her as he used to do. She acquired now an awkward habit of gazing at him with passionate intensity. He would raise his eyes and find the great moon-faced spectacles fixed upon him with a beseeching, reproachful glare in the light of them. This would irritate him intensely. He would say:

"You'll know me next time, Mary."

She would blush crimson and then, with trembling mouth, answer:

"I wasn't looking."

"Yes, you were."

"No, I wasn't."

"Of course, you were—staring as though I were an Indian or Chinaman. If my face is dirty, say so."

"It isn't dirty."

"Well, then——"

"You're always so cross."

"I'm not cross—only you're so silly——"

"You usen't always to say I was silly. Now you always do—every minute."

"So you are." Then as he saw the tears coming he would get up and go away. He didn't mean to be unkind to her; he was fond of her—but he hated scenes.

"Mary's always howling about something now," he confided to Helen.

"Is she?" Helen answered with indifference. "Mary's such a baby."

So Mary began to attribute everything to the dog. It seemed to her then that she met the animal everywhere. Cow Farm was a rambling building, with dark, uneven stairs, low-ceilinged rooms, queer, odd corners, and sudden unexpected doors. It seemed to Mary as though in this place there were two Hamlets. When, in the evening she went to her room, hurrying through the passages for fear of what she might see, stumbling over the uneven boards, sniffling the mice and straw under the smell of her tallow candle, suddenly out of nowhere at all Hamlet would appear scurrying along, like the White Rabbit, intent on serious business.

He came so softly and with so sudden a flurry and scatter when she did hear him that her heart would beat for minutes afterwards, and she would not dare that night to search, as she usually did, for burglars under her bed, but would lie, quaking, hot and staring, unable to sleep. When at last dreams came they would be haunted by a monstrous dog, all hair and eyes, who, with padding feet, would track her round and round a room from which there was no escape. Hamlet, being one of the wisest of

dogs, very quickly discovered that Mary hated him. He
was not a sentimental dog, and he did not devote his time
to inventing ways in which he might placate his enemy,
he simply avoided her. But he could not hinder a certain
cynical and ironic pleasure that he had of, so to speak,
flaunting his master in her face. He clung to Jeremy
more resolutely than ever, would jump up at him, lick
his hands and tumble about in front of him whenever
Mary was there, and then suddenly, very straight and very
grave, would stare at her as though he were the most devout
and obedient dog in the place. Indeed, he bore her no
malice; he could afford to disregard the Marys of this
world, and of women in general he had a poor opinion.
But he loved to tease, and Mary was an easy prey. He
had his fun with her.

After the affair of the sea-picnic, Jeremy was for some
time under a cloud. It was felt that he was getting too
big for anyone to manage. It was not that he was wicked,
not that he kept bad company with the boys on the farm,
or was dishonest, or told lies, or stole things—no, he gave
no one that kind of anxiety—but that he was developing
quite unmistakably a will of his own, and had a remarkable
way of doing what he wanted without being actually disobedient, which was very puzzling to his elders. Being a
little in disgrace he went off more than ever by himself,
always appearing again at the appointed time, but telling
no one where he had been or what he had been doing.
His father had no influence over him at all, whilst Uncle
Samuel could make him do whatever he wanted—and this,
as Aunt Amy said, "was really a pity."

"It's a good thing he's going to school in September,"
sighed his mother. "He's getting out of women's hands."

Mary longed with feverish longing to share in his adventures. If only he would tell her what he did on these walks of his. But no, only Hamlet knew. Perhaps, if he did not go with the dog he would go with her. When this idea crept into her brain she seized it and clutched it. That was all he wanted—a companion! Were Hamlet not there he would take her. Were Hamlet not there. . . . She began to brood over this. She wandered. . . . She considered. She shuddered at her own wickedness; she tried to drive the thoughts from her head, but they kept coming.

After all, no one need know. For a day or two Jeremy would be sorry and then he would forget. She knew the man who went round selling dogs—selling dogs and buying them.

She shuddered at her wickedness.

III

The last days of August came, and with them the last week of the holiday. Already there was a scent of autumn in the air, leaves were turning gold and red, and the evenings came cool and sudden, upon the hot summer afternoons. Mary was not very well; she had caught a cold somewhere, and existed in the irritating condition of going out one day and being held indoors the next. This upset her temper, and at night she had nightmares, in which she saw clouds of smoke crawling in at her window, snakes on the floor, and crimson flames darting at her from the ceiling. It was because she was in an abnormal condition of health that the idea of doing something with Hamlet had gained such a hold upon her. She considered the matter from every point of view. She did not want to be cruel to the dog; she supposed that after a week or two he would be quite happy with his new master, and, in any case, he had strolled in so casually upon the Cole family that he was accustomed to a wandering life.

She did not intend that anyone should know. It was to be a deep secret all of her own.

Jeremy was going to school in September, and before then she must make him friendly to her again. She saw stretching in front of her all the lonely autumn without him and her own memories of the miserable summer to make her wretched. She was an extremely sentimental little girl.

As always happens when one is meditating with a placated conscience a wicked deed, the opportunity was suddenly offered to Mary of achieving her purpose. One morning Jeremy, after refusing to listen to one of Mary's long romances, lost his temper.

"I can't stop," he said. "You bother and bother and bother. Aunt Amy says you nearly make her mad."

"I don't care what Aunt Amy says," Mary on the edge of tears replied.

"Hamlet and I are going out. And I'm sick of your silly old stories." Then he suddenly stopped and gazed at Mary, who was beginning, as usual, to weep.

"Look here, Mary, what's been the matter with you lately? You're always crying now or something. And you look at me as though I'd done something dreadful. I haven't done anything."

"I—never—said you—had," Mary gulped out. He rubbed his nose in a way that he had when he was puzzled.

"If it's anything I do, tell me. It's so silly always crying. The holidays will be over soon, and you've done nothing but cry."

"You're—never—with me—now," Mary sobbed.

"Well, I've been busy."

"You haven't. You can't be busy all—by yourself."

"Oh, yes, you can." He was getting impatient. "Anyway, you might let Hamlet and me alone. You're always bothering one of us."

"No, I'm not." She choked an enormous sob and burst out with: "It's always Hamlet now. I wish he'd never—come. It was much nicer before."

Then he lost his temper. "Oh, you're a baby! I'm sick of you and your nonsense," he cried, and stamped off.

In Mary's red-rimmed eyes, as she watched him go, determination grew.

It happened that upon the afternoon of that same day Miss Jones announced that she would take Mary for a walk; then, just as they passed through the farm gates, Hamlet, rushing out, joined them. He did not often honour them with his company, despising women most especially when they walked, but to-day his master was busy digging for worms in the vegetable garden, and, after a quarter of an hour's contemplation of this fascinating occupation, he had wandered off in search of a livelier game. He decided to join Miss Jones; he could do what he pleased, he could amuse himself with her ineffectual attempts to keep him in order, and he could irritate Mary; so he danced along, with his tail in the air, barking at imaginary rats and poking his nose into hedges.

Mary, with a sudden tightened clutching of the heart, realised that her hour was upon her. She felt so wicked as she realised this that she wondered that the ground

didn't open up and swallow her, as it had done with those
unfortunate people in the Bible. But no, the world was
calm. Little white milky clouds raced in lines and circles
across the sky, and once and again a leaf floated from a
tree, hung for a moment suspended, and then turned slowly
to the ground. The hedges were a dark black-green, high
and thick above the dusty road; there had been no rain for
weeks. Truly a stable world. Mary, glaring at Fate,
wondered how it could be so.

Miss Jones, who was happy and optimistic to-day, talked
in a tenderly reminiscent tone of her youth. This vein of
reminiscence Mary, on her normal day, loved. To-day she
did not hear a word that Miss Jones said.

"I remember my mother saying so well to my dear
brother: 'Do what you like, my boy. I trust you.' And
indeed Alfred was to be trusted if ever a boy was. It is
a remarkable thing, but I cannot remember a single occasion of dishonesty on Alfred's part. 'A white lie,' he
would often say, 'is a lie, and a lie is a sin—white or black,
always a sin'; and I remember that he would often put
mother to a serious inconvenience by his telling callers
that she was in when she had wished it to be said that she
was not at home. He felt it his serious duty, and so he
told Mother. 'Don't ask me to tell a lie, Mother,' I
remember his saying. 'I cannot do it.'"

"Like George Washington," said Mary, suddenly catching the last words of Miss Jones's sentence.

"He was like many famous characters in history, I used
to think. Once I remember reading about Oliver Crom-
well. . . . Where is that dog? Hamlet! Hamlet! Perhaps he's gone after the sheep. Ah! there he is! Hamlet,
you naughty dog!"

They were approaching one of their favourite pieces of country—Mellot Wood. Here, on the wood's edge, the ground broke away, running down in a field of corn to a little green valley with clustered trees that showed only their heads, so thickly embedded were they, and beyond the valley the sea. The sea looked quite close here, although it was in reality four miles distant. Never was such a place as this view for light and shadow. The clouds raced like the black wings of enormous birds across the light green valley, and the red-gold of the cornfield was tossed into the haze and swept like a golden shadow across the earth, bending back again when the breeze had died. Behind Mellot Wood was Mellot Farm, an old eighteenth-century house about which there was a fine tragic story with a murder and a ghost in it, and this, of course, gave Mellot Wood an additional charm. When they arrived at the outskirts of Mellot Wood Mary looked about her. It was here, on the edge of the Rafiel Road that skirted the wood, that she had once seen the dog-man eating his luncheon out of a red pocket handkerchief. There was no sign of him to-day. All was silent and still. Only the little wood uttered little sighs of content beneath the flying clouds. Hamlet, tired with his racing after imaginary rabbits, walked quietly along by Mary's side. What was she to do? She had once again the desperate feeling that something stronger than she had swept down upon her and was forcing her to do this thing. She seemed to have no will of her own, but to be watching some other commit an act whose dangerous wickedness froze her heart. How could she? But she must. Some-one was doing it for her.

And in very truth it seemed so. Miss Jones said that

now they were here she might as well call upon Miss
Andrews, the sister of the Mellot farmer. Miss Andrews
had promised her some ducks' eggs. They pushed open
the farm gate, passed across the yard and knocked on the
house door. Near Mary was a large barn with a heavy
door, now ajar. Hamlet sat gazing pensively at a flock
of geese, his tongue out, panting contentedly.

"Wait here one minute, Mary," said Miss Jones. "I
won't stay."

Miss Jones disappeared. Mary, still under the strange
sense that it was not she, but another, who did these
things, moved back to the barn, calling softly to Hamlet.
He followed her, sniffing a rat somewhere. Very quickly
she pulled back the door; he, still investigating his rat,
followed into the dark excitements of the barn. With a
quick movement she bent down, slipped off his collar,
which she hid in her dress, then shut him in. She knew
that for a moment or two he would still be pursuing his
rat, and she saw, with guilty relief, Miss Jones come out
to her just as she had finished her evil deed.

. "Miss Andrews is out," said Miss Jones. "They are
all away at Liskane Fair."

They left the farm and walked down the road. Hamlet
had not begun his cry.

IV

Miss Jones was pleased. "Such a nice servant," she
said. "One of the old kind. She had been with the
family fifty years, she told me, and had nursed Mr.
Andrews on her knee. Fancy! Such a large fat man
as he is now. Too much beer, I suppose. I suppose they
get so thirsty with all the straw and hay about. Yes, a

really nice woman. She told me that there was no place in Glebeshire to touch them for cream. I dare say they're right. After all, you never can tell. I remember at home . . ."

She broke off then and cried: "Where's Hamlet?"

Mary, wickeder than ever, stared through her spectacles down the road. "I don't know, Miss Jones," she said. They had left the wood and the farm, and there was nothing to be seen but the long white ribbon of road hemmed in by the high hedges.

"Perhaps he stayed behind at the farm," said Miss Jones.

Then Mary told her worst lie.

"Oh, no, Miss Jones. He ran past us just now. Didn't you see him?"

"No, I didn't. He's gone on ahead, I suppose. He runs home sometimes. Naughty dog! We shall catch him up."

But of course they did not. They passed through the gates of Cow Farm and still nothing of Hamlet was to be seen.

"Oh dear! Oh dear!" said Miss Jones. "I do hope that he's arrived. Whatever will Jeremy say if anything has gone wrong?"

Mary was breathing hard now, as though she had been running a desperate race. She would at this moment have given all that she possessed, or all that she was ever likely to possess, to recall her deed. If she could have seen Hamlet rushing down the road towards her she would have cried with relief; there seemed now to be suddenly removed from her that outside agency that had forced her to do this thing; now, having compelled her, it had withdrawn and left her to carry the consequences. Strangely confused in her sentimental soul was her terror of Jeremy's wrath and her own picture of the wretched Hamlet barking his heart out, frightened, thirsty, and lonely. Her teeth began to chatter; she clenched her hands together.

Miss Jones went across the courtyard, calling:

"Hamlet! Hamlet!"

The family was collected, having just sat down to tea, so that the announcement received its full measure of excitement.

"Has Hamlet come back? We thought he was ahead of us."

A chair had tumbled over. Jeremy had run round the table to Miss Jones.

"What's that? Hamlet? Where is he?"

"We thought he must be ahead of us. He ran past us down the road, and we thought——"

They thought! Silly women! Jeremy, as though he were challenging a god, stood up against Miss Jones, hurling questions at her. Where had they been? What road had they taken? Had they gone into the wood? Whereabouts had he run past them?

"I don't know," said Miss Jones to this last. "I didn't see him. Mary did."

Jeremy turned upon Mary. "Where was it you saw him?"

She couldn't speak. Her tongue wouldn't move, her lips wouldn't open; she could but waggle her head like an idiot. She saw nothing but his face. It was a desperate face. She knew so much better than all the others what the thought of losing Hamlet was to him. It was part of the harshness of her fate that she should understand him so much better than the others did.

But she herself had not realised how hardly he would take it.

"I didn't——— I couldn't——"

"There's the dog-man," he stammered. "He'll have stolen him." Then he was off out of the room in an instant.

And that was more than Mary could bear. She realised, even as she followed him, that she was giving her whole case away, that she was now, as always, weak when she should be strong, soft when she should be hard, good when she should be wicked, wicked when she should be good. She could not help herself. With trembling limbs and a heart that seemed to be hammering her body into pieces she followed him out. She found him in the hall, tugging at his coat.

"Where are you going?" she said weakly.

"Going?" he answered fiercely. "Where do you think?" He glared at her. "Just like you." He broke off, suddenly appealing to her. "Mary, *can't* you remember? It will be getting dark soon, and if we have to wait until to-morrow the dog-man will have got him. At any rate, he had his collar——"

Then Mary broke out. She burst into sobs, pushed her hand into her dress, and held out the collar to him.

"There it is! There it is!" she said hysterically.

"You've got it?" He stared at her, suspicion slowly coming to him. "But how——? What have you done?"

She looked up at him wild-eyed, the tears making dirty lines on her face, her hand out towards him.

"I took it off. I shut Hamlet into the barn at Mellot

Farm. I wanted him to be lost. I didn't want you to have him. I hated him—always being with you, and me never."

Jeremy moved back, and at the sudden look in his eyes her sobbing ceased, she caught her breath and stared at him with a silly fixed stare as a rabbit quivers before a snake.

Jeremy said in his ordinary voice:

"You shut Hamlet up? You didn't want him to be found?"

She nodded her head several times as though now she must convince him quickly of this——

"Yes, yes, yes. I did. . . . I know I shouldn't, but I couldn't help it——"

He clutched her arm, and then shook her with a sudden wave of fierce physical anger that was utterly unlike him, and, therefore, the more terrifying.

"You wicked, wicked—— You beast, Mary!"

She could only sob, her head hanging down. He let her go.

"What barn was it?"

She described the place.

He gave her another look of contempt and then rushed off, running across the courtyard.

There was still no one in the hall; she could go up to her room without the fear of being disturbed. She found the room, all white and black now with the gathering dusk. Beyond the window the evening breeze was rustling in the dark trees of the garden and the boom of the sea could be heard faintly. Mary sat, where she always sat when she was unhappy, inside the wardrobe with her head amongst the clothes. They in some way comforted her; she was not so lonely with them, nor did she feel so strongly the empty distances of the long room, the white light of the window-frames, nor the mysterious secrecy of the high elms knocking their heads together in the garden outside.

She had a fit of hysterical crying, biting the hanging clothes between her teeth, feeling suddenly sick and tired and exhausted, with flaming eyes and a dry, parched throat. Why had she ever done such a thing, she loving Jeremy as she did? Would he ever forgive her? No, never; she saw that in his face. Perhaps he would—if he found Hamlet quickly and came back. Perhaps Hamlet never would be found. Then Jeremy's heart would be broken.

She slept from utter exhaustion, and was so found, when the room was quite dark and only shadows moved in it, by her mother.

"Why, Mary!" said Mrs. Cole. "What are you doing here? We couldn't think where you were. And where's Jeremy?"

"Jeremy!" She started up, remembering everything.

"Hasn't he come back? Oh, he's lost and he'll be killed, and it will be all my fault!" She burst into another fit of wild hysterical crying.

Her mother took her arm. "Mary, explain—— What have you done?"

Mary explained, her teeth chattering, her head aching so that she could not see.

"And you shut him up like that? Whatever—— Oh, Mary, you wicked girl! And Jeremy—— He's been away two hours now——"

She turned off, leaving Mary alone in the black room.

v

Mary was left to every terror that can beset a lonely, hysterical child—terror of Jeremy's fate, terror of Hamlet's loss, terror of her own crimes, above all, terror of the lonely room, the waving elms and the gathering dark. She could not move; she could not even close the door of the wardrobe, into whose shelter she had again crept. She stared at the white sheet of the window, with its black bars like railings and its ghostly hinting of a moon that would soon be up above the trees. Every noise frightened her, the working of the "separator" in a distant part of the farm, the whistling of some farm-hand out in the yard, the voice of some boy, "coo-ee"-ing faintly, the lingering echo of the vanished day—all these seemed to accuse her, to point fingers at her, to warn her of some awful impending punishment. "Ah! you're the little girl," they seemed to say, "who lost Jeremy's dog and broke Jeremy's heart." She was sure that someone was beneath her bed. That old terror haunted her with an almost humorous persistency every night before she went to sleep, but to-night there was a ghastly certainty and imminence about it that froze her blood. She crouched up against the hanging skirts, gazing at the black line between the floor and the white sheets, expecting at every second to see a protruding black mask, bloodshot eyes, a coarse hand. The memory of the burglary that they had had in the spring came upon her with redoubled force. Ah! surely, surely someone was there! She heard a movement, a scraping of a boot upon the floor, the thick hurried breathing of some desperate villain. . . .

Then these fears gave way to something worse than

them all, the certainty that Jeremy was dead. Ridiculous pictures passed before her, of Jeremy hanging from a tree, Jeremy lying frozen in the wood, the faithful Hamlet dead at his side, Jeremy stung by an adder and succumbing to his horrible tortures, Jeremy surrounded by violent men, who snatched Hamlet from him, beat him on the head and left him for dead on the ground.

She passed what seemed to her hours of torture under these horrible imaginings, tired out, almost out of her mind with the hysteria of her loneliness, her imagination and her conscience; she passed into a kind of apathy of unhappiness, thinking now only of Jeremy, longing for him, beseeching him to come back, telling the empty moonlit room that she never meant it; that she would do everything he wanted if only he came back to her; that she was a wicked girl; that she would never be wicked again. . . . And she took her punishment alone.

After endless ages of darkness and terror and misery she heard voices—then *his* voice! She jumped out of the wardrobe and listened. Yes; it *was* his voice. She pushed back the door, crept down the passage, and came suddenly upon a little group, with Jeremy in its midst, crowded together at the top of the stairs. Jeremy was wrapped up in his father's heavy coat, and looked very small and impish as he peered from out of it. He was greatly excited, his eyes shining, his mouth smiling, his cheeks flushed.

His audience consisted of Helen, Mrs. Cole, Miss Jones, and Aunt Amy. He described to them how he had run along the road "for miles and miles and miles," how at last he had found the farm, had rung the bell, and inquired, and discovered Hamlet licking up sugary tea in the farm kitchen; there had then been a rapturous meet-

ing, and he had boldly declared that he could find his way
home again without aid. "They wanted me to be driven
home in their trap, but I wasn't going to have that. They'd
been at the fair all day, and didn't want to go out again.
I could see that." So he and Hamlet started gaily on their
walk home, and then, in some way or another, he took the
wrong turn, and suddenly they were in Mellot Wood. "It
was dark as anything, you know, although there was going
to be a moon. We couldn't see a thing, and then I got
loster and loster. At last we just sat under a tree. There
was nothing more to do!" Then, apparently, Jeremy had
slept, and had, finally, been found in the proper romantic
manner by Jim and his father.

"Well, all's well that ends well," said Aunt Amy, with
a sniff. In spite of that momentary softness over the
defeat of the Dean's Ernest she liked her young nephew
no better than of old. She had desired that he should be
punished for this, but as she looked at the melting eyes
of Mrs. Cole and Miss Jones she had very little hope.

Mary was forgotten; no one noticed her.

"Bed," said Mrs. Cole.

"Really, what a terrible affair," said Miss Jones. "And
I can't help feeling that it was my fault."

"What Mary——" began Mrs. Cole. And then she
stopped. She had perhaps some sense that Mary had
already received sufficient punishment.

Mary waited, standing against the passage wall. Jeremy,
who had not seen her, vanished into his room. She waited,
then plucking up all her courage with the desperate suffo-
cating sense of a prisoner laying himself beneath the
guillotine, she knocked timidly on his door.

He said: "Come in," and entering, she saw him, in his

braces, standing on a chair trying to put the picture entitled "Daddy's Christmas" straight upon its nail. The sight of this familiar task—the picture would never hang straight, although every day Jeremy, who, strangely enough, had an eye to such matters, tried to correct it— cheered her a little.

"Won't it go straight?" she said feebly.

"No, it won't," he began, and then, suddenly realising the whole position, stopped.

"I'm sorry, Jeremy," she muttered, hanging her head down.

"Oh, that's all right," he answered, turning away from her and pulling at the string. "It was a beastly thing to do all the same," he added.

"Will you forgive me?" she asked.

"Oh, there isn't any forgiveness about it. Girls are queer, I suppose. I don't understand them myself. There, that's better. . . . I say, it was simply beastly under that tree——"

"Was it?"

"Beastly! There was something howling somewhere— a cat or something."

"You do forgive me, don't you?"

"Yes, yes. . . . I say, is that right now? Oh, it won't *stay* there. It's the wall or something."

He came down from the chair yawning.

"Jim's nice," he confided to her. "He's going to take me ratting one day!"

"I'm going," Mary said again, and waited.

Jeremy coloured, looked as though he would say something, then, in silence, presented a very grimy cheek. "Good-night," he said, with an air of intense relief.

"Good-night," she said, kissing him.

She closed the door behind her. She knew that the worst had happened. He had passed away, utterly beyond her company, her world, her interests. She crept along to her room, and there, with a determination and a strength rare in a child so young and so undisciplined, faced her loneliness.

CHAPTER XI

THE MERRY-GO-ROUND

I

THE holidays were over. The Coles were once more back in Polchester, and the most exciting period of Jeremy's life had begun. So at any rate he felt it. It might be that in later years there would be new exciting events, lion-hunting, for instance, or a war, or the tracking of niggers in the heart of Africa—he would be ready for them when they came—but these last weeks before his first departure for school offered him the prospect of the first real independence of his life. There could never be anything quite like that again. Nevertheless, school seemed still a long way distant. It was only his manliness that he was realising and a certain impatience and rest-lessness that underlay everything that he did.

September and October are often very lovely months in Polchester; autumn seems to come there with a greater warmth and richness than it does elsewhere. Along all the reaches of the Pol, right down to the sea, the leaves of the woods hung with a riotous magnificence that is glorious in its recklessness. The waters of that silent river are so still, so glassy, that the banks of gold and flaming red are reflected in all their richest colour down into the very heart of the stream, and it is only when a fish jumps or a twig falls from the overhanging trees that the mirror is broken and the colours flash into ripples and shadows of white and grey. The utter silence of all this world makes the Cathedral town sleepy, sluggish, forgotten of all men. As the autumn comes it seems to drowse away into winter to the tune of its Cathedral bells, to the scent of its burning leaves and the soft steps of its Canons and clergy. There is every autumn here a clerical conference, and long before the appointed week begins, and long after it is lawfully concluded, clergymen, strange clergymen with soft black hats, take the town for their own, gaze into Martin the pastry-cook's, sit in the dusk of the Cathedral listening to the organ; walk, their heads in air, their arms folded behind their backs, straight up Orange Street as though they were scaling Heaven itself; stop little children, pat their heads, and give them pennies; stand outside Poole's bookshop and delve in the 2d. box for thumb-marked sermons; stand gazing in learned fashion at the great West Door, investigating the saints and apostles portrayed thereon; hurry in their best hats and coats along the Close to some ladies' tea-party, or pass with solemn and anxious mien into the palace of the Bishop himself.

All these things belong to autumn in Polchester, as Jeremy very well knew, but the event that marks the true beginning of the season, the only way by which you may surely know that summer is over and autumn is come is Pauper's Fair.

This famous fair has been, from time immemorial, a noted event in Glebeshire life. Even now, when fairs have yielded to cinematographs as attractions for the people, Pauper's Fair gives its annual excitement. Thirty years ago it was the greatest event of the year in Polchester. All our fine people, of course, disliked it extremely. It disturbed the town for days, the town rocked in the arms of crowds of drunken sailors, the town gave shelter to gipsies and rogues and scoundrels, the town, the decent, amiable, happy town actually for a week or so seemed to invite the world of the blazing fire and the dancing clown. No wonder that our fine people shuddered. Only the other day—I speak now of these modern times —the Bishop tried to stop the whole business. He wrote to the *Glebeshire Morning News,* urging that Pauper's Fair, in these days of enlightenment and culture, cannot but be regretted by all those who have the healthy progress of our dear country at heart. Well, you would be amazed at the storm that his protest raised. People wrote from all over the County, and there were ultimately letters from patriotic Glebeshire citizens in New Zealand and South Africa. And in Polchester itself! Everyone—even those who had shuddered most at the fair's iniquities—was indignant. Give up the fair! One of the few signs left of that jolly Old England whose sentiment is cherished by us, whose fragments nevertheless we so readily stamp upon. No, the fair must remain and will remain, I have no doubt, until the very end of our national chapter.

Nowadays it has shed, very largely, I am afraid, the character that it gloriously maintained thirty years ago. Then it was really an invasion by the seafaring element of the County. All the little country ports and harbours poured out their fishermen and sailors, who came walking, driving, singing, laughing, swearing; they filled the streets, and went peering, like the wildest of ancient Picts, into the mysterious beauties of the Cathedral, and late at night, when the town should have slept, arm in arm they went roaring past the dark windows, singing their songs, stamping their feet, and every once and again ringing a decent door-bell for their amusement. It was very seldom that any harm was done. Once a serious fire broke out amongst the old wooden houses down on the river, and some of them were burnt to the ground, a fate that no one deplored; once a sailor was murdered in a drunken squabble at "The Dog and Pilchard," the wildest of the riverside hostelries; and once a Canon was caught and stripped and ducked in the waters of the Pol by a mob who resented his gentle appeals that they should try to prefer lemonade to gin; but these were the only three catastrophes in all the history of the fair.

During the fair week the town sniffed of the sea—of lobster and seaweed and tar and brine—and all the tales of the sea that have ever been told by man were told during these days in Polchester.

The decent people kept their doors locked, their children at home, and their valuables in the family safe. No upper class child in Polchester so much as saw the outside of a gipsy van. The Dean's Ernest was accustomed to boast that he had once been given a ride by a gipsy on a donkey, when his nurse was not looking, but no one credited the story, and the details with which he supported it were feeble and unconvincing. The Polchester children in general were told that "they would be stolen by the gipsies if they weren't careful," and, although some of them in extreme moments of rebellion and depression felt that the life of adventure thus offered to them might, after all, be more agreeable than the dreary realism of their natural days, the warning may be said to have been effective.

No family in Polchester was guarded more carefully in

this matter of the Pauper's Fair than the Cole family.
Mr. Cole had an absolute horror of the fair. Sailors and
gipsies were to him the sign and seal of utter damnation,
and although he tried, as a Christian clergyman, to believe that they deserved pity because of the disadvantages
under which they had from the first laboured, he confessed
to his intimate friends that he saw very little hope for
them either in this world or the next. Jeremy, Helen and
Mary were, during Fair Week, kept severely within doors;
their exercise had to be taken in the Cole garden, and the
farthest that they poked their noses into the town was their
visit to St. John's on Sunday morning. Except on one
famous occasion. The Fair Week of Jeremy's fifth year
saw him writhing under a terrible attack of toothache,
which became, after two agonised nights, such a torment
and distress to the whole household that he had to be conveyed to the house of Mr. Pilter, who had his torture-
chamber at No. 3 Market Square. It is true that Jeremy
was conveyed thither in a cab, and that his pain and his
darkened windows prevented him from seeing very much
of the gay world; nevertheless, in spite of the Jampot,
who guarded him like a dragon, he caught a glimpse of
flags, a gleaming brass band and a Punch and Judy show,
and he heard the trumpets and the drum, and the shouts
of excited little boys, and the blowing of the Punch and
Judy pipes, and he smelt roasting chestnuts, bad tobacco,
and beer and gin. He returned, young as he was, and
reduced to a corpse-like condition by the rough but kindly
intentioned services of Mr. Pilter, with the picture of a
hysterical, abandoned world clearly imprinted upon his
brain.

"I want to go," he said to the Jampot.

"You can't," said she.

"I will when I'm six," said he.

"You won't," said she.

"I will when I'm seven," said he.

"You won't," said she.

"I will when I'm eight," he answered.

"Oh, give over, do, Master Jeremy," said she. And now he was eight, very nearly nine, and going to school in a fortnight. There seemed to be a touch of destiny about his prophecy.

II

He had no intention of disobedience. Had he been once definitely told by someone in authority that he was not to go to the fair he would not have dreamt of going. He had no intention of disobedience—but he had returned from the Cow Farm holiday in a strange condition of mind.

He had found there this summer more freedom than he had been ever allowed in his life before, and it had been freedom that had come, not so much from any change of rules, but rather from his own attitude to the family— simply he had wanted to do certain things, and he had done them and the family had stood aside. He began to be aware that he had only to push and things gave way— a dangerous knowledge, and its coming marks a period in one's life.

He seemed, too, during this summer, to have left his sisters definitely behind him and to stand much more alone than he had done before. The only person in his world whom he felt that he would like to know better was Uncle Samuel, and that argued, on his part, a certain tendency towards rebellion and individuality. He was no longer rude to Aunt Amy, although he hated her just as he had always done. She did not seem any longer a question that mattered. His attitude to his whole family now was independent.

Indeed, he was, in reality, now beginning to live his independent life. He was perhaps very young to be sent off to school by himself, although in those days for a boy of eight to be plunged without any help but a friendly word of warning into the stormy seas of private school life was common enough—nevertheless, his father, conscious that the child's life had been hitherto spent almost entirely among women, sent him every morning during these last weeks at home down to the Curate of St. Martin's-in-the-Market to learn a few words of Latin, an easy sum or two, and the rudiments of spelling. This young curate, the Rev. Wilfred Somerset, recently of Emmanuel College, Cambridge, had but two ideas in his head—the noble game of cricket and the jolly qualities of Mr. Surtees's novels. He was stout and strong, red-faced, and thick in the leg, always smoking a large black-looking pipe, and wearing trousers very short and tight. He did not strike Jeremy with fear, but he was, nevertheless, an influence. Jeremy, apparently, amused him intensely. He would roar with laughter at nothing at all, smack his thigh and shout, "Good for you, young 'un," whatever that might mean, and Jeremy, gazing at him, at his pipe and his trousers, liking him rather, but not sufficiently in awe to be really impressed, would ask him questions that seemed to him perfectly simple and natural, but that, nevertheless, amused the Rev. Wilfred so fundamentally that he was unable to give them an intelligible answer.

Undoubtedly this encouraged Jeremy's independence.

He walked to and from the curate's lodging by himself, and was able to observe many interesting things on the way. Sometimes, late in the afternoon, he would have some lesson that he must take to his master who, as he lodged at the bottom of Orange Street, was a very safe and steady distance from the Coles.

Of course Aunt Amy objected:

"You allow Jeremy, all by himself, into the street at night, and he only eight. Really, you're too strange!"

"Well, in the first place," said Mrs. Cole, mildly, "it isn't night—it's afternoon; in the second place, it is only just down the street, and Jeremy's most obedient always, as you know, Amy."

"I'm sure that Mr. Somerset is wild," said Aunt Amy.

"My dear Amy, why?"

"You've only got to look at his face. It's 'flashy.' That's what I call it."

"Oh, that isn't the sort of man who'll do Jeremy harm," said Mrs. Cole, with a mother's wisdom.

Certainly, he did Jeremy no harm at all; he taught him nothing, not even "mensa," and how to spell "receive" and "apple." The only thing he did was to encourage Jeremy's independence, and this was done, in the first place, by the walks to and fro.

He had only been going to Mr. Somerset's a day or two when the announcements of the Fair appeared on the walls of the town. He could not help but see them; there was a large one on the boarding half-way down Orange Street, just opposite the Doctor's; a poster with a coloured picture of "Wombwell's Circus," a fine affair, with spangled ladies jumping through hoops, elephants sitting on stools, tigers prowling, a clown cracking a whip, and, best of all, a gentleman, with an anxious face and a scanty but elegant costume, balanced above a gazing multitude on a tight-rope. There was also a bill of the Fair setting forth that there would be a "Cattle Market, Races, Round-about, Swings, Wrestling, Boxing, Fat Women, Dwarfs, and the Two-Headed Giant from the Caucasus." During a whole week, once a day, Jeremy read this bill from the top to the bottom; at the end of the week he could repeat it all by heart.

He asked Mr. Somerset whether he was going.

"Oh, I shall slip along one evening, I've no doubt," replied that gentleman. "But it's a bore—a whole week of it—upsets one's work."

"It needn't," said Jeremy, "if you stay indoors."

This amused Mr. Somerset immensely. He laughed a great deal.

"We always have to," said Jeremy, rather hurt. "We're not allowed farther than the garden."

"Ah, but I'm older than you are," said Mr. Somerset. "It was the same with me once."

"And what did you do? Did you go all the same?"

"You bet, I did," said the red-faced hero, more intent on his reminiscences than on the effect that this might have on the morals of his pupil.

Jeremy waited then for the parental command that was always issued. It was: "Now, children, you must promise me never to go outside the house this week unless you have asked permission first." And then: "And on no account to speak to any stranger about anything what-ever." And then: "Don't look out of the back windows, mind." (From the extreme corners of the bedroom windows you could see a patch of the meadow whereon the gipsy-vans settled.) These commands had been as regular as the Fair, and always, of course, the children had promised obedience. Jeremy told his conscience that if, this year, he gave his promise, he would certainly keep it. He wondered, at the same time, whether he might not possibly manage to be out of the house when the commands were issued. He formed a habit of suddenly slipping out of the room when he saw his father's mouth assuming the shape of a "command." He took the utmost care not to be alone with his father.

But he need not have been alarmed. This year no command appeared. Perhaps Mr. Cole thought that it was no longer necessary; it was obvious that the children were not to go, and they were, after all, old enough now to think for themselves. Or, perhaps, it was that Mr. Cole had other things on his mind; he was changing curates just then, and a succession of white-faced, soft-voiced, and loud-booted young men were appearing at the Coles' hospitable table.

"Here's this tiresome Fair come round again," said Mrs. Cole.

"Wicked!" said Aunt Amy, with an envious shudder. "Satan finds work, indeed, in this town."

"I don't suppose it's worse than anywhere else," said Mrs. Cole.

On the late afternoon of the day before the opening, Jeremy, on his way to Mr. Somerset's, caught the tail-end of Wombwell's Circus Procession moving, in misty splendour, across the market.

He could see but little, although he stood on the pedestal of a lamp-post; but Britannia, rocking high in the air, flashing her silver sceptre in the evening air, and followed by two enormous and melancholy elephants, caught his gaze. Strains of a band lingered about him. He entered Mr. Somerset's in a frenzy of excitement, but he said nothing. He felt that Mr. Somerset would laugh at him.

He returned to his home that night haunted by Britannia. He ate Britannia for his supper; he had Britannia for his dreams; and he greeted Rose as Britannia the next morning when she called him. Early upon that day there were borne into the heart of the house strains of the Fair. It was no use whatever to close the windows, lock the doors, and read Divinity. The strains persisted, a heavenly murmur, rising at moments into a muffled shriek or a jumbling shout, hanging about the walls as a romantic echo, dying upon the air a chastened wail. No use for Mr. Cole to say:

"We must behave as though the Fair was not."

For a whole week it would be there, and everyone knew it.

Jeremy did not mean to be disobedient, but after that glimpse of Britannia he knew that he would go.

III

It had, at first, been thought advisable that Jeremy should not go to Mr. Somerset's during Fair Week. Perhaps Mr. Somerset could come to the Coles'? No, he was very sorry. He must be in his rooms at that particular hour in case parishioners should need his advice or assistance.

"Pity for him to miss all this week, especially as there

will be only four days left after that. I am really anxious for him to have a little grounding in Latin."

Mrs. Cole smiled confidently. "I think Jeremy is to be trusted. He would never do anything that you wouldn't like."

Mr. Cole was not so sure. "He's not quite so obedient as I should wish. He shows an independence——"

However, after some hesitation it was decided that Jeremy might be trusted.

But even after that he was never put upon his honour. "If I don't promise, I needn't mind," he said to himself, and waited breathlessly; but nothing came. Only Aunt Amy said:

"I hope you don't speak to little boys in the street, Jeremy." To which he replied scornfully: "Of course not."

He investigated his money-box, removing the top with a tin-opener. He found that he had there 3s. 3½d.; a large sum, and enough to give him a royal time.

Mary caught him.

"Oh, Jeremy, what are you doing?"

"Just counting my money," he said, with would-be carelessness.

"You're going to the Fair?" she whispered breathlessly.

He frowned. How could she know? She always knew everything.

"Perhaps," he whispered back; "but if you tell anyone I'll——"

"Of course I wouldn't tell," she replied, deeply offended.

This little conversation strengthened his purpose. He had not admitted to himself that he was really going. Now he knew.

Wednesday would be the night. On Wednesday evenings his father had a service which prevented him from returning home until half-past eight. He would go to Somerset's at half-past four, and would be expected home at half-past six; there would be no real alarm about him until his father's return from church, and he could, therefore, be sure of two hours' bliss. For the consequences he did not care at all. He was going to do no harm to anyone or anything. They would be angry, perhaps, but that would not hurt him, and, in any case, he was going to school next week. No one at school would mind whether he had been to the Fair or no.

He felt aloof and apart, as though no one could touch him. He would not have minded simply going into them all and saying: "I'm off to the Fair." The obvious drawback to that would have been that he would have been shut up in his room, and then they might make him give his word. . . . He would not break any promises.

When Wednesday came it was a lovely day. Out in the field just behind the Coles' house they were burning a huge bonfire of dead leaves. At first only a heavy column of grey smoke rose, then flames broke through; little, thin golden flames like paper; then a sudden fierce red tongue shot out and went licking up into the air until it faded like tumbling water against the sunlight. On the outer edge of the bonfire there was thin grey smoke through which you could see as through glass. The smell was heavenly, and even through closed windows the crackling of the burnt leaves could be heard. The sight of the bonfire excited Jeremy. It seemed to him a signal of encouragement, a spur to perseverance. All the morning the flames crackled, and men came with wheelbarrows

full of leaves and emptied them in thick heaps upon the
fire. At each emptying the fire would be for a moment
beaten, and only the white, thick, malicious smoke would
come through; then a little spit of flame, another, another;
then a thrust like a golden hand stretching out; then a
fine, towering, quivering splendour.

Under the full noonday sun the fire was pale and so
unreal, weak, and sickly, that one was almost ashamed to
look at it. But as the afternoon passed, it again gathered
strength, and with the faint, dusky evening it was a giant
once more.

"You come along," it said to Jeremy. "Come along!
Come along!"

"I'm going to Mr. Somerset's, Mother," he said, putting
two exercise books and a very new and shining blue Latin
book together.

"Are you, dear? I suppose you're safe?" Mrs. Cole
asked, looking through the drawing-room window.

"Oh, it's all right," said Jeremy

"Well, I think it is," said Mrs. Cole. "The street seems
quite empty. Don't speak to any odd-looking men, will
you?"

"Oh, that's all right," he said again.

He walked down Orange Street, his books under his
arm, the 3s. 3½d. in his pocket. The street was quite
deserted, swimming in a cold, pale light; the trees, the
houses, the church, the garden-walls, sharp and black; the
street, dim and precipitous, tumbling forward into the blue,
whence lights, one, two, three, now a little bunch together,
came pricking out.

The old woman opened the door when he rang Mr.
Somerset's bell.

"Master's been called away," she said in her croaking voice. "A burial. 'E 'adn't time to let you know. 'Tell the little gen'l'man,' 'e said, 'I'm sorry.'"

"All right," said Jeremy; "thank you."

He descended the steps, then stood where he was, in the street, looking up and down. Who could deny that it was all being arranged for him? He felt more than ever like God as he looked proudly about him. Everything served his purpose.

The jingling of the money in his pocket reminded him that he must waste no more time. He started off.

Even his progress through the town seemed wonderful, quite unattended at last, as he had always all his life longed to be. So soon as he left Orange Street and entered the market he was caught into a great crowd. It was all stirring and humming with a noise such as the bonfire had all day been making. It was his first introduction to the world—he had never been in a large crowd before—and it is not to be denied but that his heart beat thick and his knees trembled a little. But he pulled himself together. Who was he to be afraid? But the books under his arm were a nuisance. He suddenly dropped them in amongst the legs and boots of the people.

There were many interesting sights to be seen in the market-place, but he could not stay, and he found himself soon, to his own surprise, slipping through the people as quietly and easily as though he had done it all his days, only always he kept his hand on his money lest that should be stolen and his adventure suddenly come to nothing.

He knew his way very well, and soon he was at the end of Finch Street which in those days opened straight into fields and hedges.

Even now, so little has Polchester grown in thirty years, the fields and hedges are not very far away. Here there was a stile with a large wooden fence on either side of it, and a red-faced man saying: "Pay your sixpences now! Come along . . . pay your sixpences now." Crowds of people were passing through the stile, jostling one another, pressing and pushing, but all apparently in good temper, for there was a great deal of laughter and merriment. From the other side of the fence came a torrent of sound, so discordant and so tumultuous that it was impossible to separate the elements of it one from another —screams, shrieks, the bellowing of animals, and the monotonous rise and fall of scraps of tune, several bars of one and then bars of another, and then everything lost together in the general babel; and to the right of him Jeremy could see not very far away quiet fields with cows grazing, and the dark grave wood on the horizon.

Would he venture? For a moment his heart failed him—a wave of something threatening and terribly powerful seemed to come out to him through the stile, and the people who were passing in looked large and fierce. Then he saw two small boys, their whole bearing one of audacious boldness, push through. He was not going to be beaten. He followed a man with a back like a wall. "One, please," he said.

"Come along now . . . pay your sixpences . . . pay your sixpences," cried the man. He was through. He stepped at once into something that had for him all the elements of the most terrifying and enchanting of fairy tales. He was planted, it seemed, in a giant world. At first he could see nothing but the high and thick bodies of the people who moved on every side of him; he peered under shoulders, he was lost amongst legs and arms, he walked suddenly into waistcoat buttons and was flung thence on to walking sticks.

But it was, if he had known it, the most magical hour of all for him to have chosen. It was the moment when the sun, sinking behind the woods and hills, leaves a faint white crystal sky and a world transformed in an instant from sharp outlines and material form into coloured mist and rising vapour. The Fair also was transformed, putting forward all its lights and becoming, after the glaring tawdiness of the day, a place of shadow and sudden circles of flame and dim obscurity.

Lights, even as Jeremy watched, sprang into the air, wavered, faltered, hesitated, then rocked into a steady glow, only shifting a little with the haze. On either side of him were rough, wooden stalls, and these were illuminated with gas, which sizzled and hissed like angry snakes. The stalls were covered with everything invented by man; here a sweet stall, with thick, sticky lumps of white and green and red, glass bottles of bulls' eyes and peppermints, thick slabs of almond toffee and pink cocoanut icing, boxes of round chocolate creams and sticks of liquorice, lumps of gingerbread, with coloured pictures stuck upon them, saffron buns, plum cakes in glass jars, and chains of little sugary biscuits hanging on long red strings. There was the old-clothes' stall with trousers and coats and waistcoats, all shabby and lanky, swinging beneath the gas, and piles of clothes on the boards, all nondescript and unhappy and faded; there was the stall with the farm implements, and the medicine stall, and the flower stall, and the vegetable stall, and many, many another. Each place had his or her guardian, vociferous, red-faced, screaming out the wares, lowering the voice to cajole, raising it again to draw back a retreating customer, carrying on suddenly an intimate conversation with the next-door shopkeeper, laughing, quarrelling, arguing.

To Jeremy it was a world of giant heights and depths. Behind the stalls, beyond the lane down which he moved, was an uncertain glory, a threatening peril. He fancied that strange animals moved there; he thought he heard a lion roar and an elephant bellow. The din of the sellers all about him made it impossible to tell what was happening beyond there; only the lights and bells, shouts and cries, confusing smells, and a great roar of distant voices.

He almost wished that he had not come, he felt so very small and helpless; he wondered whether he could find his way out again, and looking back, he was for a moment terrified to see that the stream of people behind him shut him in so that he could not see the stile, nor the wooden barrier, nor the red-faced man. Pushed forward, he found himself at the end of the lane and standing in a semi-circular space surrounded by strange-looking booths with painted pictures upon them, and in front of them platforms with wooden steps running up to them. Then, so unexpectedly that he gave a little scream, a sudden roar burst out behind him. He turned and, indeed, the world seemed to have gone mad. A moment ago there had been darkness and dim shadow. Now, suddenly, there was a huge whistling, tossing circle of light and flame, and from the centre of this a banging, brazen, cymbal-clashing scream issued—a scream that, through its strident shrillness, he recognised as a tune that he knew—a tune often whistled by Jim at Cow Farm. "And her golden hair was hanging down her back." Whence the tune came he could not tell; from the very belly of the flaming monster, it seemed; but, as he watched, he saw that the huge circle whirled ever faster and faster, and that up and down on the flame of it coloured horses rose and fell, vanishing from light to darkness, from darkness to light, and seeming of their own free will and motion to dance to the thundering music.

It was the most terrific thing that he had ever seen. The most terrific thing. . . . He stood there, his cap on the back of his head, his legs apart, his mouth open; forgetting utterly the crowd, thinking nothing of time or danger or punishment—he gazed with his whole body.

As his eyes grew more accustomed to the glare of the hissing gas, he saw that in the centre figures were painted standing on the edge of a pillar that revolved without pause. There was a woman with flaming red cheeks, a gold dress and dead white dusty arms, a man with a golden crown and a purple robe, but a broken nose, and a minstrel with a harp. The woman and the king moved stiffly their arms up and down, that they might strike instruments, one a cymbal and the other a drum.

But it was finally the horses that caught Jeremy's heart. Half of them at least were without riders, and the empty ones went round pathetically, envying the more successful ones and dancing to the music as though with an effort. One especially moved Jeremy's sympathy. He was a fine horse, rather fresher than the others, with a coal-black mane and great black bulging eyes; his saddle was of gold and his trappings of red. As he went round he seemed to catch Jeremy's eye and to beg him to come to him. He rode more securely than the rest, rising nobly like a horse of fine breeding, falling again with an implication of restrained force as though he would say: "I have only to let myself go and there, my word, you *would* see where I'd get to." His bold black eyes turned beseechingly to Jeremy—surely it was not only a trick of the waving gas; the boy drew closer and closer, never moving his gaze from the horses who had hitherto been whirling at a bacchanalian pace, but now, as at some sudden secret command, suddenly slackened, hesitated, fell into a gentle jog-trot, then scarcely rose, scarcely fell, were suddenly still. Jeremy saw what it was that you did if you wanted to ride. A stout dirty man came out amongst the horses and, resting his hands on their backs as though they were less than nothing to him, shouted: "Now's your chance, lidies and gents! Now, lidies and gents! Come along hup! Come along hup! The ride of your life now! A 'alfpenny a time! A 'alfpenny a time, and the finest ride of your life!"

People began to mount the steps that led on to the platform where the horses stood. A woman, then a man and a boy, then two men, then two girls giggling together, then a man and a girl.

And the stout fellow shouted: "Come along hup! Come along hup! Now, lidies and gents! A 'alfpenny a ride! Come along hup!"

Jeremy noticed then that the fine horse with the black mane had stopped close beside him. Impossible to say whether the horse had intended it or no! He was staring now in front of him with the innocent stupid gaze that animals can assume when they do not wish to give themselves away. But Jeremy could see that he was taking it for granted that Jeremy understood the affair. "If you're such a fool as not to understand," he seemed to say, "well, then, I don't want you." Jeremy gazed, and the reproach in those eyes was more than he could endure. And at any moment someone else might settle himself on that beautiful back! There, that stupid fat giggling girl! No—she had moved elsewhere. . . . He could endure it no longer and, with a thumping heart, clutching a scalding penny in a red-hot hand, he mounted the steps. "One ride—little gen'elman. 'Ere you are! 'Old on now! Oh, you wants that one, do yer? Right yer are—yer pays yer money and yer takes yer choice." He lifted Jeremy up. "Put yer arms round 'is neck now—'e won't bite yer!"

Bite him indeed! Jeremy felt, as he clutched the cool head and let his hand slide over the stiff black mane, that he knew more about that horse than his owner did. He seemed to feel beneath him the horse's response to his clutching knees, the head seemed to rise for a moment and nod to him and the eyes to say: "It's all right. I'll look after you. I'll give you the best ride of your life!"

He felt, indeed, that the gaze of the whole world was upon him, but he responded to it proudly, staring boldly around him as though he had been seated on merry-go-rounds all his days. Perhaps some in the gaping crowd knew him and were saying: "Why, there's the Rev. Cole's kid——" Never mind; he was above scandal. From where he was he could see the Fair lifted up and translated into a fantastic splendour. Nothing was certain, nothing defined—above him a canopy of evening sky, with circles and chains of stars mixed with the rosy haze of the flame of the Fair; opposite him was the Palace of "The Two-Headed Giant from the Caucasus," a huge man as portrayed in the picture hanging on his outer walls, a giant naked, save for a bearskin, with one head black and one yellow, and white protruding teeth in both mouths.

Next to him was the Fortune Teller's, and outside this a little man with a hump beat a drum. Then there was "The Theatre of Tragedy and Mirth," with a poster on one side of the door portraying a lady drowning in the swiftest of rivers, but with the prospect of being saved by a stout gentleman who leaned over from the bank and grasped her hair. Then there was the "Chamber of the Fat Lady and the Six Little Dwarfs," and the entry to this was guarded by a dirty sour-looking female who gnashed her teeth at a hesitating public, before whom, with a splendid indifference to appearance, she consumed, out of a piece of newspaper, her evening meal.

All these things were in Jeremy's immediate vision, and beyond them was a haze that his eyes could not penetrate. It held, he knew, wild beasts, because he could hear quite clearly from time to time the lion and the elephant and the tiger; it held music, because from somewhere through all the noise and confusion the tune of a band penetrated; it held buyers and sellers and treasures and riches, and all the inhabitants of the world—surely all the world *must* be here to-night. And then, beyond the haze, there were the silent and mysterious gipsy caravans. Dark with their little square windows, and their coloured walls, and their round wheels, and the smell of wood fires, and the noise of hissing kettles and horses cropping the grass, and around them the still night world with the thick woods and the dark river.

He did not see it all as he sat on his horse—he was, as yet, too young; but he did feel the contrast between the din and glare around him and the silence and dark beyond, and, afterwards, looking back, he knew that he had found in that same contrast the very heart of romance. As it was, he simply clutched his horse's beautiful head and waited for the ride to begin. . . .

They were off! He felt his horse quiver under him, he saw the mansions of the Two-Headed Giant and the Fat Lady slip to the right, the light seemed to swing like the skirt of someone's dress, upwards across the floor, and from the heart of the golden woman and the king and the minstrel a scream burst forth as though they were announcing the end of the world. After that he had no clear idea as to what occurred. He was swung into space, and all the life that had been so stationary, the booths, the lights, the men and women, the very stars went swinging with him as though to cheer him on; the horse under him galloped before, and the faster he galloped the wilder was the music and the dizzier the world. He was exultant, omnipotent, supreme. He had long known that this glory was somewhere if it could only be found, all his days he seemed to have been searching for it; he beat his horse's neck, he drove his legs against his sides. "Go on! Go on! Go on!" he cried. "Faster! Faster! Faster!"

The strangest things seemed to rise to his notice and then fall again—a peaked policeman's hat, flowers, a sudden flame of gas, the staring eyes and dead white arms of the golden woman, the flying forms of the horses in front of him. All the world was on horseback, all the world was racing higher and higher, faster and faster. He saw someone near him rise on to his horse's back and stand on it, waving his arms. He would like to have done that, but he found that he was part of his horse, as though he had been glued to it. He shouted, he cried aloud, he was so happy that he thought of no one and nothing. . . . The flame danced about him in a circle, he seemed to rise so high that there was a sudden stillness, he was in the very heart of the stars; then came the supreme moment when, as he had always known, that one day he would be, he was master of the world. . . . Then, like Lucifer, he fell. Slowly the stars receded, the music slackened, people rocked on to their feet again. . . . The Two-Headed Giant slipped back once more into his place, he saw the sinister lady still devouring her supper, women looking up at him gaped. His horse gave a last little leap and died.

This marvellous experience he repeated four times, and every time with an ecstasy more complete than the last.

He rushed to a height, he fell, he rushed again, he fell, and at every return to a sober life his one intention was instantly to be off on his steed once more. He was about to start on his fifth journey, he had paid his halfpenny, he was sitting forward with his hands on the black mane, his eyes, staring, were filled already with the glory that he knew was coming to him, his cheeks were crimson, his hat on the back of his head, his hair flying. He heard a voice, quiet and cool, a little below him, but very near:

"Jeremy. . . . Jeremy. Come off that. You've got to go home."

He looked down and saw his Uncle Samuel.

IV

It was all over; he knew at once that it was all over. As he slipped down from his dear horse he gave the glossy dark mane one last pat; then, with a little sigh, he found his feet, stumbled over the wooden steps and was at his uncle's side.

Uncle Samuel looked queer enough with a squashy black hat, a black cloak flung over his shoulders, and a large cherry-wood pipe in his mouth. Jeremy looked up at him defiantly.

"Well," said Uncle Samuel sarcastically. "It's nothing to you, I suppose, that the town-crier is at this moment ringing his bell for you up and down the Market Place?"

"Does father know?" Jeremy asked quickly.

"He does," answered Uncle Samuel.

Jeremy cast one last look around the place; the merry-go-round was engaged once more upon its wild course, the horses rising and falling, the golden woman clashing the cymbals, the minstrel striking, with his dead eyes fixed upon space, his harp. All about men were shouting; the noise of the coconut stores, of the circus, of the band, of the hucksters and the charlatans, the crying of children, the laughter of women—all the noise of the Fair bathed Jeremy up to his forehead.

He swam in it for the last time. He tried to catch one last glimpse of his coal-black charger, then, with a sigh, he said, turning to his uncle: "I suppose we'd better be going."

"Yes, I suppose we had," said Uncle Samuel.

They threaded their way through the Fair, passed the wooden stile, and were once again in the streets, dark and ancient under the moon, with all the noise and glare behind them. Jeremy was thinking to himself: "It doesn't matter what Father does, or how angry he is, *that* was worth it." It was strange how little afraid he was. Only a year ago to be punished by his father had been a terrible thing. Now, since his mother's illness in the summer, his father had seemed to have no influence over him.

"Did they send you, or did you just come yourself, Uncle?" asked Jeremy.

"I happened to be taking the air in that direction," said Uncle Samuel.

"I hope you didn't come away before you wanted to," said Jeremy politely.

"I did not," said his uncle.

"Is Father very angry?" asked Jeremy.

"It's more than likely he may be. The Town Crier's expensive."

"I didn't think they'd know," explained Jeremy. "I meant to get back in time."

"Your father didn't go to church," said Uncle Samuel. "So your sins were quickly discovered."

Jeremy said nothing.

Just as they were climbing Orange Street he said:

"Uncle Samuel, I think I'll be a horse-trainer."

"Oh, will you? . . . Well, before you train horses you've got to train yourself. Think of others beside yourself. A fine state you've put your mother into to-night."

Jeremy looked distressed. "She'd know if I was dead, someone would come and tell her," he said. "But I'll tell Mother I'm sorry. . . . But I won't tell Father," he added.

"Why not?" asked Uncle Samuel.

"Because he'll make such a fuss. And I'm not sorry. He never told me not to."

"No, but you knew you hadn't to."

"I'm very good at obeying," explained Jeremy, "if someone says something; but if someone doesn't, there isn't anyone to obey."

Uncle Samuel shook his head. "You'll be a bit of a prig, my son, if you aren't careful," he said.

"I think it will be splendid to be a horse-trainer," said Jeremy. "It was a lovely horse to-night. . . . And I only spent a shilling. I had three and threepence halfpenny."

At the door of their house Uncle Samuel stopped and said:

"Look here, young man, they say it's time you went to school, and I don't think they're far wrong. There are things wiser heads than yours can understand, and you'd better take their word for it. In the future, if you want to go running off somewhere, you'd better content yourself with my studio and make a mess there."

"Oh, may I?" cried Jeremy delighted.

That studio had been always a forbidden place to them, and had, therefore, its air of enchanting mystery.

"Won't you really mind my coming?" he asked.

"I shall probably hate it," answered his uncle; "but there's nothing I wouldn't do for the family."

The boy walked to his father's study and knocked on the door. He did have then, at the sound of that knock, a moment of panic. The house was so silent, and he knew so well what would follow the opening of the door. And the worst of it was that he was not sorry in the least. He seemed to be indifferent and superior, as though no punishment could touch him.

"Come in!" said his father.

He pushed open the door and entered. The scene that followed was grave and sad, and yet, in the end, strangely unimpressive. His father talked too much. As he talked Jeremy's thoughts would fly back to the coal-black horse.

and to that moment when he had seemed to fly into the very heart of the stars.

"Ah, Jeremy, how could you?" said his father. "Is obedience nothing to you? Do you know how God punishes disobedience? Think what a terrible thing is a disobedient man!" Then on a lower scale: "I really don't know what to do with you. You knew that you were not to go near that wicked place."

"You never said——" interrupted Jeremy.

"Nonsense! You knew well enough. You will break your mother's heart."

"I'll tell her I'm sorry," he interrupted quickly.

"If you *are* really sorry——" said his father.

"I'm not sorry I went," said Jeremy, "but I'm sorry I hurt Mother."

The end of it was that Jeremy received six strokes on the hand with a ruler. Mr. Cole was not good at this kind of thing, and twice he missed Jeremy's hand altogether, and looked very foolish. It was not an edifying scene. Jeremy left the room, his head high, his spirit obstinate; and his father remained, puzzled, distressed, at a loss, anxious to do what was right, but unable to touch his son at all.

Jeremy went up to his room. He opened his window and looked out. He could smell the burnt leaves of the bonfire. There was no flame now, but he fancied that he could see a white shadow where it had been. Then, on the wind, came the music of the Fair.

"Tum—te—Tum . . . Tum—te—Tum . . . Whirr— Whirr—Whirr—Bang—Bang."

Somewhere an owl cried, and then another owl answered.

He rubbed his sore hand against his trousers; then, thinking of his black horse, he smiled.

He was a free man. In a week he would go to school; then he would go to College; then he would be a horse-trainer.

He was in bed; faintly into the dark room stole the scent of the bonfire and the noise of the Fair.

"Tum—te—Tum . . . Tum—te—Tum . . . "

He was asleep, riding on a giant charger across boundless plains.

CHAPTER XII

HAMLET WAITS

I

THE last day! Jeremy, suddenly waking, realised this with a confusion of feeling as though he were sentenced to the dentist's, but, oddly enough, looked forward to his visit. Going to school, one had, of course, long ago perceived, was a mixed business; but the balance was now greatly to the good. It was a step in the right direction towards liberty and freedom. Thank Heaven! No one in the family was likely to make a fuss about his departure, unless it were possibly Mary, and she had, of late, kept very much to herself and worried him scarcely at all. Indeed, he felt guilty about Mary. He was fond of her, really. . . . Funny kid. . . . If only she didn't make fusses!

Yes, it was unlike his family to make fusses. He realised that very plainly to-day. Everyone went about his or her daily business with no implication whatever that something extraordinary was going to happen to-morrow. Perhaps they were all secretly relieved that he was off. He had been, he knew, something of a failure during these last months; one trouble after another; the scandal of his visit to the Fair as the grand finale. He felt that there was, in some way, some injustice in all this. He had no desire to be bad or rebellious—on the

contrary he wished to do all that his elders ordered him—
but he could not prevent the rising of his own individuality, which showed him quite clearly whether he should
do a thing or no. It was as though something inside him
pushed him . . . whereas they, all of them, only checked
him.

He loved his mother best, and he was secretly disappointed to find how ordinary an affair his departure was
to her. He realised, with a perception that was beyond
his years, that the infant Barbara was now rapidly occupy-
ing the position, as centre of the family, that he had held.
Barbara, everyone declared, was a charming baby—the
house revolved, to some extent, round Barbara. But, then
again, this isolation was entirely his own fault. During
the summer holidays he had gone his own way, and had
wanted no one but Hamlet as his companion. He had
no right to complain.

After breakfast he did not know quite what to do, and
it was obvious, also, that no one knew quite what to do
with him.

Mrs. Cole said: "Jeremy, dear, Ponting has never sent
that letter paper and envelopes that he promised, and
Father must have them to-day. Would you go down and
bring them back with you? Father will write a note."

No one seemed to realise what an abysmal change from
earlier conditions this casual sentence marked. That he
should go to Ponting's, which was on the farther side of
the town, alone and unattended, seemed to no one peculiar;
and yet, only six months ago, a walk without Miss Jones
was undreamt of; and, before her, no more than nine
months back, there was the Jampot! He was delighted to
go; but, of course, he did not show his delight.

All he said was: "Yes, Mother."

He was in his new clothes: stiff black jacket, black knickerbockers, black stockings, black boots. No more navy suits with white braid and whistles! Perhaps he would see the Dean's Ernest. It was his most urgent desire!

He started off, accompanied by a barking, bounding Hamlet, who showed no perception of the calamity that threatened to tumble upon him. For Jeremy, leaving Hamlet was a dreadful affair. In three months a dog can change more swiftly than a human being, and Hamlet, although not a supremely greedy dog, had shown of late increasing signs of a love of good food, and a regrettable tendency to fawn upon the giver of the same, even when it was Aunt Amy. Jeremy had checked this tendency, and had issued punishments when necessary, and Hamlet had accepted the same without a murmur. So long as Jeremy was there Hamlet's character was secure; but now, during this long absence, anything might happen. There was no one to whom Jeremy might leave him; no one who had the slightest idea what a dog should do and what he should not.

These melancholy thoughts filled Jeremy's mind when he started upon his walk, but soon he was absorbed by his surroundings. He realised even more drastically than the facts warranted that he was making his farewell to the town.

He was not making his final farewell; he would not make that until his death, and, perhaps, not then; but he was making farewell to some of his sense of his wonder in it, only not, thank God, to the sense of wonder itself!

As he went he met the daily figures of all his walks,

and he could not help but speculate on their realisation of the great change that was coming to him. It was absurd to suppose that they were saying to themselves: "Ah, there's young Jeremy Cole! He's off to school to-morrow. I wonder what he feels about it! . . ." No, that was incredible, and yet they must realise something of the adventure.

He, on his part, stared at them with a new interest. They had before shared in the inevitable background without individuality. But now that he was leaving them, and they would grow, as it were, without his permission, he was forced to grant them independence. At the bottom of Orange Street he met Mr. Dawson, the Cathedral Organist; he was a little, plump man, in a very neat grey suit, a shiny top hat, and very small spats. He was always dressed in the same fashion, and carried a black music-case under his arm. He had an eternal interest for Jeremy because, whenever he was mentioned, the phrase was: "Poor little Mr. Dawson!" Why he was to be pitied Jeremy did not know. He looked spruce and bright enough, and generally whistled to himself as he walked; but "poor" was an exciting adjective, and Jeremy, when he passed him, felt a little shudder of drama run down his spine.

Outside Poole's bookshop there was, of course, Mr. Mockridge. Mr. Mockridge was the poorest of the Canons; so poor, that it had become a proverb in the place: "As poor as Mr. Mockridge"; and also another proverb, I am afraid, from the same source: "As dirty as Mr. Mockridge." He was a very long, thin man, with a big, pointing nose, coloured red, not from indigestion, and most certainly not from drink, but simply, I think, because the wind

caught it. His passion was for books, and he might be
seen every afternoon, between three and four o'clock, bending over Poole's 2d. box, a dirty handkerchief flying out
of the tail of his long, black coat, and a green, bulging
umbrella, pointing outwards, under his arm, to the infinite
danger of all the passers-by. He was so commonplace a
figure to Jeremy that, on ordinary days, he was shrouded
by an invisibility of tradition. But, to-day, he was fresh
and strange. "He'll be here to-morrow poking his nose
into that box just the same, and I shall be——"

Then, on the outskirts of the Market Place, Jeremy
paused and looked about him. There was all the usual
business of the place—the wooden trestles with the flower-
pots, the apple-woman under her umbrella, the empty
cattle-pens, where the cows and sheep stood on market
days, and behind them the dark, vaulted arches of the
actual market, now empty and deserted. Bathed in sunlight it lay very quiet and still; some pigeons pecking at
grain, a dog or two, and children playing round the empty
cattle-stalls. From the hill above the square the Cathedral boomed the hour, and all the pigeons rose in a flight,
hovered, then slowly settled again.

Jeremy sighed, and, with a strange pain at his heart
that he could not analyse, moved up the hill. The High
Street is, of course, the West End of Polchester, and in
the morning, between ten and one, every lady in the town
may be seen at her shopping. It had always been the
ambition of the Cole children to be taken for their walk
up High Street in the morning; but it was an ambition
very rarely gratified, because they stopped so often and
were always in everyone's way. And here was Jeremy, at
this gay hour, strolling up the High Street all by himself.

He lifted his head, pushed out his chest, and looked the world in the face. He might meet the Dean's Ernest at any moment. The first people whom he saw were the Misses Cragg—always known, of course, as "The Cragg girls." They were, perhaps, Polchester's most constant and obvious feature. There were four of them, all as yet unmarried, all with brown-red faces and hard straw hats, short skirts, and tremendous voices; forerunners, in fact, of a type now almost universal. They played croquet and lawn-tennis, were prominent members of the Archery Club, and hunted when their fathers would let them. They were terrible Dianas to Jeremy. He had met one of them once at a Children's Dance, and she had whirled him around until, with a terrified scream, he broke, howling, from her arms, and hid himself in the large bosom of the Jampot. He was always ashamed of this memory, and he could never see them without blushing; but, to-day, he seemed less afraid of them, and actually, when he passed them, touched his hat and looked them in the face. They all smiled and nodded to him, and when they had gone he was so deeply astonished at this adventure that he had to stop and consider himself. If the Craggs were nothing to him, what might he not face?

"Come here, Hamlet. How dare you?" he ordered in so sharp and military a voice that Hamlet, who had merely cast a most innocent glance at a disdainful and conceited white poodle, looked up at his master with surprise.

Nevertheless, his new-found hardihood received, in the very midst of his self-congratulation, its severest test. He stumbled into the very path of the Dean's wife.

Mrs. Dean could never have seemed to anyone a large woman, but to Jeremy she had always been a terror. She was thick and hard, like a wall, and wore the kind of silken clothes, that rustled—like the whispering of a whole meeting of frightened clergymen's wives—as she moved. She had a hard, condemnatory voice, and she spoke as though she were addressing an assembly; but, worst of all, she had black, beetling eyebrows, and these frightened Jeremy into fits. He did not, of course, know that the poor lady suffered continually from nervous headaches.

He suddenly heard that voice in his ear: "Good morning, Jeremy, and where are you off to so early?" Mrs. Dean was never so awful as when she was jolly, and Jeremy, caught up by the eyebrows as though they had been hooks and hung thus in mid-air for all the street to laugh at, nearly lost his command of his natural tongue. He found his voice just in time:

"To Ponting's," he said.

"All alone? Ah, no, I see you have your little dog. Nice little dog. And how's your mother?"

"She's quite well, thank you."

"That's right—that's right. We haven't seen you lately. You must come up to tea with your sisters. I'm afraid you won't find Ernest, he's gone back to school—but I dare say you're not too big to play with little girls."

Jeremy felt some triumph at his heart.

"I'm going to school to-morrow," he said. But if he expected Mrs. Dean to be pitiful at this statement he was greatly mistaken.

"Are you, indeed? Such a pity you couldn't have gone with Ernest—but he'd be senior to you, of course. . . . Good-bye. Good-bye. Give my love to your mother," and she pounded her way along.

"She's a beastly woman anyway," thought Jeremy. "I

wish I'd found something to say to her. I wonder whether she knows I knocked Ernest down in the summer and trod on him?"

But the sight of the High Street soon restored his equanimity. On other occasions he had been pushed through it, either by the Jampot or Miss Jones, so rapidly that he could gather only the most fleeting impressions. To-day he could linger and linger; he did. The two nicest shops were Mannings' the hairdressers and Ponting's the book-shop, but Rose the grocer's, and Coulter's the confectioner's were very good. Mr. Manning was an artist. He did not simply put a simpering bust with an elaborate head of hair in his window and leave it at that—he did, indeed, place there a smiling lady with a wonderful jewelled comb and a radiant row of teeth, but around this he built up a magnificent world of silver brushes, tortoise-shell combs, essences and perfumes and powders, jars and bottles and boxes. Manning was the finest artist in the town. Ponting, at the top of the street just at the corner of the Close, was an artist too, but in quite another fashion. Ponting was the best established, most sacred and serious bookseller in the county. In the days when the new "Waverley" was the sensation of the moment Mr. Ponting, grandfather of the present Mr. Ponting, had been in quite constant correspondence with Mr. Southey, and Mr. Coleridge, and had once, when on a visit to London, spoken to the great Lord Byron himself. This tradition of aristocracy remained, and the present Mr. Ponting always advised the Bishop what to read and was consulted by Mrs. Lamb, our only authoress, on questions of publishers and editions and such technical points. For all this Jeremy, at his present stage of interest, would have cared nothing

even had he known it, but what he did care for were the
rows of calf-bound books with little ridges of gold, that
made a fine wall across the window with an old print of
the Cathedral and the Close in the middle of them. Inside
Pontings there was a hush as of the study and the church
combined. It was a rather dark shop with rows and rows
of books disappearing into the ceiling, and one grave and
unnaturally old young man behind the counter. Jeremy
did not know what he should do about Hamlet, so he
brought him inside, only to discover to his horror that the
fiercest of all the Canons, Canon Waterbury, held the floor
of the shop. Canon Waterbury had a black beard and a
biting tongue. He had once warned Jeremy off the
Cathedral grass in a voice of thunder, and Jeremy had
never forgotten it. He glared now and pulled his beard,
but Hamlet fortunately behaved well, and the old young
man discovered Jeremy's notepaper within a very short
period.

Then suddenly the Canon spoke.

"Dogs should not be inside shops," he said, as though
he were condemning someone to death.

"I know," said Jeremy frankly. "I wanted to tie him
up to something and there was nothing to tie him up to."

"What did you bring him out for at all?" said the
Canon.

"Because he's got to have exercise," said Jeremy, discovering, to his own delighted surprise, that he was not
frightened in the least.

"Oh, has he? I don't know what people keep dogs for."

And then he stamped out of the shop.

Jeremy regarded this in the light of a victory and
marched away, his head more in the air than ever. He

should now have hurried home. The midday chimes had
rung out and Jeremy's duties were performed. But he
lingered, listening to the last notes of the chimes, hearing
the cries of the Cathedral choir-boys as they moved across
the green to the choir-school, watching all the people hurry
up and down the street. Ah, there was the Castle carriage!
Perhaps the old Countess was inside it. He had only seen
her once, at some service in the Cathedral to which his
mother had taken him, but she had made a great impression on him with her snow-white hair. He had heard
people speak of her as "a wicked old woman." Perhaps
she was inside the carriage . . . but he only saw the
Castle coachman and footman and the coronet on the
door. It rolled slowly up the hill with its fine air of
commanding the whole world—then it disappeared around
the corner of the Close.

Jeremy decided then that he would go home across the
Green and down Orchard Lane. He had a wish to enter
the Cathedral for a moment; such a visit would, after all,
complete the round of his experiences. He had never
entered the Cathedral alone, and now, as he saw it facing
him, so vast and majestic and quiet, across the sun-
drenched green, he felt a sudden fear and awe. He found
a ring in a stone near the west end through which he
might fasten Hamlet's lead, then, slowly pushing back the
heavy door, he passed inside. The Cathedral was utterly
quiet. The vast nave, stained with reflections of purple
and green and ruby, was vague and unsubstantial, all the
little wooden chairs huddled together to the right and left,
leaving a great path that swept up to the High Altar under
shafts of light that fell like searchlights from the windows.
The tombs and the statues peered dimly from the shadow,

and the great east end window, with its deep purple light, seemed to draw the whole nave up into its heart and hold it there. All was space and silence, light and dusk; a little doll of a verger moved in the far distance, an old woman, so quiet that she seemed only a shadow, passed him, wiping the little chairs with a duster.

It seemed to Jeremy that he had never been in the Cathedral before; he stood there, breathless, as though in a moment something must inevitably happen. Although he did not think of it, the moment was one of a sequence that had come to him during the year—his entry into the theatre with his uncle, his first conversation with the sea-captain, the hour when his mother had been so ill, the evening on the beach when Charlotte had been frightened, the time when Hamlet had been lost and he had slept with him under a tree. All these moments had been something more than merely themselves, had had something behind them or inside them for which simply they stood as words stand for pictures. He analysed, of course, nothing, being a perfectly healthy small boy, but if afterwards he looked back these were the moments that he saw as one sees stations on a journey. One day he would know for what they stood.

He simply now waited there as though he expected something to happen. Thoughts slipped through his mind quite casually, whether Hamlet were behaving well outside, what the old lady did when she was tired of dusting, who the stone figure lying near him might be, a figure very fine with his ruff and his peaked beard, his arms folded, his toes pointing upwards, whether the body were inside the stone like a mummy, or underneath the ground somewhere; how strangely different the nave looked now from its Sunday show, and what fun it would be to run races all the way down and see who could reach the golden angels over the reredos first; he felt no reverence, and yet a deep reverence, no fear, but, nevertheless, awe; he was warm and happy and comfortable, and yet suddenly, giving a little shudder, he slipped out into the sunlight, released Hamlet and started for home.

II

Back again in the bosom of his family he felt that they were beginning to be aware of his departure.

"What shall we do this evening, Jeremy—your last evening?" said his mother.

Everyone looked at him.

"Oh, I don't know," he said uncomfortably. "Just as usual, I suppose."

"You're making him feel uncomfortable," said Aunt Amy, who loved to explain quite obvious things. "You want it to be just an ordinary evening, dear, don't you?"

"Oh, I don't know," he said again, hating his aunt.

"I don't think that quite the way to speak to your aunt, my son," said his father. "We only inquire out of kindness, thinking to please you. No, Mary, no more. Friday —one helping——"

"Jeremy might have another as it's his last day, I suggest," said Aunt Amy, who was determined to be pleasant.

"I don't want any, thank you," said Jeremy, although it was treacle pudding, which he loved.

"Well, I think," said Mrs. Cole, "that we'll have high

tea at half-past seven, and the children shall stay up afterwards and we'll have 'Midshipman Easy.'"

Jeremy loved his mother intensely at that moment. How did she know so exactly what was right? She made so little disturbance, was so quiet and was never angry, and yet she was always right when the others were always wrong. She knew that above all things he loved high tea —fish pie and boiled eggs and tea and jam and cake— a horrible meal that his later judgment would utterly condemn, but nevertheless something so cosy and so comfortable that no later meal would ever be able to rival it in those qualities.

"Oh, that will be lovely!" he said, his face shining all over.

Nevertheless, as the afternoon advanced a strange new sense of insecurity, unhappiness and forlornness crept increasingly upon him. He realised that he had that morning said good-bye to the town, and now he felt as though he had, in some way, hurt or insulted it.

And, all the afternoon, he was saying farewell to the house. He did not wander from room to room, but rather sat up in the schoolroom pretending to mend a fishing rod which Mr. Monk had given him that summer. He did not really care about the rod—he was not even thinking of it. He heard all the sounds of the house as he sat there. He could tell all the clocks, that one booming softly the half hours was in his mother's bedroom, there was a rattle and a whirr and there came the cuckoo-clock on the stairs, there was the fast, cheap careless chatter of the little clock on the schoolroom mantelpiece, there was the whisper of Miss Jones's watch which she had put out on the table to mark the time of Mary's sewing by. There were all the regular sounds of the house. The distant closing of doors, deep down in the heart of the house someone was using a sewing machine somewhere, voices came up out of the void and faded again, someone whistled, someone sang. His gloom increased. He was exchanging a world he knew for a world that he did not know, and he could not escape the feeling that he was, in some way, insulting this world that he was leaving. He bothered himself all the afternoon with unnecessary stupid affairs to cover his deep discomfort. He whistled carelessly and out of tune, he poked the fire and walked about. He was increasingly aware of Hamlet and Mary. Mary was determined so hard that she would show no emotion at all that she was a painful sight to witness. She scarcely spoke to him, and only answered in monosyllables if he asked her something.

And Hamlet had suddenly discovered that the atmosphere of the house was unusual. He had expected, in the first place, to be taken for a walk that afternoon; then his master was very busy doing nothing, which was most unusual. Then at tea time his worst suspicions were confirmed. Jeremy suddenly made a fuss of him, pouring his tea into his saucer, giving him a piece of bread and jam and an extra lump of sugar. Hamlet drank his tea and ate his bread and jam thoughtfully. They were very nice, but what was the matter?

He looked up through his hair and discovered that his master's eyes were restless and unhappy, and that he was thinking of things that disturbed him. He went away to the fire and, sitting on his haunches, gazing in his metaphysical way at the flames, considered the matter. Jeremy came over to him and, drawing him back to him, laid his head upon his knee and so held him. Hamlet did not move, save occasionally to sigh, and, once or twice, to snap in a sudden way that he had at an imaginary fly. He thought that in all probability his master had been punished for something, and in this he was deeply sympathetic, never seeing why his master need be punished for anything and resenting the stupidity of human beings with their eternal desire to be, in some way or other, asserting their authority.

Gradually, in front of the hot fire, both boy and dog fell asleep. Jeremy's dreams were confused, bewildered, distressing; he was struggling to find something, was always climbing higher and higher to discover it, only to be told that, in the end, he was in the place where he had begun.

Hamlet's dream was of an enormous succulent bone that was pulled away from him so soon as he snapped at it.

They both awoke with a start to find that it was time for high tea.

III

Throughout the evening Jeremy was more and more lonely. He had never before felt so deep an affection for the family and never been so utterly unable to express it. It was as though, during the whole year he had, by his own will, been slipping away from them, and now they had gone too far for him to call them back.

He sat on the floor at his mother's feet whilst she read "Midshipman Easy." It was all so cosy, the room was so comfortable with all the familiar pictures and photographs and books, and Helen and Mary diligently sewing, and Hamlet stretched out in front of the fire, his nose on his paws—six months ago Jeremy would have felt utterly and absolutely part of it. Now he was outside it and, at the same time, was inside nothing else. It might be that in a week's time he would be so familiar with his new world that he would be as happy as a cricket—he did not know. He only knew that at this moment he would have given all that he had to fling his arms round his mother's neck, to be hugged and kissed and nursed by her, and that, at the same time, he would have died rather than do such a thing.

The evening came to an end. The girls got up and said good-night. His mother kissed him, holding him perhaps for a moment longer than usual, but at that same instant she said:

"Oh, I must remind Ella about the half-past seven breakfast again, she always has to be told everything twice."

The girls went on ahead, Jeremy and Hamlet following close behind. Jeremy found himself alone in the school-room, where the fire was very low, giving only little spurts and flashes that ran like golden snakes suddenly through the darkness.

Moved by an impulse, he went to the toy-cupboard and, opening it, put his hand quite by chance on the toy village. The toy village! He laid it out and spread it on the floor. He could not see, but he knew every piece by heart, and he laid it all out, the church and the flower garden, and the Noah's house and the village street, the animals and the Noahs. What centuries ago that birthday was, what worlds away! How excited he had been, and now——!

With a sudden impatient gesture he tumbled the pieces over on to their sides, then quickly, as though he were afraid of the dark, went into his bedroom and began to undress.

IV

In the morning events moved too quickly for thought. He had still the same lonely pain at his heart, but now he simply was not given time to consider it.

His father called him into the study. He gave him ten shillings and a new prayer-book. Jeremy knew that he was trying to come close to him and be a friend of a new kind to him.

He heard in a distance such words as: ". . . a new world, full of trial and temptation. God sees us. . . . Work at your Latin . . . cricket and football . . . prayers every night. . . ." But he could feel no emotion, nothing but terror lest some sudden stupid emotional scene should occur. Nothing occurred. He kissed his father and went.

Then, quite suddenly, just as he came down in his hat and coat and heard that the cab was there, his restraint melted; he was free and impulsive and natural. He kissed Mary, telling her:

"You may have my toy village. I'd like you to—— Yes, rather. I mean it."

He kissed Helen and Barbara, and then held to his mother, not caring whether all the world was there to see. The old life was going with him! He was not leaving it after all. The town and the house, and all the things to which he had thought that he had said good-bye, were going with him.

Hamlet! He found the dog struggling to get into the cab. That was more than he could stand. He was not going to make a fool of himself, but the only way to be secure was to get into the cab and hide there. He caught Hamlet's head, gave it a kiss, then jumped in, catching a last glimpse of the family grouped at the door, the servants at the window, the old garden with the dead leaves gathered upon it, Hamlet held, struggling, in Mary's arms.

He choked down his sobs, felt the ten shillings in his pocket, then with a mighty resolve, to which it seemed that the labours of Hercules were as nothing, leaned out and waved his hand.

The cab rolled off.

Hamlet lay down upon the mat just inside the hall-door. Someone tried to pull him away. He growled, showing his teeth. His master had gone out. He would wait for his return—and no one should move him.

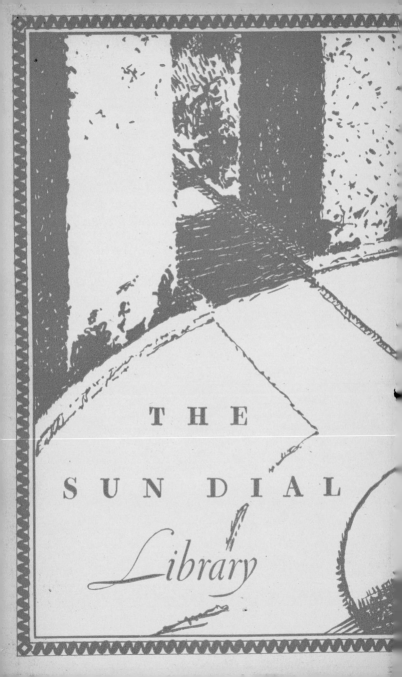

THE

SUN DIAL

Library